A Chanticleer Press Edition

ASTRONOMY

Donald H. Menzel

Paine Professor of Practical Astronomy
Harvard University

Sky Maps and Illustrations
by Ching-Sung Yü
Professor Emeritus of Astronomy
Hood College

RANDOM HOUSE · NEW YORK

Second Printing

Photographs on the half-title, title, and
contents pages are from Lick Observatory

Published in the United States by Random House, Inc.,
New York. Distributed in Canada by Random House
of Canada Limited, Toronto

Planned and produced by Chanticleer Press, New York

Manufactured by Amilcare Pizzi S.p.A. in Milan, Italy

Library of Congress Catalog Number 70-127542

Contents

Preface

As a special feature, this book contains a series of sky maps, which are, I believe, unique. Twenty-four maps cover the entire sky in much the same way that a geographical atlas presents the various continents and parts thereof. Some years ago, in writing for young people, I developed a special technique to facilitate the orientation of such maps. The maps presented here, exquisitely drawn by my old friend, Professor Ching-Sung Yü, Professor Emeritus of Astronomy at Hood College, Maryland, are a greatly improved version of this early work. I wish to thank the editors of *Highlights for Children* for permission to use the original material. The constellation forms used for the sky maps were based on the design by H. A. Rey for his books *The Stars* and *Find the Constellations;* I used these in *A Field Guide to the Stars and Planets*. Houghton Mifflin published all three of these books.

I again thank Professor Yü for his expert execution of the many diagrams in this book. And I wish to thank my former colleague Dr. Gerald Anderson, now of the National Science Foundation, for assisting me in the preparation of Chapters 12, 13, and 14, which are concerned chiefly with the planets, meteors, and comets. To some extent I have drawn from a series of lectures entitled *The Universe in Action*, delivered in 1955 at Birmingham-Southern College under sponsorship of the Rushton Lectures. Portions of these appeared in *The Atlantic Monthly* in November and December 1955.

I would be remiss if I did not acknowledge the pleasurable experience of working with Milton Rugoff and Susan Weiley of Chanticleer Press, whose editorial skill and understanding patience have materially contributed to *Astronomy*.

Introduction

During the past two decades, astronomy has experienced a growth unmatched by any other area of human knowledge. It has even been said that this growth has equaled the total advance of astronomical knowledge in the three centuries since the death of Galileo.

Many discoveries and inventions in other areas of science and engineering have helped in this sensational advance. For example, developments in atomic engineering have confirmed what astronomers had long suspected: the fusion of light atoms into heavier ones could liberate enough energy to account for the heat radiated by the sun and other stars over billions of years. The knowledge about such atomic reactions was so precise that astronomers were able to construct by calculation the internal structure of stars. They could, moreover, determine the course of a star's evolution, from its prenatal state as a contracting cloud of gas and dust through its life as a stable, shining star, to its extinction in a gigantic explosion or in slow decline into a cold, black clinker coursing through interstellar space. At last man, despite his living on a perpetually beclouded planet, could accomplish what Sir Arthur Eddington, the great British astronomer, had suggested several decades earlier: he could take pencil and paper and deduce the stars.

The electronics industry developed increasingly powerful radio transmitters and ever more sensitive receivers. Experts in communication had become aware that the sun, the moon, various planets and galaxies, and a multitude of other celestial objects were the source of radio noise ranging from a smooth purring to bursts of cosmic static. As our radio antennas and receivers were improved, still stranger sources of radio noise came to our attention. These included the blue points of light that came to be known as quasi-stellar objects, or "quasars," because they resembled stars except for the outpouring of radio energy. And then there were the still more mysterious "pulsars," objects that sent out pulses of radio energy so regularly that some astronomers at first thought they might be a form of cosmic radio beacon from beings on some distant planet. Soon, however, astronomers were able to identify the source as a rapidly rotating neutron star of very advanced age that had been compressed to extreme density.

But astronomers were tantalized by the possibility that intelligent beings might exist elsewhere in the universe. For a time, an exploratory program carried out a continuous recording of radio emissions entering our atmosphere from various directions. There was plenty of radio noise and static, but nothing suggesting intelligent messages. And so the program, called "Project Ozma," was discontinued.

Industrial research and engineering made great improvements in the efficiency of optical telescopes. Melted quartz and special ceramics such as Cer-vit provided astronomers with a far more efficient substitute for the glass previously used in large telescope mirrors. Unlike the best of the glasses, the new products were very stable under extreme conditions of heat and cold. New methods of telescope mounting, special controls, automatic guiding, and new accessory instruments were developed. One of these, known as an "image tube," greatly increased the efficiency of a telescope through amplification of the light by electronic means. New detectors enhanced the ability to record the intensity of radiation in the infrared region of the spectrum.

The earth's atmosphere, although transparent to certain regions of the radio spectrum and the visible spectrum and slightly into the ultraviolet and infrared, is opaque to immense ranges of the electromagnetic spectrum. Employing the latest rockets, scientists found that they could raise some of their equipment above the earth's atmosphere and study thitherto inaccessible ultraviolet and X-ray regions. The results were indeed astonishing, for they showed that the sun and many other celestial bodies were emitters of ultraviolet radiation of high intensity. And the development of extended space programs, first by the Soviet Union and later by the United States, opened up vast new vistas of astronomical research.

Orbiting telescopes began to record the appearance of the universe in various wavelengths. Such studies revealed X-ray sources in distant realms of the galaxy. And as the space vehicles increased in efficiency so that they could leave the environs of the earth and travel through our solar system, astronomers were able to acquire first-hand knowledge of our moon and the planets. The Russians were the first to photograph the moon's far side, which man had never seen. Later, American vehicles photographed the entire lunar surface with a detail impossible from earth-bound telescopes. Probes sent to Venus confirmed what we had already suspected: the surface of this cloud-covered planet is very hot. And probes sent to Mars transmitted detailed photographs of its crater-pitted surface. Finally man achieved the goal of landing on the moon; he explored it briefly and brought back rocks for analysis. All of these space programs required the development of special instrumentation, such as the cameras that took and automatically developed photographs in space, then turned the photographic records into electronic pulses that our great radio receivers could capture. Electronic computers then reconverted these pulses back into high-resolution pictures of the photographed object.

Photographic film has been greatly improved. In particular, the incorporation of special dyes into the emulsion has increased the sensitivity of the film in regions such as the far-red and infrared. From the laboratories of other sciences came entirely new methods for the chemical analysis of rocks, meteorites, and especially the samples recently returned from the moon. These studies have shed new light on their nature and evolution.

High-speed digital computers have revolutionized astronomical calculation. A computer can now perform in a few seconds the calculations that would have taken an early astronomer a full year to carry out. The accuracy of the calculations has also been vastly increased. Without these computing facilities, the space program would have been impossible. Computers check and assess every detail of a space flight from liftoff to splashdown. They have furthermore been vital in the design and performance of multi-stage rockets.

Computers have also played an important part in other astronomical experiments. Our great radio telescopes send pulses of radio energy into space, where they may be reflected from the surface of the moon or one of the planets. The signal, much weakened, returns to earth, where receivers transmit the data to a computer. This highly sophisticated application of radar has yielded valuable information about distances within our solar system, the size and rotation of planets, and irregularities on their surface. And flashes of light from a laser beam have fixed the distance to the moon to within a foot.

Such studies have also led to great improvement in our measurement of time. Half a century ago, an astronomer was satisfied if he could measure time to a hundredth or even a tenth of a second. Today scientists confidently measure intervals even shorter than a nanosecond (10^{-9} sec). And special clocks, using atomic or molecular vibrations to control their movements, are more accurate timekeepers than our earth, which up to recently was the standard measure of time.

Such are some of the explosive developments that have revolutionized astronomy. After we have reviewed the history of the science, we shall examine these developments in full detail.

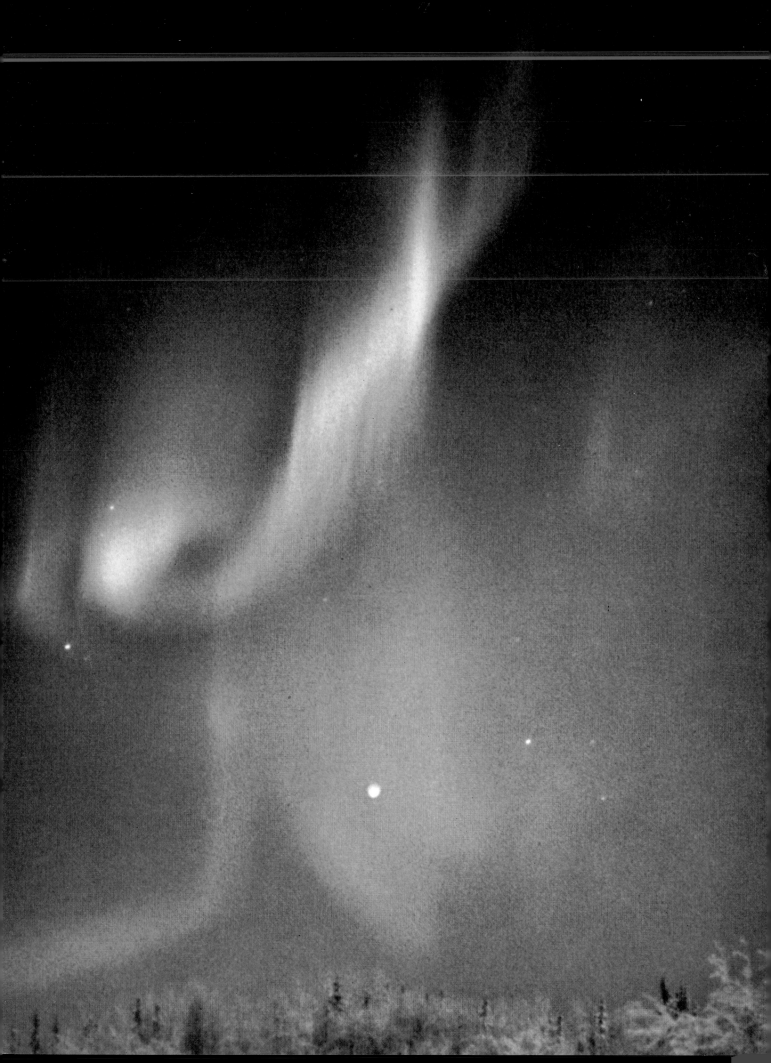

The Birth of Astronomy

Let us try to reconstruct man's early struggle to understand the world around him. No matter how limited his curiosity, primitive man certainly noticed the sun and recognized it as the giver of light and warmth. He became aware of its rising and setting. He learned to associate the changing altitude of the sun with the changing seasons, and the departure of summer and the onset of winter with days growing shorter and shorter.

The moon, brilliant luminary, doubtless attracted almost as much attention as the sun. Man surely observed its changing shape, from crescent to full and back to crescent again, and wondered what it signified. And he measured time by the moon's circuit of the sky; today we still recognize and use this measurement of the "moonth," or rather, month.

Ancient man probably realized that most of the bright points of light in the sky, which we call stars, did not change their relative positions each night as they traced circles around the sky. He also noted that a few of the bright stars "wandered" with respect to the "fixed" stars in a path roughly parallel to that of the moon. Today we call these special "stars" the planets, a word derived from the Greek *planēt*, meaning "wanderer."

Astronomy and the Cycle of Life

The sun regulates the behavior of all living things, animal and vegetable. The alternation of night and day controls the lives of man and beast. Primitive people were almost instinctively able to determine the time of day from visual estimates of the altitude and direction of the sun. Recognition and prediction of the sequence of the seasons were even more important. At high latitudes the marked difference between a beneficent summer and a hostile winter posed problems for the very survival of primitive man. And equally important problems confronted tribes living near the equator, where there was an alternation of dry seasons and torrential monsoons. Man eventually realized that the altitude of the sun at noon had something to do with the changing seasons, and he used the gnomon, a vertical pole that cast a shadow, to determine the position of the sun in the sky and establish a solar calendar.

When the barbarism of the nomadic tribes gave way to communal association and the development of agriculture, sometime between 4000 B.C. and 2000 B.C., the need for an accurate calendar increased. For much of this period, historic records clearly show the importance of astronomy and astronomical observations, especially in the fertile valleys of China, Mesopotamia, India, and Egypt. At certain seasons the rivers of these regions—the Hwang Ho, the Tigris, the Euphrates, and the Nile—overflowed their banks and covered valley floors with a layer of fertile alluvial silt. The water could at times be devastating if it was not properly controlled by dikes or canals. To maintain effective agricultural operations, accurate predictions of water levels became imperative; for without proper control, potential garden areas were ruined and the people starved.

The Original Meaning of Meteors

Today we use the word "meteor" in astronomy to denote what is sometimes called a shooting star. This phenomenon is the result of a fragment of iron or

2. A detail from the eleventh-century Bayeux Tapestry vividly illustrates the wonder aroused by a comet that passed in 1066. Six centuries later it became known as Halley's Comet when Edmund Halley discovered that it reappeared periodically. (Photographie Giraudon)

11

rock entering the earth's atmosphere at high speed and being heated to incandescence by friction. It burns for a few seconds as it traverses the sky and then disappears in a shower of sparks. The ancients had a much more general interpretation of the word meteor, using it to mean anything falling from the sky or seen in the sky, with the exception of the sun, moon, stars, and five planets.

There were, first of all, the "aerial meteors," which consisted mainly of winds, whose direction so obviously controlled the weather, and of clouds, which scuttled across the sky and clearly were moved by the wind. The "aqueous meteors" signified such phenomena as fog, dew, rain, hail, sleet, and snow. "Luminous meteors" included rainbows (fig. 1–1), but also much rarer phenomena associated with mist or fog—such as the "ghost of the Brocken"—and with ice crystals—such as the frightening apparitions known technically as parhelia or paraselene, and more popularly as sundogs or moondogs. The series of circles and arches resulting from the passage of sunlight or moonlight through layers of fine ice crystals can produce an apparition suggestive of an enormous, fiery chariot standing in the sky (fig. 1–2). The Aurora Borealis (Aurora Australis in the southern hemisphere), also considered a luminous meteor, was equally frightening, with brilliant curtains hanging in the north and pulsing streamers converging toward what we call the magnetic zenith, but which then appeared to be a corridor into the upper regions of the starry realm (color plates 1, 24). Miscellaneous halos and other unusual optical apparitions were also regarded as luminous meteors. Finally, there were the "igneous meteors," which included lightning flashes as well as ordinary fireballs and the shooting stars called bolides.

The Birth of Meteorology

It is easy to see how the ancients became confused in their attempts to interpret the complex phenomena of the heavens, the various kinds of meteors, and miscellaneous astronomical objects. The weather, of course, was their prime concern. And thus was born the science of meteorology, which included the interpreting of all the heavenly meteors. We still use the term today but in a far more restricted sense.

Only by conjecture can we reconstruct the simultaneous development in

The mariner's card from the *Grooten Atlas*, 1652, shows the winds as personal forces—a conception widely held by the ancients. (M. Laffineur, Institut d'Astrophysique, Paris)

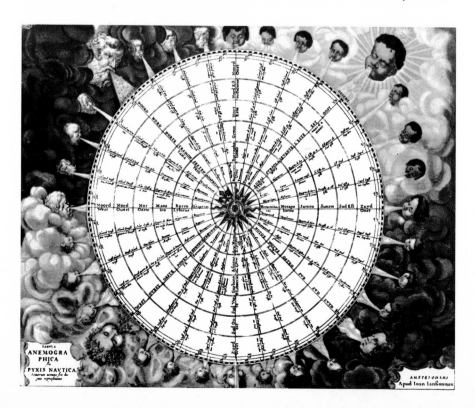

Such mysterious apparitions in the sky as mock suns, or sun dogs, were very frightening to the ancients. This picture, drawn in 1563, clearly refers to such parhelic phenomena. (Zentral Bibliothek, Zurich)

their early stages of the sister sciences, meteorology and astronomy. For example, the ancients correctly concluded that the sun was the most important of all the celestial bodies. They attempted to map its course through the sky, although this was difficult because the sun by its very brightness made the stellar backdrop invisible. Even so, they were able to trace the steady eastward motion of the sun throughout the year, ascribing to it a diagonal path that made it appear sometimes north and sometimes south of the equator. The apparent circular path of the sun across the sky, called the *ecliptic*, is broadly delineated by the twelve constellations of the zodiac. The *zodiac*, a word signifying "zone of the animals," is approximately 10° wide and is centered in the ecliptic. Because of its importance, almost all primitive peoples mapped it, organizing the brighter stars into constellations and giving them names. Clearly noting that the seasons were somehow associated with the position of the sun along the zodiac, they tried to find an astronomical explanation for all meteorological phenomena.

An example of their scientific "logic" was the belief that since water falls from the sky, in some form, as the presence of aqueous meteors indicates, there must be large bodies of water somewhere in the heavens, restrained from falling to the earth by a transparent barrier through which we see the stars. Thus the ancients came to visualize a crystalline vault of heaven, called the "firmament," which held the waters back and kept them from falling on the earth. Occasionally a leak would develop. In Genesis, we find the following description of the Great Flood: "... the windows of heaven were opened. And the rain was upon the earth forty days and forty nights."

Since most of the patterns of rainfall repeat themselves seasonally, the ancients reasoned that the position of the sun in the sky was the factor that controlled the weather. It can be no accident that they located three adjacent

13

zodiacal constellations, all related to water, in that part of the sky occupied by the sun during the season of the worst storms. Several other aquatic constellations—such as Cetus, the whale or sea monster, and Piscis Austrinus, the southern fish—shared this area of the sky with Capricornus, the sea goat; Aquarius, the water bearer; and Pisces, the fish. Farther to the south lay the constellation of the great ship Argo Navis, in legend used by the Argonauts in their search for the Golden Fleece and then stranded on the shore of the vast Heavenly Sea.

The ancients must have found further justification for their theory of the direct effect of the sun on the weather in the obvious relation between the moon and the tides. The more perceptive could not help noticing that the high tides followed the moon, occurring at different times of day as the moon moved eastward along its orbit. They could easily have discovered that the sun also had an effect on the tides: high tides were higher and low tides lower at new and full moon, when the moon and sun were in what astronomers call *syzygy*—that is, when the sun, moon, and earth lay in a straight line (fig. 1–3). They also probably noted that the human female menstrual cycle coincides almost exactly with the lunar month and may have interpreted this coincidence as further proof of the direct effect of the heavenly bodies on affairs terrestrial.

If, as seemed to be the case, the sun and moon exerted control over the weather and, apparently, over human beings, what about the effect exerted by other moving objects, the planets? Thus, confusing cause and effect, the ancients over the centuries built up an elaborate scheme for predicting man's destiny as well as the weather. This was the beginning of astrology and its extraordinary influence on civilization.

Order from Chaos

The ancients, believing that a relationship existed between the heavenly bodies, the gods, the weather, and other natural phenomena, concluded that if they could learn enough about the motions of these bodies, they could better forecast the weather and, in particular, the occurrence of destructive natural events. The motion of the moon was the simplest to measure, because it was fairly regular and because, unlike the sun, it was not so brilliant that it obscured the background of reference stars. The diurnal rotations of the various heavenly bodies made determination of the north-south line relatively easy. Man found that the moon's monthly path was approximately circular, inclined in such a way that the moon sometimes came toward the north and sometimes receded toward the south. He could have found that the moon takes a little less than thirty days to go from full back to full. Hence, in one day, it would move about $1/30$ of a 360°-circle, or about 13° a day, according to our modern calculations.

The sun was harder to observe, as we have said, because its brilliance makes

Aurora borealis near Bamberg in December 1560. Superstitious people, seeing such flashing lights in the northern sky, often explained them as sparks from the clashing of swords. (Zentral Bibliothek, Zurich)

14

Medieval representation of a meteor that appeared after a thunderstorm over Esseck in 1687. (From a print by T. Duell)

the starry background invisible. On the other hand, at full moon, the sun is always directly opposite the moon. Man found by observation of the starry background that successive full moons do not occur at the same position with respect to the constellations. The moon makes a complete circuit in relation to the stars in about $27\frac{1}{3}$ days, as compared with the $29\frac{1}{2}$ days from full moon to full moon. One can readily determine, therefore, that successive full moons are spaced 29.1° apart along the circle of the moon's motion. And this figure, then, represents the mean motion of the sun per lunation.

We shall later discuss in more detail the apparent motion of the moon and the sun. For the moment it is accurate enough to say that both the moon and the sun describe apparent circles around the earth, the former moving at approximately 13° and the latter slightly less than 1° per day. Indeed, our present division of a circle into 360° undoubtedly stems from this coincidence. In addition, 360 is a much more convenient number to divide than is 365. Within the accuracy of these elementary determinations, the motion of both the sun and the moon would also have been uniform along their respective

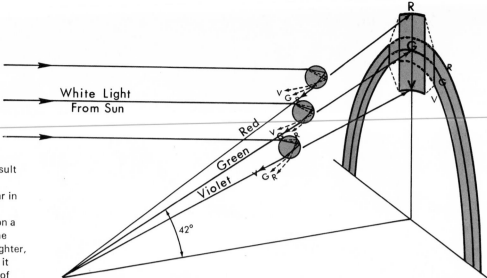

Figure 1–1. A rainbow's colors result from the refraction of sunlight by raindrops. Rainbows always appear in the sky opposite the sun, with the center of the rainbow circle lying on a line drawn from the sun through the observer. Since the primary, or brighter, rainbow has a radius of about 42°, it will not appear unless the altitude of the sun is less than that. The secondary bow, with the colors displayed in reverse order, has a radius of about 50°.

orbital circles. This statement is not precisely true, but any inaccuracies of motion cancel out in the long run.

The Motions of the Planets

We shall consider the motions of the "inner planets," Mercury and Venus, and the "outer planets," Mars, Jupiter, and Saturn, since these were the only planets known to the ancients. All exhibited a motion very different from that of the moon and the sun. Where the sun and moon progress uniformly eastward across the sky, the inner planets progress eastward from the sun into the evening sky until they reach a maximum distance from the sun. They then reverse direction, move westward, pass the sun, and move into the morning sky, where they again come to a stop, reverse and start moving eastward again. Venus, more brilliant than Mercury, gets more than 47° away from the sun. Mercury, shy and difficult to see, is usually lost in the rays of the setting or rising sun. Its maximum distance from the sun is 28°.

The three outer planets behave very differently. Their normal motion is eastward, like the sun and moon, but at a certain stage they come to a stop, reverse, and start moving backward. This retrograde motion takes place most rapidly when the planets are 180° from the sun, rising when the sun is setting, and vice versa. Finally the westward drift stops. The planet reverses again and resumes its eastward motion. The retrograde loop is longest for Mars, less for

Figure 1–2. When sunlight filters through fine ice crystals instead of raindrops, the refractions produce two circles of light around the sun, one with a radius of 22° and the other of 45°. Sometimes bright patches appear on either side of the sun; these are known as mock suns, or sun dogs. The entire phenomenon is known as parhelia.

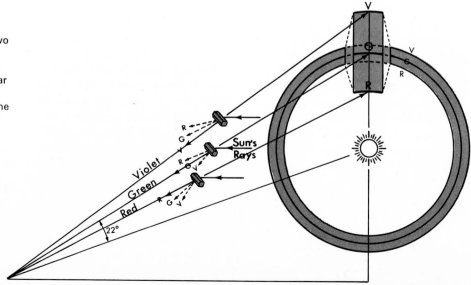

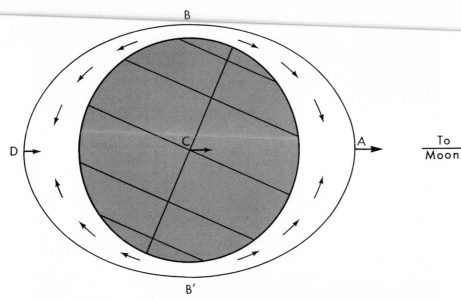

Figure 1–3. The ancients recognized the relationship of the moon and the tides. As shown here, the attraction of the moon (and secondarily of the sun) causes tides. When the sun and moon are in line, the attraction is greatest and the tides are at their extreme highs and lows. Point *A* on the earth, which is closest to the moon, is strongly attracted and has high tides. Tides are also high at *D,* because there the solid earth is attracted to the moon and pulls away, so that the sea level rises relative to the earth's crust. At *B* and *B'* the sea level decreases to make up for the rise at *A* and *D.*

Jupiter, and still smaller for Saturn. This reversal of motion posed a problem for the early astronomers, who regarded the earth as the center of the universe, with the stars and planets revolving about it. The sun and moon behaved sensibly; but how could one account for the peculiar reversal of motion exhibited by the various planets? We shall return to this point in a later chapter.

Ecliptic, Zodiac, and Moon Stations

We have already recognized the importance of the apparent path of the sun, moon, and planets in their course through the heavens. The ancients conceived of the background of fixed stars as a great sphere rotating about a definite axis. One pole of rotation lies above the horizon; the other is invisible. Halfway between the two poles we draw a circle from the east to the west point of the horizon. This circle we call the *celestial equator.* If the observer were precisely on the terrestrial equator, the celestial equator would go through the overhead point, the *zenith,* and the two poles would be respectively at the north and south points of the horizon.

The circle denoting the path of the sun throughout the year, the ecliptic, is inclined to the equator, making an angle of about $23\frac{1}{2}°$ with respect to it, so that sometimes the sun is north of the equator and sometimes south. The paths of the moon and the five planets are inclined only slightly to the ecliptic. Mercury's orbit is tilted $7°$; that of the moon, $5°$. The moving heavenly bodies, therefore, are always to be found in the zodiacal belt. The division of the zodiac into twelve parts clearly resulted from the fact that, on the average, 12.4 full moons occur during the year. Hence, successive full moons always occurred in the neighboring, eastward zodiacal constellation. This circumstance provided a method, primitive and inaccurate but nevertheless scientific, of keeping track of the passage of time throughout the year.

For a different purpose, the ancients sometimes divided the ecliptic into a number of "moon stations." Since the Arabs, Indians, Chinese, and other primitive cultures employed the same notation, they must have inherited it from one another, though we do not know where the concept originated. The division of the zodiac into 27 or 28 subdivisions also had calendric significance. Spaced approximately $13°$ apart, each station was occupied on successive days by the moon in the course of its monthly revolution around the earth. The moon stations, therefore, provided a means of keeping track of the passage of days. Although we no longer find the moon stations useful, they did serve a very important purpose in early times.

Lightning strokes form a complex pattern of electrical breakdown. Because it could start fires, split open trees, and kill men, the ancients considered lightning one of the malevolent meteors. (National Center for Atmospheric Research)

The Constellations

Calling on imagination and folklore, the ancients delineated about three dozen constellations in the heavens in addition to those of the zodiac. The pictorial interpretation of the constellations differed, of course, among the various cultures. The Egyptians figured the bull's hind leg in place of what we call the Big Dipper. The little bear became a hippopotamus; and a crocodile, a lion, a sparrow, and a hawk were also added. Apparently most of the ancient constellations we now recognize originated in Mesopotamia. Minstrels, wandering from one nomadic tribe to another, spun fabulous yarns about the gods and their relation to mankind. They illustrated these lusty stories with the heavens as a backdrop—a primitive substitute for modern motion pictures. The more popular of these stories eventually came down to us in the form of Greek mythology.

Methods of Observation

Until the introduction of the photographic plate in the latter part of the nineteenth century, the human eye was the fundamental detector in astronomical observations. From simple instruments like the gnomon, men in early times went on to construct more elaborate devices for solving special problems, such as the prediction of the beginning of spring or the forecasting of eclipses. One of the most spectacular of these is the arrangement of huge monolithic stones at Stonehenge, England, which almost certainly was a solar observatory. Another special astronomical observatory, this one in the western hemisphere, is El Caracol (the Snail), built by the Maya near Mérida, Yucatán.

Although we have to use our imaginations to reconstruct these early

3. Armillary sphere depicting the geometry of the heavens. (Instituto e Museo di Storia della Scienzia, Florence)

4. Below: Early mariner's compass. (Instituto e Museo di Storia della Scienzia, Florence)

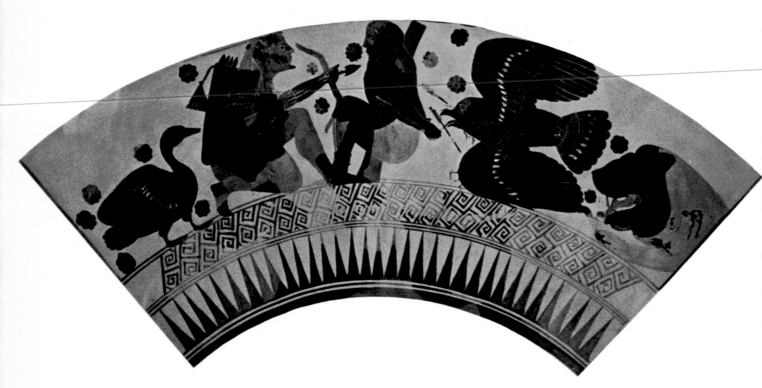

scientific ventures, it seems clear that simple mappings of the sky itself, perhaps first on a flat surface and later on a sphere, gave man a way of recording and tracing all kinds of astronomical events. By 1500 B.C., observational astronomy had attained a relatively high degree of precision. For more than a thousand years, the astronomer observed and measured the positions of the various heavenly bodies. Probably because of its great brilliance, they devoted special attention to the planet Venus. Many clay tablets, inscribed in cuneiform script, contain records of these observations.

The Birth of Astrology

Near the beginning of the first millenium B.C., a new power appeared in the plains of Mesopotamia—the Assyrians. They continued to make astronomical observations, but the objective began to change. Whereas in the beginning the calendar, the keeping of time, the forecasting of weather, and the planning of agricultural programs had been the primary aim, a new influence began to dominate man's thought. Perhaps it was inevitable that man, firmly believing in the influence of the heavenly bodies on terrestrial meteorology, should carry his reasoning one step further and apply it to human affairs as well. The various "meteors," in the most general sense, came to be regarded as omens, which one versed in such matters could use to foretell the future. And thus astrology, stepdaughter of astronomy and meteorology, was born.

The basic concepts of astrology were by no means new. Even primitive man believed in omens and in the influence of unseen things upon his destiny. It was natural for him to invoke the aid of nature's gods in various ways, whether by offerings, sacrifices, incantations, or exorcism. He felt that it was vital for him to seek their favor or appease their hostility. As early as 2500 B.C., for example, we find an inscription on a stone cylinder that indicates a favorable time for building a temple.

In Assyria from 800 to 700 B.C., such random and disorganized beliefs began to take on a new significance. The court astrologers became more powerful and exerted a great influence on the affairs of men. They constantly "consulted" the heavens, especially the moon and planets, as well as the other "meteors" mentioned earlier. Eclipses of the sun or moon and the un-

Babylonian tablet. Inscribed on it are the observations of Jupiter from 131 B.C. to 59 B.C. The cuneiform text records the passage of the planet through the constellations of the zodiac. Chaldean records reveal a surprising knowledge of both mathematics and the motions of the planets. (British Museum)

5. Facing page, top: Greek amphora of about 582 B.C. shows Hercules shooting an arrow, Sagitta, toward an eagle, Aquila, and a duck-like creature that may represent the constellation of Cygnus, the Swan. The human figure in the center is probably Prometheus. (Donald Menzel. Original in National Museum, Athens)

6. Bottom: Astrolabe. An early instrument used for determining the positions of stars and planets. (Instituto e Museo di Storia della Scienzia, Florence)

heralded appearance of a bright comet, its tail stretching across the sky, were particularly frightening. Perhaps the advent of such a comet happened to coincide with the death of a king. For to this day it is a firmly-ingrained tenet of astrology that comets generally presage the death of rulers.

Astrology provided a new impetus for improved and more accurate astronomical observations. Instead of just recording where the heavenly bodies had been, men had a powerful motive to foretell their positions in the future. The attitude was that if the planets were to exert an influence on the world, including mankind, one should at least be able to predict their positions. They redoubled their efforts to improve their observations and to develop sophisticated methods for forecasting the motions of the planets.

The Curious Influence of Astrology

Many of our sciences originated as handmaidens of astrology. Mathematics, for example, had to be applied to observational data in order to make systematic predictions possible. Medicine developed because one objective of astrology was predicting the health of an individual. Many early recipes for medicines, such as the preparation of herbal infusions, contained such astrological directions as that the ingredients should be mixed under the light of the full moon, and so forth. As a result of medical experiments, the science of chemistry developed, along with the elements of biology. Then there was the

A reconstruction, based on a photograph of El Caracol, or the Snail, in Yucatán, Mexico. It was erected by the Maya and is believed to have been used as a solar observatory.
(American Museum of Natural History)

Stonehenge, in southern England, is also believed to have been erected as a solar temple. At the vernal equinox, the rays of the rising sun show directly on the Heel stone. The monument may have been even more commonly used as a type of computer of ancient eclipses. (Paul Caponigro)

pseudoscience, alchemy, whose relationship to chemistry essentially parallels that of astrology to astronomy. Where astrology attempted to predict the future of man for his health or good fortune, alchemy was intended for gain in that it endeavored to find a recipe for changing base metal into precious gold.

Man's study turned him toward the earth as well as toward the stars. He noted the rocks and began to develop a curiosity about what we now call geology. As he became more mobile, he acquired a conception of geography. And in an endeavor to understand his environment and to systematize all of accumulated knowledge, man developed philosophy—of nature, of the universe, and of man himself.

Over the centuries, astrology has always had a special appeal, for man has thought that if he could know the future, he could perhaps exercise some control over his destiny, take advantage of propitious moments, and avoid the pitfalls of less favorable times. For something like three millenia, charlatans have preyed on the credulous and self-deluded. Astrology is not, as has often been claimed, the father of astronomy. Astronomy existed long before man used the stars to try to predict the future. As for astrology itself, there is not one iota of evidence to support the claims made for it.

Early Astronomy

The science of cosmology, dealing with the nature of the universe and its parts, goes back to the ancients. Challenged by the complexity of the universe around them, they tried to figure out what it consisted of and how it had been put together. Since their primitive concepts of the world were usually completely wrong, or at least incomplete, their cosmologies were quite unsuccessful. They nevertheless persisted in recording the motions of the heavenly bodies and over the centuries accumulated a wealth of data concerning those motions. Much of this information was collected for the purposes of astrology, but in the end it contributed most effectively to the development of scientific thought.

The Babylonians and Egyptians

The cosmologist must "mind the why and wherefore" of the universe. The primitive cosmologist had little to go on, partly because of misconceptions and preconceptions. As an example of the kind of conceptions that developed in early civilizations, let us examine what the people of Babylonia believed at about the first millenium B.C.

Basic astronomical knowledge was possessed principally by the astrologer-priests, who controlled the calendar and established rites for the worship of the heavenly bodies. Such knowledge was closely guarded, so that the ignorant populace based its concept of the world more on mythology than on observations. According to these popular beliefs, water was the source of everything. The land had sprung from the ocean, which still surrounded the land. And beyond the ocean stream the sungod pastured his cattle. The ancients regarded the sky as a solid vault that held back the "upper waters," above which were the heavens and the dwelling place of the gods.

Every morning, at sunrise, the sun came out through a door on the eastern horizon, performed his circuit of the sky, and disappeared through a similar door on the western horizon at sunset. The ancients regarded the moon, planets and stars as living beings, moving in their special paths. The earth itself was hollow, supported by pillars. The interior was the abode of the dead, which the spirit entered through a door in the west. The cosmology was simple because there were so fews facts to explain.

These early concepts spread widely. They must have had a profound influence on those who later wrote the Bible, for we find in it many references suggestive of the Babylonian universe. The Scriptures mention the horizon as a "circle (or compass) upon the face of the deep." (Prov. viii.27) Or, again, "It is he that sitteth upon the circle of the earth, and the inhabitants thereof are as grasshoppers; that stretcheth out the heavens as a curtain, and spreadeth them out as a tent to dwell in." (Isa. xl.22) We also hear of the "pillars" or "foundations" as in "the pillars of the earth are the Lord's and He hath set the world upon them." (1 Sam. ii.8) The concept of the firmament and the upper waters is clearly set forth in the following: "And God said, Let there be a firmament in the midst of the waters, and let it divide the waters from the waters. And God made the firmament, and divided the waters which were under the firmament from the waters which were above the firmament." (Gen. i.6,7).

Facing page: The Egyptian goddess Nu forms the sky as she bends over the earth. The carving dates from the fifth century B.C. (Metropolitan Museum of Art)

The Egyptian King Akhenaton (c. fourteenth century B.C.) and Queen Nefertiti and their daughter standing with offerings for the sun god Aton. His rays, ending in the form of a human hand, bestow the key of life on the royal family. (Metropolitan Museum of Art)

The Egyptians held roughly similar views. The universe was a large, rectangular box, of which the earth was the floor. The top was sometimes regarded as vaulted, with numerous lamps suspended from it or carried by various deities. The sun god Ra, reborn in the east every morning, traversed the sky in a boat. The Egyptians regarded the Milky Way as a heavenly Nile flowing through regions inhabited by the spirits of the dead.

Early Greek Philosophers

Our knowledge of the early Greeks comes mainly through indirect references, for none of their original works has survived. The earliest nature philosopher of whom we have a record is Thales of Miletus (640–546 B.C.). To Thales, the earth was a flat disk floating on a vast body of water. Although he recognized the vaulted heavens, he said nothing concerning the motions of stars or planets. However, the historian Herodotus recorded that Thales had actually predicted a solar eclipse, though perhaps he merely forecast the year in which it would happen.

Anaximander (611–547 B.C.), a contemporary of Thales, promoted the popular philosophical idea that water is a prime substance from which all the universe evolved. He theorized that the earth must be a cylinder floating freely in space. The height of the cylinder, he obscurely concluded, was one-third of the circular face. The idea of a free-floating earth was a marked advance over earlier thinking, which had always assumed that the earth needed some sort of support. And his arguments in favor of this proposition still have some validity. Since the earth was in the center of the universe, it would have no tendency to fall out of that position; hence it did not require a special support. Apparently Anaximander was the first to regard the heavens as a complete sphere that encased the earth's atmosphere like the bark of a tree.

During the sixth century B.C., two great schools of thought developed independently, that of Xenophanes (ca. 570–500 B.C.) and that of Pythagoras (ca. 580–500 B.C.). The former founded what became known as the Eleatic School of philosophy. Xenophanes' astronomical concepts were considerably less advanced than those of his predecessors. He thought of the earth as infinite and flat, and believed that the heavenly bodies were extinguished in the west and rekindled every morning in the east.

The cosmology of Pythagoras represented a marked step forward in that it was based in part on observation. Certainly the Pythagoreans and probably Pythagoras himself realized that the earth was a sphere. This fact came to be known because mariners, more venturesome than ever before, made more extensive voyages. As they sailed southward along the west coast of Africa they saw the northern stars sink below the horizon while new and unfamiliar stars rose before them in the south.

Pythagoras was widely traveled and may himself have noted some of these phenomena. However, he relied more on mathematical views of the universe, which at times bordered on the mystical. The spherical shape of the heavens led him to suppose that the earth, in order to be geometrically compatible, must have a similar shape. But none of the Pythagoreans supported the idea that the earth itself, although spherical, was rotating.

The Pythagoreans introduced a rather novel cosmological model for the solar system. To them the number 10 was "perfect" because it was the sum of the first four integers. They could see only nine celestial bodies: the sun, the earth, the moon, the five planets, and the fixed stars. To satisfy their ideas of perfection and symmetry, they postulated the existence of a tenth planet, the Antichthon, or counter-earth. They set all ten of these bodies, including the sun, in orbit around a central fire, which men could never see because the counter-earth perpetually obscured it from view. This cosmology, based more on philosophical principles than on observation, had at least one remarkable feature. It regarded the earth, for the first time in human history, as one of the planets in individual orbit, if not around the sun, at least around the central fire.

We can understand, even if we cannot accept, the basic principles of Pythagorean philosophy. For Pythagoras himself had deduced the famous Pythagorean theorem, not from measurement, but from the application of simple mathematical reasoning. To him, as indeed to us, triangles are not necessarily abstract, but something real, a part of the visible universe.

If Pythagoras was the first to apply such reasoning, he was certainly not the last. Kepler, some twenty-one centuries later, also tried to account for the separations of planets in our solar system in terms of the regular geometrical solids. He was unsuccessful, but he regarded this "law" as one of his great achievements. And we must admit, as we look at various aspects of Einstein's theory of relativity, that certain principles of symmetry apply here as well. One of its postulates—that the laws of nature should be independent of the motion of an observer—has a distinctly Pythagorean slant.

Anaxagoras

A large meteorite fell in Greece in the year 467 B.C. This fiery interloper from outer space made an impression on the philosopher Anaxagoras (ca. 500–428 B.C.). He recognized its extraterrestrial origin and regarded it as a piece of the sun. From this fact he deduced that the sun was a mass of molten iron, and only slightly larger than the Peloponnesus, the southern peninsula of Greece. He said that the moon was also about the same size, that it contained "plains and valleys," and shone by light reflected from the sun.

Anaxagoras regarded the earth as flat. It is not difficult to see how he may have come to his conclusions. As a traveler moves southward, he will see the sun and the moon rise in the sky by one degree for about every 70 miles traversed. We know, of course, that this changing altitude results from the fact that the earth is a sphere and we are simply seeing the distant heavenly bodies a little bit more overhead as the result of our moving southward along the curved earth. Anaxagoras, however, ascribed the change in altitude to the flatness of the earth and concluded that the sun was about 4000 miles away and had a diameter of some 35 miles, not too different from that of the Peloponnesus. Anaxagoras apparently understood the nature of both solar and lunar eclipses. However, there is a curious contradiction in his conclusion that the sun and moon were of the same size, for he does not place them at the same distance from the earth.

The reaction of Anaxagoras' compatriots to his cosmological models was harsh and swift. He was accused of heresy, for his views denied the popular interpretation of the heavenly bodies as deities. The eloquence of his friend Pericles saved him from death, but he was banished from Athens and died in exile.

An example of the difficulty many people had in visualizing a spherical earth and the consequences thereof is the doubt that the historian Herodotus (ca. 484–425 B.C.) expressed concerning the reports of Phoenician sailors. They claimed to have seen the rising sun on their right as they sailed westward from the Indian Ocean, around the Cape of Good Hope, and into the Atlantic.

Plato

Although Plato (ca. 427–347 B.C.) owes his fame to his philosophical writings, he had much to say on astronomical topics. To him the stars were living beings, but he regarded the universe, exemplified by the solar system, as eternal. He subscribed to the geometric theory and proposed a mechanical system for the motion of the various planets. He refined and extended the concepts of Pythagoras concerning the musical spheres, interpreting the spacing and motions of the planets in terms of the harmony of Greek music. His reasoning was essentially Pythagorean in character. Starting with the two geometrical progressions, 1, 2, 4, 8, and 1, 3, 9, 27, he superimposed them and related them, as follows, to the distance of the seven heavenly bodies: moon—1; sun—2; Venus—3; Mercury—4; Mars—8; Jupiter—9; Saturn—27.

In this sequence of numbers Plato saw the superimposition of four octaves and a major sixth.

Many of Plato's astronomical arguments were vague and fanciful. However, he evidently did attribute the apparent diurnal motion of the heavenly bodies to the axial rotation of the earth. He was also reported by Plutarch and others as having in his old age "repented of having given to the earth the central place in the universe, which did not belong to it." The implication is that Plato either began to think of a heliocentric theory or, more probably, that he leaned toward the Pythagorean doctrine of a central fire.

Eudoxus

The philosopher Eudoxus (ca. 408–355 B.C.) contributed a new and important principle to cosmology. He clearly enunciated the doctrine that the heavens consisted of a number of perfectly transparent, crystalline, concentric spheres rotating about various axes. The fixed stars were the simplest of all. To represent their motion, he imagined them attached to a large sphere rotating once every 24 sidereal hours. Because of the eastward apparent motion of the sun, a sidereal day is approximately four minutes shorter than a solar day, a difference that adds up to one full day in a year. To account for the motion of the sun, Eudoxus postulated a similar sphere, rotating once every 24 sidereal hours. Inside this sphere was a second sphere, the pole of its rotation $23\frac{1}{2}°$ away from the pole of the diurnal rotation. The sun, attached to the equator of the second sphere, moved slowly eastward, completing a revolution once a year. Thus it was sometimes north of the equator and sometimes south. The slow eastward motion of the sun accounted for the difference between sidereal and solar time. Somehow or other, Eudoxus fitted a third sphere into this picture, probably because he had found such a sphere necessary to account for the motion of the moon.

Of the three concentric spheres accounting for the lunar motion, the outer one rotated in a sidereal day. The second one had an axis of $23\frac{1}{2}°$ from the diurnal pole, as for the sun. The third and inner sphere, the one that actually held the moon, had its axis some 5° away from the axis of the second. The inner sphere rotated in $27\frac{1}{2}$ days to account for the monthly revolution of the moon and its changing phases. It explained why the orbit of the moon is inclined 5° with respect to the ecliptic. But Eudoxus undoubtedly knew that although the inclination of 5° remained constant, the actual path of the moon is a slow spiral around the sky, taking about 19 years for a revolution. Hence, he had the second sphere, to which the third was attached, rotate around the pole of the ecliptic once every 19 years. This model of the solar system actually gave a very good representation of the lunar motion.

The planets were much more complex. We have seen that the paths of the sun and moon are relatively simple in as much as both progress regularly eastward across the heavens. The planets, however, slow down, come to a halt, and then move westward, exhibiting retrograde motion for a part of their orbits. To account for this retrograde motion, Eudoxus postulated an ingenious mechanical system. It consisted of two concentric spheres, the inner one containing the planets on its equator, and the outer one, to which the inner is attached, rotating independently in the opposite direction and with the same period. Now, if the two poles coincide, the rotation of the inner sphere undoes the opposite rotation of the outer and the planet remains stationary. If, on the other hand, the two axes do not coincide, but are displaced, say, 10° or so, the oppositely rotating sphere will carry the planet in a path like a number eight. And over half the cycle, if we set the long axis of the figure eight parallel to the ecliptic, the planet will be moving in a retrograde manner. Eudoxus called this path a "hippopede," after a favorite exercise in riding schools.

Applying this model to the planets, Eudoxus set the rotation period of the two synchronous spheres equal to the synodic period of the planet, namely the interval between successive appearances 180° from the sun. But he was not content to have the planet just make a figure eight in the sky: it must progress eastward as well. Hence, he gave to the outer of the two spheres a rotation about the axis of the ecliptic with a period equal to the sidereal period of the planet. Thus the hippopede was carried along with reference to the stars while the planet executed alternately retrograde and forward motions. Finally, the first and outermost sphere, as before, revolved once a sidereal day.

This model, of course, did not take into account the fact that the orbits of the planets do not coincide precisely with the ecliptic. To achieve his system, Eudoxus had had to postulate 27 spheres, one for the stars, three each for the sun and moon, and four each for the five planets. Evidently to improve the agreement, Callippus (ca. 370–300 B.C.) added six more. Even then, the agreement was poor for Mercury, Venus, and Mars. And the observations themselves left something to be desired. Eudoxus, however, was more of a mathematician than an astronomer. He regarded his "spheres" as an interesting mathematical device more as a model useful for prediction and calculation than as an actual physical fact.

With respect to the motion of the sun, Eudoxus had neglected one point that Callippus attempted to correct. The ancient Babylonians had recognized that the four seasons are not equally long: $94\frac{1}{2}$ days for spring, $92\frac{1}{2}$ days for summer, $88\frac{3}{4}$ days for fall, and $89\frac{1}{2}$ days for winter. Callippus tried to account for this difference by introducing two extra spheres for the sun, with hippopedes that slowed the sun during spring and summer and speeded it up during fall and winter. He similarly postulated two extra spheres for the moon.

The basic problem of the calendar, as we have seen, lies in the fact that the year contains not 12 but 12.3344 lunations from full moon to full moon. Hence the solar year exceeds the 12-month lunar year by about one-third of a month, and thus seasons in this system become disorganized. The priest in charge of the calendar would accumulate the additional days and, about every three years, insert an extra month, much as we do when we accumulate the extra quarters of a day and add a leap day every four years. The ancient Babylonians had discovered that 235 lunar months or 6940 days almost exactly equalled 19 solar years. If we divide 6940 by 19, we obtain the quotient of 365 and $5/16$ days, which exceeds the year of $365\frac{1}{4}$ by only about $1/16$ of a day. The Greek astronomer, Meton (b. 460 B.C.), working

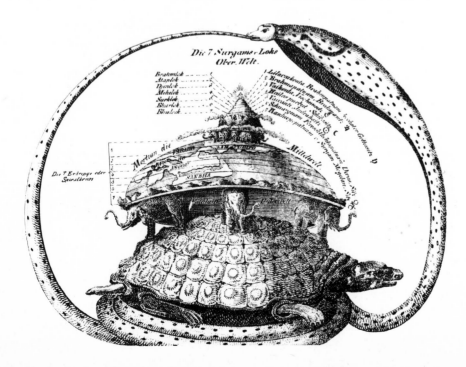

The Hindu concept of the universe designed by Brahmin. According to Hindu belief, the tortoise, symbol of force and creative power, rests on the great serpent, the emblem of eternity. The three worlds consist of the upper region of the gods; the second, or intermediate, region of the earth; and the third, the infernal region. The triangle, symbol of creation, unites the three worlds. (Bettmann Archive)

with Euctemon in about 432 B.C., rediscovered this interval, which has since then been referred to as the Metonic cycle. This principle makes clear that, however calendars differ from year to year during the 19 years, the same sequence of calendars could be used over and over again during each 19-year cycle. The 19-year cycle, therefore, consisted of 12 years having 12 lunations or "months" and 7 with 13 "months." As long as a lunar calendar was deemed necessary, this method was one of the best for reconciling the two schemes. Of course, the inequality of even $1/16$ of a day would accumulate over the years and require the subtraction of one day every 16 years.

How Aristotle Saw the World

Aristotle (384–322 B.C.), a pupil of Plato, delivered treatises on most of the sciences of his day—physics, astronomy, geology, biology, mathematics—in addition to politics, ethics, and art.

Although he was somewhat less successful in astronomy than in other fields of natural philosophy, Aristotle managed to depict a universe that was essentially consistent with the known facts of his time. He regarded the earth and heavens as spherical. He declared that all motion was either straight up or down, away from or toward the center of the earth, or parallel to its surface, that is, in circles around the earth's center, or a combination of both. This theorem is unquestionably true, for any motion whatever can be represented as combinations of radial and tangential components.

It is not surprising that Aristotle began by accepting the spheres of Eudoxus, for just as the circle was regarded as the most perfect of all plane figures, so the sphere was presumed the most perfect of solid bodies. Since Callipus had added additional spheres to those of Eudoxus, Aristotle—apparently more on philosophical grounds than on the basis of observation—assigned three new spheres each to Saturn and Jupiter, and four each to Mars, Venus, Mercury, and the sun. The moon, he claimed, did not need an extra sphere: being an inner sphere, there was nothing to disturb its motion. Thus he increased the total number of spheres to 55 in order more effectively to isolate the various celestial bodies from one another and from the sphere of fixed stars on the outside.

Aristotle devoted considerable attention to the composition of the universe. He followed Plato in assuming four fundamental elements: earth, water, air, and fire, in order of lightness. Earth sank to the bottom of the water, bubbles of air floated to the top, and fire rose upward in the air. The natural motions of the four basic elements, Aristotle noted, were up or down. They must, therefore, differ from the stars and other heavenly bodies, whose motions tended to be circular. For the composition of celestial objects, he postulated the existence of a perfect fifth substance, the essence or, literally, quintessence.

As for the earth, Aristotle held remarkably modern views. He gave two compelling reasons for regarding it as spherical. First, the shadow of the earth falling on the moon during a lunar eclipse has a curved edge. Second, new stars appear over the southern horizon as one moves south. He gave 12,000 miles for the earth's diameter, a figure some 50 per cent too large. He discusses but dismisses the idea that the sun, rather than the earth, may be the center of the solar system. If it were, he reasons, the orbital motion of the earth would cause the stars to reflect that motion. The argument is sound, except for the fact that the stars are so far away that their reflected motions can be detected only with telescopes of high precision, instruments not available in Aristotle's times.

Aristotle certainly recognized the moon as smaller than the earth and shining like the earth by reflected sunlight. He declared that some "stars" were larger than the earth, but it is not clear whether he meant the fixed stars or the wandering ones, the planets. From the fact that the moon occasionally moved in front of the stars and planets, "occulting" them, he deduced that it was the nearest of all the heavenly bodies. However, by some obscure and faulty logic, he also placed the sun nearer than the planets. The aurora, shooting

The Farnese Globe, with the early constellations and the heavens held up by Atlas. The ship Argo Navis is clearly visible. (Alinari Art Reference Bureau)

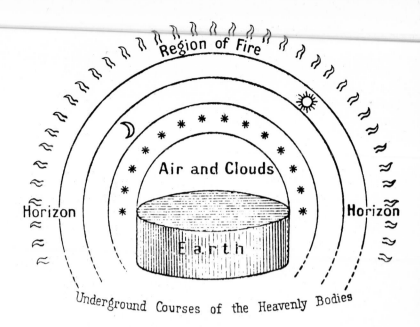

stars, and comets were, he stated, exhalations of the earth's upper atmosphere that became ignited by their motion.

The philosophy of Aristotle was a blend of scientific information and skillful argument, seasoned with his preconceptions as to what constituted a good and perfect universe. The general acceptance of Aristotle as the ultimate authority—particularly during the medieval period—obscured the fallacies in his arguments and conclusions. Adherence to that authority contributed appreciably to the scientific regression that marked the Middle Ages. But we should not hold Aristotle at fault for the dark ages of science. Had he been alive during that era, he most certainly would have fought the bigots who, by denying the evidence of their eyes and by quoting from irrelevant works, sought to stifle every attempt of science to advance.

A contemporary of Aristotle, Heraclides (ca. 388–315 B.C.), held relatively modern views concerning the world. He supposed the universe to be infinite, with the spherical earth rotating about an axis. He described the planets as separate worlds, each with its own atmosphere. To account for the fact that neither Mercury nor Venus strays very far from the sun, he put them in orbit around the sun. But he did not go so far as to make the sun the center of the solar system. His earth-centered model somewhat resembled the system proposed by Tycho Brahe in 1583, except that Tycho placed all the planets in orbit around the sun, which in turn revolved around the stationary earth.

An Early Heliocentric System

Aristarchus of Samos (ca. 312–230 B.C.) proposed a truly heliocentric system, antedating Copernicus by more than eighteen centuries. The idea may not have been entirely original, since Aristotle, a century or so earlier, had discussed the possibility and dismissed it on observational grounds. But the contributions of Aristarchus went far beyond his cosmological system. By logical reasoning and sound application of geometry he obtained an approximate idea of both the moon's size and distance. The diameter of the moon, he reasoned, was about one-third (rather than one-fourth, the modern figure) that of the earth.

In trying to determine the distance of the sun, he used arguments that were sound, but he went astray because of unavoidable observational inaccuracy. The argument was simple. As shown in Figure 2–1, we continue to watch the moon until it appears exactly half illuminated. This is the phase we call first (or last) quarter. When that occurs the angle at M must be a right angle. If at that moment we measure the angle at E, between the moon and sun, we have enough data to calculate the distance of the sun, ES. Aristarchus, from

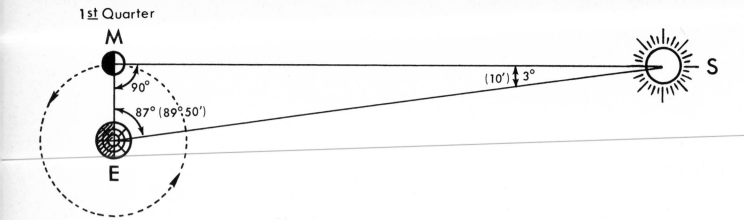

Figure 2-1. Aristarchus attempted to determine the distance of the sun by measuring the angles of the right triangle formed by the sun, earth, and the first quarter moon. His determinations of 87° and 3° were incorrect because of unavoidable observational error. The actual values are 89°50' and 10'. As a result, Aristarchus substantially underestimated the distance of the sun.

some unknown source—perhaps his own observations—estimates that the angle *E* is 87°, so that the angle *S* is only 3°. Simple geometry (or trigonometry) therefore gave the distance to the sun as 19 times that of the moon.

Since the sun and moon, as seen from the earth, have the same apparent diameter, Aristarchus then concluded that the sun's true diameter would be 19 times that of the moon or slightly more than 6 times that of the earth. Perhaps it was the overpowering size of the sun that led Aristarchus to the view that it would be more fitting for the earth to revolve around the sun than vice versa. The figure 19 is a tremendous underestimate, of course. The true value is nearer 400 and the angle at *S* is closer to 10 ' (minutes of arc), so that the angle *E* is only 10 ' less than a right angle. The point is that the crude observational methods of those days could not possibly have measured an angle that small. Furthermore, the terminator, as we call the boundary between the moon's dark and illuminated hemispheres, is not sharp since the apparent angular diameter of the sun itself is only 30 ', or half a degree. The terminator is consequently blurred by a similar amount when the sun is either rising or setting.

Eratosthenes Measures the Earth

As we have seen, various individuals had attempted to determine the diameter of the spherical earth. Eratosthenes (ca. 276–194 B.C.) is noted principally for the care he took in his measurements and the accuracy of his final result. He had noted that the difference in altitude of the noonday sun on June 21, at Syene and at Alexandria, Egypt, amounted to about 7° or, as he phrased it, $1/50$ of a circle. Hence the distance between these two stations, which lay very nearly on the same meridian, was $1/50$ of the circumference of the earth. The distance between the two cities, in terms of measurements known as *stadia*, was 5000 stadia, so that the circumference came out to 250,000 stadia. Later, Eratosthenes changed the figure to 252,000 stadia, probably to make it divisible by 360° and thus give exactly 700 stadia per degree.

The true circumference, in modern terms, depends therefore on the length of a stadium. Authorities disagree on that, but there seems to be some basis for considering a stadium equal to 157.5 meters, which would make the earth's circumference 24,662 miles, corresponding to a diameter of 7850 miles, some 50 miles less than the earth's polar diameter. The almost exact accord between the old and modern values must be accidental. Since the figures used—$1/50$ and 5000—were round numbers, the inherent errors just chanced to cancel. In any event, the value was more accurate than that determined later by Posidonius (ca. 135–50 B.C), who is also credited with suggesting that the sun was much more distant than any previous estimate. His figure for the solar distance was 500,000,000 stadia, approximately 200 times farther than the moon, as compared with the older value of 19 times. However, the observational basis for this estimate is not entirely clear. It may well have been little more than an exercise in mathematics based on unsupported hypotheses. Man had come a long way in understanding the universe around him. But he still had far to go.

Stone of the Sun, generally recognized
as depicting the Aztec calendar.
Around the border lie numbers,
designated in the vigesimal system
(based on 20 instead of 10). Original
in Archeological Museum, Mexico
City. (American Museum of Natural
History)

3

The Mechanistic Universe

Eudoxus' ingenious scheme of rotating, nesting spheres for each celestial body, with a separate pole for each sphere, represents quite well, as we have noted, the complex apparent motion of each body. In fact, with a sufficiently large number of spheres, one could still use this model to predict planetary positions far into the future. This representation, however, had a serious defect, one that the more discerning ancient scientists clearly recognized. As they move, the planets vary in brightness, often markedly, and the most natural explanation for these variations is changes in distance; in the Eudoxus spheres, the distances of the planets from the central earth remained constant. It was apparent that something was wrong with the model, because it did not allow the distances to change.

As an alternative, the scientists of ancient Greece began to think of the solar system as a huge machine whose secrets they thought they could discover by measurements and schematic interpretations. So they devised accurate methods for measuring the positions of the planets relative to the stars and conceived ingenious schemes for interpreting those observations.

Figure 3–1. Epicycle and the orbit of Mars. Early astronomers devised elaborate mathematical models utilizing devices called deferents and epicycles to account for departures from the circular motions of heavenly bodies. The deferent was an earth-centered circle; the epicycle revolved counter-clockwise around a point on the epicycle. In this diagram, Mars circles a point Q on a deferent circling the earth, thus representing the apparent motion of the planet as seen from the earth.

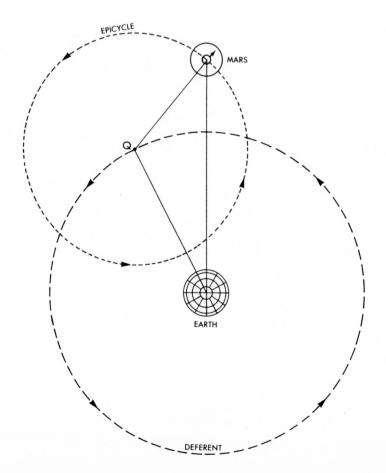

The Puzzle of the Sun

The sun presented the simplest problem. To the first observers it appeared to progress regularly and almost uniformly in a circular path around the sky. But then they discovered that the four seasons have unequal lengths, spring and summer requiring nine days longer than fall and winter. We know, today, that the elliptical form of the earth's orbit causes this discrepancy. The earth moves more rapidly in winter, when it is nearer the sun, than in summer, when it is farther away. And the apparent annual motion of the sun in a circle around the sky merely reflects the earth's non-uniform orbital motion. The ecliptic, the apparent circular path of the sun, and the zodiacal constellations that lie along it provide a useful reference system for locating the sun, moon, and planets.

To account for departures of heavenly bodies from uniform circular motion, early astronomers devised an elaborate system, based on mechanical or mathematical models. In its simplest form, the system employs an earth-centered circle called a *deferent*. The second circle, called an *epicycle*, has a

Eighteenth-century concept of the world showing (I) Ptolemaic and (II) Copernican systems and spheres with signs of zodiac. A partially modified version of the system proposed by Tycho is shown (III), and a more modern version of the universe (IV) indicates the relative sizes of the sun and planets. (Bettmann Archive)

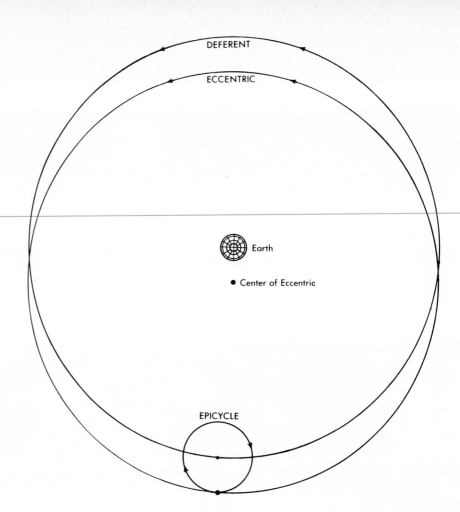

DEFERENT

ECCENTRIC

⊕ Earth

● Center of Eccentric

EPICYCLE

Figure 3–2. Early astronomers explained the irregular motion of the sun by saying that the center of the circle it describes does not coincide with that described by the earth. Hipparchus showed, however, that the sun's eccentric circle was the same as the deferent around the earth combined with an epicycle that rotated counterclockwise.

Below: Figure 3–3. The relationship of the moon's orbit to the ecliptic. Because the moon's rate of movement changes during the month and its orbit is inclined 5° with reference to the ecliptic, it crosses the ecliptic at a point called the node (☊) at a different point each month. This is known as the regression of the nodes.

center, Q, which lies on the deferent and revolves uniformly counterclockwise around the earth from west to east. The point Q was said to be "immaterial," since it did not contain matter. The celestial body, meanwhile, revolves uniformly around Q on the epicycle circle. This second motion can be either clockwise or counterclockwise. The apparent motion of the body relative to the earth is the combined motion in the two circles (fig. 3–1).

To explain the irregular motion of the sun, Hipparchus (fl. 130 B.C.), often referred to as the father of modern astronomy, favored the idea—advanced by the earlier astronomers—that the sun moved in a circle whose center does not coincide with the earth. Hipparchus proved, however, that such an eccentric circle is identical with an earth-centered, circular deferent rotating counterclockwise combined with an epicycle that rotates clockwise (fig. 3–2) and has the same period as the deferent. Hipparchus clearly recognized the equivalence of these two concepts, but preferred the epicyclic description. This model was accurate enough to account for the motion of the sun to within less than a minute of arc, a negligible error then and for more than seventeen centuries thereafter.

The Motion of the Moon

The motion of the moon proved, of course, to be much more complex than that of the sun. Applying reasoning similar to that used by Aristarchus, the ancients had long realized that the sun was very much farther away than the

Moon's Path one month later

Moon's Path in the Sky

5°

E

Ecliptic

W

☊   ☊

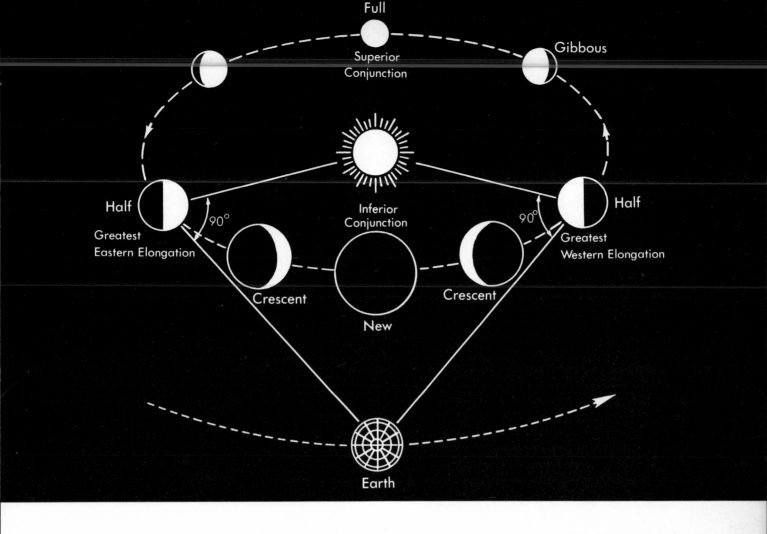

Figure 3–4. Phases and relative sizes of Venus as seen from earth.

moon. They had come to recognize that the changing phases of the moon were clearly those of a sphere illuminated from different directions by sunlight.

Some of the difficulties in predicting the moon's position by means of the earlier theories arose because the actual orbit is much more elliptical than the orbit of the earth around the sun. As a consequence, the moon moves much faster during one part of the month and more slowly during the next part. The ancients could only partially explain this effect—as they did for the sun—in terms of uniform motion in an eccentric circle. Actually the problem had other complications, as Figure 3–3 shows. The orbit of the moon is inclined 5° with reference to the ecliptic. But the point where it crosses the ecliptic, called the *node*, slowly moves.

There are actually two nodes. The *ascending node*, designated by the symbol ☊, is the point where the moon crosses the ecliptic from south to north. The *descending node*, ☋, marks the crossing from north to south. Successive crossings occur 27.21222 days apart, an interval called the *Draconitic month*. In other words, the moon's path is not a true circle but a spiral, with successive loops spaced about a degree and a half apart. The node drifts slowly westward, a direction opposite to that of the normal motion of the planets. This phenomenon is called *regression* of the nodes. One complete revolution of the nodes requires 18.61 years, an interval known as the *nutation* period. Nutation means "wobbling," and indeed the orbit does wobble, like a wheel on a bent shaft.

The peculiar spiral pattern of the lunar motion taxed the early astronomers to find an acceptable mathematical or mechanical representation of it. The moon moved around the rim of the eccentric wheel once in a Draconitic month, while the wheel shaft slowly revolved in 18.61 years.

This model had many defects, of which the ancients were aware. At the

37

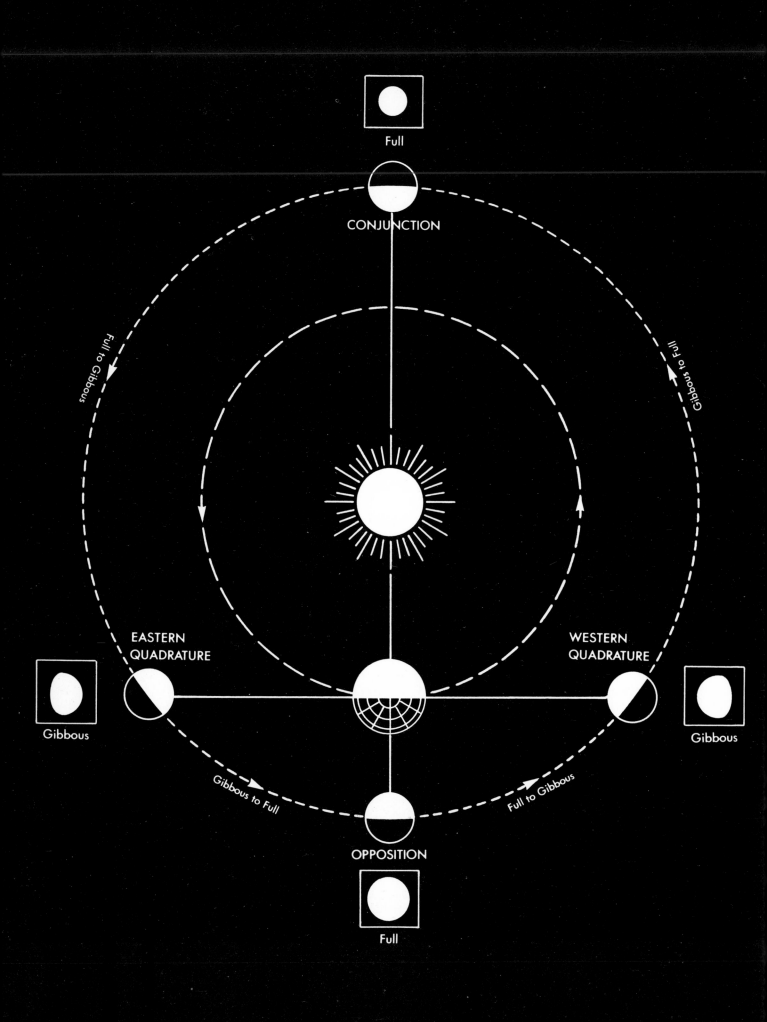

Full

CONJUNCTION

Full to Gibbous

Gibbous to Full

EASTERN
QUADRATURE

WESTERN
QUADRATURE

Gibbous

Gibbous

Gibbous to Full

Full to Gibbous

OPPOSITION

Full

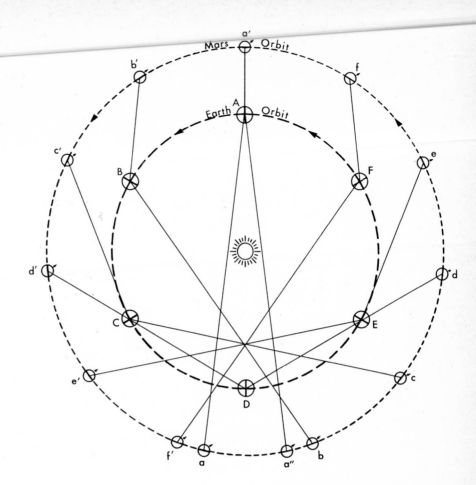

Left: Figure 3–5. The configuration and phases of a superior planet.

Right: Figure 3–6. Orbit of Mars in the Copernican System.

basis of these faults lay the impossibility of representing the actual orbital ellipse by an eccentric circle. Ptolemy (fl. 150 A.D.) vastly improved earlier observations and developed much more accurate models of the solar system. He devoted great attention to the moon, making accurate measures throughout the lunation. The theory that Ptolemy developed to explain his observations is needlessly complicated. It was a great improvement over earlier theories, except that it made the moon's distance vary much more than it actually does, a fact that Ptolemy could scarcely have failed to notice. His main objective, however, was to represent past observations and successfully predict the position of the moon in the future.

Too little note has been taken of one point in Ptolemy's contribution to the subject. Where earlier philosophers usually rigidly adhered to their conceptions of how the universe should work, Ptolemy showed a remarkable flexibility. He regarded observations themselves as sacred. And he modified theoretical models to fit the data. He subscribed to a phrase widely used in his and later eras: "Save the phenomena." By this he meant that the theories of interpretation must be modified if they fail to represent the observations—a philosophical approach that is the cornerstone of modern scientific method.

Hipparchus and Planetary Motion

Hipparchus tried to explain the motions of the five planets as well as the motion of the sun and moon, but in this area he was much less successful. Let us examine the problem in the light of modern knowledge of the solar system, but, for simplicity, with the planets moving in circular instead of elliptical orbits.

Mercury and Venus, whose orbits lie inside that of the earth, we call *inferior* planets, solely because of their relative position. Analogously, we term Mars and other bodies with orbits outside that of the earth *superior* planets. When a planet lies in the same direction from the earth as the sun, we

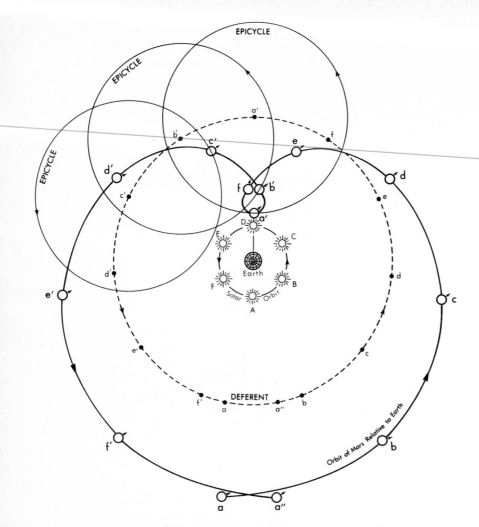

Figure 3–7. Orbit of Mars in the Ptolemaic System.

say that it is in *conjunction* with the sun (fig. 3–4). An inferior planet has two such configurations: a *superior conjunction* when the planet lies beyond the sun, and in *inferior conjunction* when it lies between the sun and the earth. A planet, after passing superior conjunction, moves into the evening sky, setting in the west after the sun. Slowly it draws away from the sun until it reaches the maximum distance east from the sun, a point known as the *eastern elongation*. As seen through a telescope, a planet at this point looks like the moon at first quarter, presenting half an illuminated hemisphere toward the earth. The planet continues to draw nearer the earth, meanwhile increasing somewhat in brightness, the diminished distance more than compensating for the decrease in size of the illuminated crescent seen from the earth. After reaching its greatest brightness, the planet rapidly draws in toward the sun and passes inferior conjunction. It then appears in the morning sky as it again attains greatest brightness and reaches maximum *western elongation*.

The phases of a superior planet are as follows (fig. 3–5): after passing conjunction, the planet slowly moves eastward into the evening sky, finally reaching quadrature, 90° from the sun, when the planet appears on the meridian near sunset. The planet continues on to a position opposite the sun, and rises at sunset, a phase termed *opposition*. Later it reaches the second quadrature, 90° from the sun.

The Motion of the Planets

The apparent motion of any planet, inferior or superior, is the result of the combined motion of the earth and planet. Let us see how the ancients tried to reconcile the observed motions with their belief in an earth-centered solar system.

40

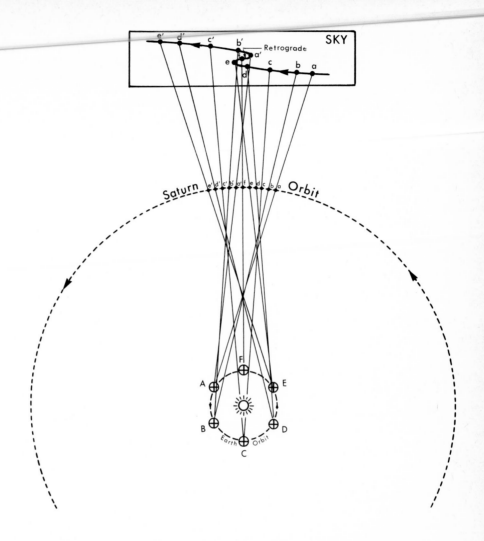

Figure 3–8. Orbit of Saturn in the
Copernican System.

The behavior of Mars, for example, did not accord with the concept of uniform revolution around the earth. The earth takes 365.25636 days to execute a full revolution with respect to the stars—which constitutes what is called the *sidereal year*. Mars on the other hand has a much longer sidereal period of 686.980 days. Hence, while the earth completes a full revolution of 360°, Mars has moved through only 191°, slightly more than one-half a circuit. In Figure 3–6, showing the relative motions of the earth and Mars, the letters *A*, *B*, *C*, *D*, *E*, and *F* on the inner circle represent the positions of the earth at two-month intervals. If we assume that Mars lies at *a* in its orbit, on the far side of the sun near conjunction, two months later the two planets will be at *Bb*; then *Cc*; and so on. The rapidly moving earth is thus catching up to Mars and getting ready to pass it. After a year, the earth is again at *A*, but now Mars lies at *a'*, at opposition and minimum distance.

As the faster-moving earth passes Mars, the slower planet appears to drift backward or westward, a direction opposite to the normal motion. (This retrograde motion is illustrated in the actual path of Mars in the sky during the opposition of 1969, Figure 12–2.) The phenomenon was well known to the ancients. A tablet at Nineveh reads, "When the star of Mars becomes powerful, its brightness increases: seven days, fourteen days, twenty-one days it journeys backward, and then it continues on its prescribed course." The actual duration of the retrograde motion is nine to eleven weeks. As the earth continues its motion through a second year, the two planets occupy the positions *Aa'*, *Bb'*, *Cc'*, *Dd'*, *Ee'*, and *Ff'*. Then the earth continues on to *A* and Mars to *a"*, passing through conjunction during this last interval. In the course of two full years, the earth has made two complete orbits, while Mars has executed just one, together with the small segment of the circle

41

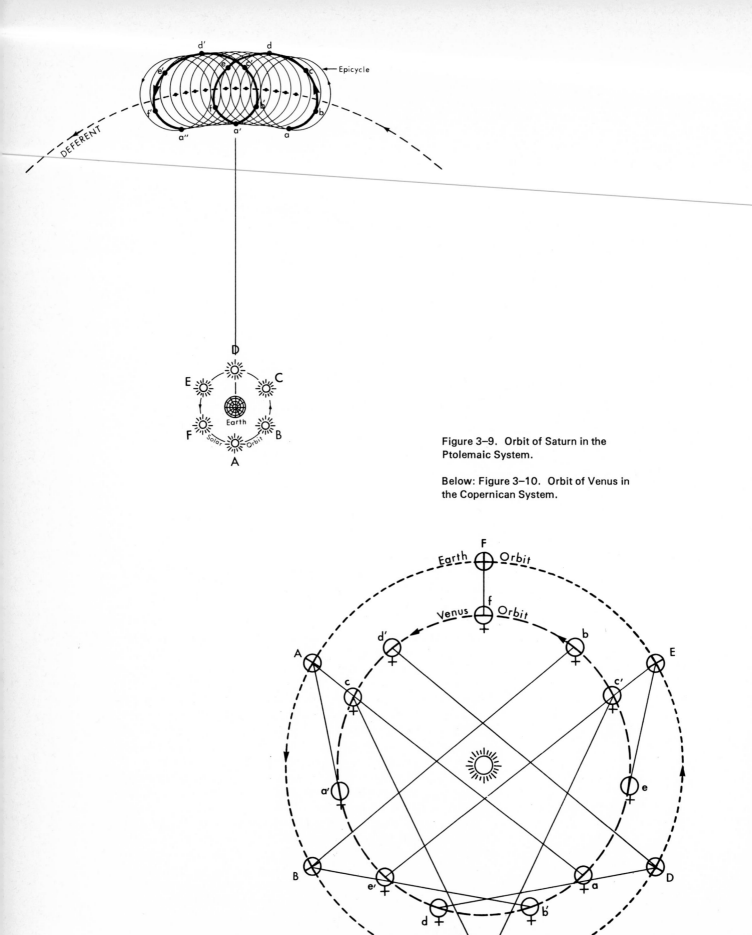

Figure 3–9. Orbit of Saturn in the Ptolemaic System.

Below: Figure 3–10. Orbit of Venus in the Copernican System.

between *a* and *a"*. Meanwhile Mars has swung in from distant conjunction to near opposition and receded again in conjunction.

If we adopt the view that the earth is stationary, we can represent the position of Mars relative to the earth by a heart-shaped curve (fig. 3–7). The letter pairs have the same meaning as in Figure 3–6, except that we have made the sun revolve about the earth in a year, occupying the successive positions *A, B, C, D*, etc., in an orbit of arbitrary radius. To see how the ancients reconciled the peculiar heart-shaped orbit with their model of deferent and epicycle, we may turn again to Figure 3–1. The deferent has a radius equal to that of the orbit of Mars, and point *Q* revolves around the earth in 687 days, the sidereal period of Mars. The radius of the epicycle equals that of the earth's orbit around the sun, and the planet executes one complete sidereal revolution in a terrestrial year. In Figure 3–1, the deferent, the motion of the epicycle along the deferent, and the apparent motion of the planet are all firmly attached to the epicycle. Two circular motions combine to represent the motion of Mars relative to the earth as a center, duplicating exactly the heart-shaped curve of Figure 3–7. Similar representations of the orbit of Saturn appear in Figures 3–8 and 3–9.

The Orbit of Venus

Let us now consider the orbit of an inferior planet, Venus, relative to the earth. In this comparison, Venus, nearer the sun, is the speedster, with a sidereal period of 224.701 days. The two planets start out together (at *Aa* in Figure 3–10) just before superior conjunction. Ten months later the earth is lagging behind at *F* and Venus is at inferior conjunction. The motion continues for the second year, represented by the positions *Aa ', Bb '*, to *Ee '*.

The relative earth-centered orbit (fig. 3–11) also forms a heart-shaped loop. The mechanical representation, as for Mars, consists of a deferent and

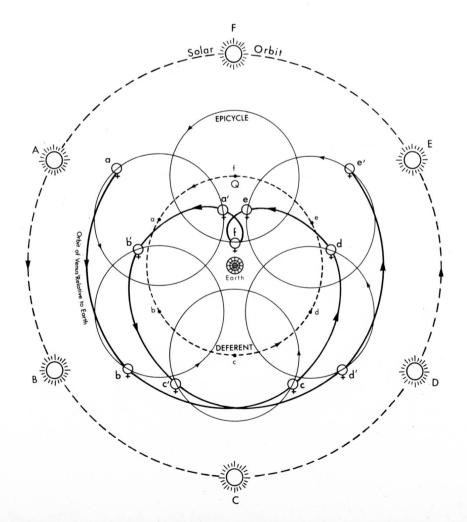

Figure 3–11. Orbit of Venus in the Ptolemaic System.

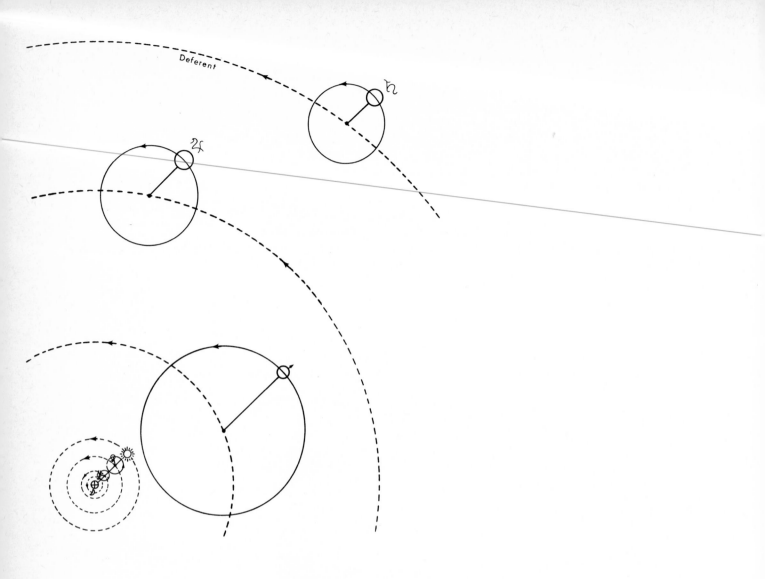

Figure 3–12. The solar system of the ancients, constructed so that the epicycles of no two planets would interfere with one another.

Deferent

an epicycle (fig. 3–1). Unlike the model for Mars, however, the deferent has a radius equal to that of the earth's orbit, with the immaterial point, Q, revolving once a year. The radius of the epicycle equals that of the orbit of Venus and it revolves once in the sidereal period of Venus. The assumed orbit of the sun always lies outside those of Venus and Mercury. The ancients could have represented the motion more accurately, however, if they had put the solar orbit midway between that of Mercury and Venus, so that the sun would at times be closer to the earth and at other times more distant than either of these planets.

The Solar System of the Early Astronomers

Having determined the relative epicycles and deferents for all seven of the celestial bodies, including the sun and moon, the ancients put all of them together in a complex scheme (fig. 3–12). This arrangement might be considered the most economical apportionment of space, since no two bodies in it would ever collide as a result of their motion. None of the "wheels" actually touches another. Thus the epicycle of Mars is barely tangent externally to the circular orbit of the sun, the epicycle of Venus is internally tangent to the solar orbit, and so on. Various other arrangements are possible with this approach, since it ignores the scale of the solar system and treats each body, except the sun, separately.

The early astronomers were by no means unaware of the heliocentric alternative. But they rejected it, for they concluded, quite correctly, that if the earth were moving in an annual orbit, the nearer (and brighter) stars

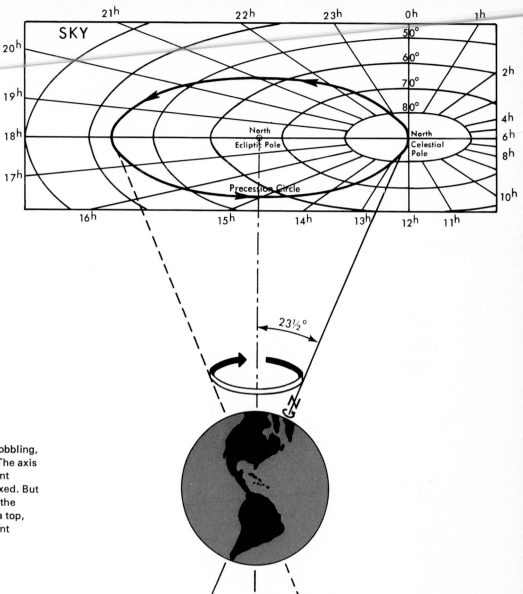

Figure 3–13. Precession, or wobbling, of the earth's pole of rotation. The axis of the earth (shown in its present position) remains essentially fixed. But the whole earth, tilted 23.5° to the plane of its orbit, wobbles like a top, with the axis pointing to different regions of the sky in turn.

would oscillate relative to the more distant (and fainter) stars. Such shifts do occur, but they are very minute because the stars are vastly more distant than the ancients ever imagined. It was not until 1838, long after the invention of the telescope, that the astronomer F. W. Bessel finally detected this annual shift, known as *parallax*, of the near star 61 Cygni.

Our analysis of planetary motion based on the hypothesis of circular orbits around the sun failed entirely to represent the positions of Mercury and Mars, whose orbits are the most elliptical of all planetary orbits. The deferents and epicycles used in ancient times were a poor substitute for reality, and Ptolemy tried other devices to bring theory into line with observation. For one thing, the orbits are not, in general, parallel to the ecliptic. So he used an inclined deferent but set the epicycle parallel to the ecliptic. This decision was truly a stroke of genius, since the epicycles, as we have seen, merely reflect the earth's orbital motion. For the inner planets, he correctly assumed that the deferent was parallel to the ecliptic and to the inclined epicycle. But among the phenomena he could not explain was the fact that the length of the retrograde arc of Mars varied significantly from opposition to opposition.

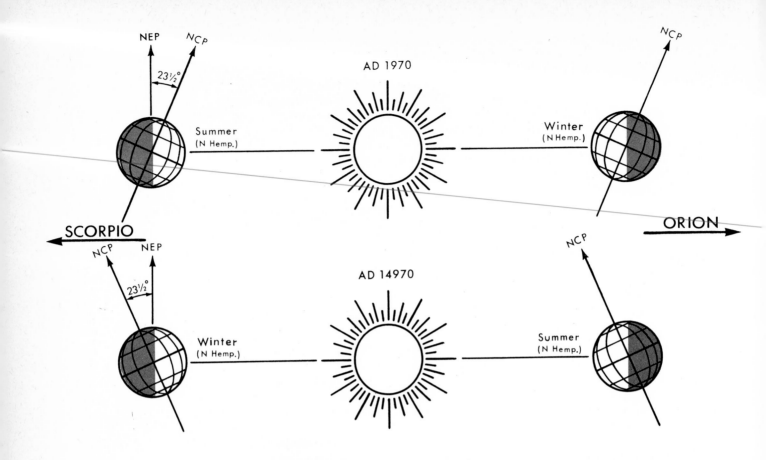

Figure 3–14. Shift in zodiacal constellations because of precession. The drift in the vernal equinox resulting from the shifting of the pole causes the equinox to move over the centuries from one zodiacal constellation to the next. In the course of the next 13,000 years, for example, the relationship between Orion, which is now high in the sky, and Scorpio, which is now low, will be completely reversed. NCP is the north celestial pole, and NEP is the north ecliptic pole.

The Errors of Early Astronomy

We should not be too critical of the early astronomers for imperfections in their theoretical models of the solar system. They were, of course, wrong in their basic assumption that one could define the system of the world by applying geometrical principles alone. But they had found that a concept such as the Pythagorean theorem was valid within the physical universe, even though it in no way derived from experiment. The ancients were also led astray by their mystical belief in the significance of the circle and circular motion. The fact that all circles, unlike ellipses, possessed the same shape, irrespective of size, suggested to them some sort of perfection.

Nor did the ancients all agree on the sequence of the planets in order of their distance from the earth. Plato, Aristotle, and others favored the following sequence: Moon, Sun, Venus, Mercury, Mars, Jupiter, Saturn. But Hipparchus and those who followed him chose this arrangement: Moon, Mercury, Venus, Sun, Mars, Jupiter, Saturn. Some writers gave a kind of philosophical reason for the second list, namely that it set the sun at the center of the system, a commanding position befitting its importance. But this explanation fails to account for the transposition of Venus and Mercury. More probably, the second list derived from the sidereal periods of the objects, which had by then become known through the theory of epicycles.

The Drifting Equinox

The *vernal equinox* is that point on the celestial sphere where the sun, moving along the ecliptic, crosses the equator from south to north. Astronomers have often found it convenient to represent the positions of stars with reference to the ecliptic. They reckon *celestial longitude* eastward from the vernal equinox and *celestial latitude* north or south of the ecliptic. The system resembles, but should not be confused with, that used for locating points on the surface of the earth.

Hipparchus prepared a major catalog of stars, their positions and their apparent magnitudes. Comparing the positions of stars from his own observations with those of Timocharis, made a century and a half earlier, Hipparchus was surprised to find that the longitudes had all increased. From these studies Hipparchus concluded that the vernal equinox was slowly drifting westward among the stars at 45 or 46 seconds of arc per year. The figure was remarkably correct since the modern value is 50″ 23 (or 50.23 seconds of arc) per year. Ptolemy gave a less accurate figure of 36″ per year, which may have been "rounded off" from a rough estimate of 1° per century.

The phenomenon these ancient astronomers had noted is known as *precession of the equinox*. In the course of 25,800 years the equinox drifts entirely around the sky, occupying each of the zodiacal constellations in turn. In the time of Hipparchus and Ptolemy it lay in the constellation of Aries. Now, some 2000 years later, it has moved about 100,000″ or 28°. Since the zodiac contains twelve constellations, one for each 30° of longitude, the vernal equinox no longer lies in Aries but in the neighboring constellation of Pisces.

Our Wobbling Earth

Precession has a relatively simple explanation. Like the earth, the celestial sphere has two poles, north and south, defined by the apparent rotation (fig. 3–13). Our North Star, Polaris, currently lies near one of these poles. But these poles are not fixed in the sky. The earth is slowly wobbling like a top, tilted 23.5° to the plane of its orbit. As the pole moves, delineating a small circle in the sky, the celestial equator, which is a circle 90° from either pole, also moves. The intersection of the equator drifts along the ecliptic, causing precession of the equinox.

We must recall that the original motivation for these celestial studies stemmed from the wish to predict the occurrence of the vernal equinox and to forecast the flooding of the Nile and other rivers that marked the onset of spring. The vernal equinox occurred then, as now, at the precise moment when the sun, moving diagonally across the sky from south to north, crossed the equator.

The discovery of precession must have shocked the astrologers, who had maintained that the passage of the sun from one zodiacal constellation to the next controlled events on earth, including the seasons (fig. 3–14). When they realized that the seasons remained fixed with reference to the vernal equinox and not to the star constellations, the astrologers had to find an acceptable answer. And they did—one that they still use to this day. They invented the signs of the zodiac, which are distinguished from the constellations in that the signs remain permanently attached to the vernal equinox. Hence, the purported influence of the heavenly bodies on weather or on man was supposed to derive from these mythical and mystical signs and not from the constellations or stars therein. Currently the "sign of Aries" lies on the border of the constellation of Pisces, or in what astrologers assign to the edge of Aquarius. This fact accounts for the recent publicity about the "Age of Aquarius." Such sophistry appears to satisfy those who believe in astrology; indeed, most believers, unaware of these facts, fail to distinguish between the signs and the constellations.

4

The Rebirth of Science

Ptolemy, who lived in the second century A.D., was the last great figure before the renaissance of science. His collected works, *Thirteen Books of the Mathematical Composition*, comprise the best guide to his ideas and the contributions of those who preceded him. Although beclouded here and there with vague philosophical ideas and superstitions, the Greek concept of the universe was the product of careful observation, logical deduction, and the application of basic geometrical principles. Without telescopes and with only primitive measuring devices, the Greeks compiled a tremendous amount of observational data concerning the motions of the planets with respect to the stars. And their mechanical model of deferents and epicycles yielded, as we have seen, a reasonably accurate representation of their observations.

Peace and prosperity continued to reign until about the end of the second century A.D. Then a series of catastrophes dissolved the Roman Empire and all but destroyed civilization itself. Decadent political and social systems collapsed. The exhaustion of gold and silver coins, as the Spanish mines ran out of the precious minerals, paralyzed commerce. A horrible pestilence, brought back from Asia by the military, struck down the population at the rate of two thousand persons per day. Barbarian tribes pressed in, conquering and devastating southern Europe.

The centuries that followed were sad times for science. Deprived of comfort in this world, people looked forward to solace in a better world hereafter, and turned away from the science of the past. Christianity, the major force during the Middle Ages, brought with it a growing desire to reconcile science in general and concepts of the universe in particular with the literal statements of the Scriptures. Lactantius ridiculed the concept of a spherical earth. Most people came to believe that the earth was flat, square, and supported by four pillars, one at each corner. Under such circumstances, contributions to science were few. The "meteors" (in the general sense in which the term is used in chapter 1) became signs in the sky prophetic of events, evil or good, about to happen on the earth. Superstition and fear were the motivating forces in astronomical thought for many centuries.

For a time the torch of learning passed into hands of the Arabs. They made few advances, but at least they preserved in the *Almagest* the writings of Ptolemy, and they continued to make a few observations of the motions of the heavenly bodies. The *Koran*, fortunately, was silent on questions that related to concepts of the earth and the universe. By the end of the twelfth century, interest was rekindled in learning, in agriculture, craft, commerce, and in science. But an aura of superstition, mysticism, and magic continued to obstruct the development of the sciences, especially astronomy and chemistry.

The pseudoscience of alchemy, bearing a relationship to chemistry similar to that of astrology to astronomy, burgeoned. There was a widespread belief that with the use of magic, potions, and incantations one could turn base metal into gold or silver. Failure did not discourage the alchemists and magicians. From time to time they even made, by accident, some useful chemical discovery. In such an atmosphere, it is not surprising that astrology flourished. The idea that God, through the stars, could influence mankind was not unacceptable to the church fathers. And so, with the full approval of the church, astrologers continued to cast horoscopes.

The medieval concept of the sky as a star-studded globe, through which a fortunate traveller might poke his head and view the glories of Heaven beyond. The interlocked wheels were those described by Ezekiel, which in reality are parhelic phenomena caused by ice crystals in the earth's atmosphere. (Bettmann Archive)

Observational astronomy began again early in the sixteenth century. Belief in a flat earth began to recede and in its place came an understanding of the universe as visualized by Ptolemy. Attention was again turned to Aristotle and the other pagan philosophers.

The Advent of Copernicus

In 1473, Niklas Koppernigk, known as Copernicus, was born in Poland. At the University of Cracow he took an interest in astronomy and astrology. He was a voracious reader and his growing knowledge led him to speculate about the world system. In particular, he began to revive the postulate, proposed some seventeen centuries earlier by Aristarchus, that the sun was the center of the solar system and that the planets went around the sun. Analyzing observational data in terms of this hypothesis, he developed a model of the solar system that was remarkably modern, except that he substituted the old deferents and epicycles of Hipparchus, Ptolemy, and their predecessors for true elliptical orbits. He worked out a detailed theory of the moon in orbit and set the distance of the moon, in essential agreement with Ptolemy, at about 60 times the earth's radius, a figure very close to the one we use today. Copernicus noted that the moon's orbit was not an earth-centered circle.

49

Left: God creating the stars, with the planetary spheres shown inside, according to the Ptolemaic order. (Verlag Karl Alber, Freiburgh Museum)

Right: The astronomer Ptolemy observing the heavens with a primitive quadrant. On the wall behind him appear representations of the zodiacal constellations Capricornus, Aquarius, and Pisces. Detail from a fresco in the Campanile of the Duomo, Florence. (Alinari Art Reference Bureau)

He also concluded that the earth definitely was a planet. Ptolemy had once argued against the rotation of the earth by saying that so rapid a motion would have caused the mountains to tear loose from the surface and be scattered over the heavens. Copernicus countered this by saying that Ptolemy should have been even more afraid that the heavens, rotating in the same interval but with vastly greater radius, would be even more likely to break. He investigated the old question of the precession of the equinoxes and arrived at a value for its magnitude that is consistent with the modern figure. Although he did not realize that Ptolemy had mistakenly asserted that the precession is irregular, Copernicus was the first to recognize the true cause of precession as a slow wobbling of the earth's axis in relation to the perpendicular to the earth's orbital plane. He also correctly located the positions of Mercury and Venus, the two inferior planets, and correctly accounted for the variable lengths of the retrograde motion of the three outer planets. His values for the relative mean distances of planets from the sun agree, to within a few per cent, with ours.

After describing his system of the world, Copernicus justifies his conclusions thus:

"... in the midst of all stands the sun. For who could in this most beautiful temple place this lamp in another or better place than that from which it can at the same time illuminate the whole? Which some not unsuitably call the light of the world, others the soul or the ruler. Trismegistus calls it the visible God, the Electra of Sophocles, the all-seeing. So indeed does the sun, sitting on the royal throne, steer the revolving family of stars."

For all of its advantages, Copernicus was dissatisfied with the results of his model. He had hoped to predict the positions of the planets within ten minutes of arc, a modest objective, but his figures were far less accurate. The discrepancies lay in the failure of deferents and epicycles to reproduce precisely the true motions of the planets. It fell to the lot of Kepler, half a century later, to discover this fact and thus vastly increase the accuracy of prediction. Dying in 1543, the year his monumental work was published, Copernicus escaped the criticism that his revolutionary hypotheses later aroused.

Tycho Brahe

Following Copernicus, the Danish nobleman Tycho Brahe (1546–1601) began his astronomical studies. He achieved much greater precision than had any earlier astronomer. Tycho, as he is known, became interested in astronomy in 1572 when a "new star" sudently blazed out in the constellation Cassiopeia. Known technically as a *nova*, it was considered unique in the history of astronomy. It far outshone any of the fixed stars and rivaled the planet Venus in its brilliance. One could see it even in the daytime. Today we realize what happened: a star had truly exploded, increasing millions of times in brightness as it expelled fragments into space—a type of outburst generally called a *supernova*.

But in 1572, ignorant and superstitious people thought it had a deeper meaning. One philosopher supposed it to be a reappearance of the Star of Bethlehem, presaging the second coming of Christ. Others speculated about the calamities it might bring. And how did it fit into the cosmic scheme of things? After all, Aristotle, in his vast authority, had asserted that the world of stars was eternal and invariable. Or was it a mere exhalation of the earth, a luminous vapor akin to comets?

Tycho sought an answer to some of these questions through direct observation, carefully measuring the distance between the nova and Polaris, the North Star. He also fixed the position of the nova with reference to the neighboring stars of Cassiopeia. These measures clearly established that the body did not change position and thus lay in the realm of the fixed stars. Had it been nearer, Tycho would have detected a displacement as it moved in its diurnal circle around the sky. He came, therefore, to the conclusion—startling at that time—that, contrary to Aristotle's teaching, the stars were not invariable. The nova soon began to decline in brightness and, with colors changing from yellow, to red, to white, finally faded from view in 1574. People still wondered about it, and Tycho advanced the hypothesis that the star had perhaps formed as a condensation from dark matter of the Milky Way. He even pointed out a dark area from which such a condensation might have occurred.

The appearance of this star stimulated interest in astronomy. After extensive travels to study the methods of other astronomers, Tycho finally built his own observatory, a palace of astronomy known as "Uraniborg," near Copenhagen. There, for two decades, this nobleman carried out systematic measurements of the positions of stars, planets, and the other heavenly bodies. To do this he devised a new and more accurate instrument than any then available. He also studied the comets and he concluded, as he had about the nova, that these objects were not exhalations of the earth but part of interplanetary realms. In 1598, when a lunar eclipse that he had calculated occurred one and a half hours too late, he correctly concluded that the error resulted from his failure to allow for the fact that the sun was nearer the earth and moved more rapidly in winter than in summer.

Medieval astronomer in his study, surrounded by his tools. (Metropolitan Museum of Art)

Although Tycho was fully aware of the model solar system of Copernicus, he rejected it for the same reason that Ptolemy had given many centuries earlier: the stars failed to show any motion caused by a reflection of the earth's orbital movement around the sun. Hence Tycho, in an attempt to reconcile the geocentric and heliocentric systems, devised still another mechanical model (fig. 4–1). He set the earth, stationary, at the center, letting the moon and sun orbit around it, but with the five planets circling the sun rather than the earth. Mechanically, Tycho's system is identical with that of Copernicus, except that it avoids the difficulty of the earth's annual revolution.

When his patron, King Frederic, died, Tycho moved to Prague and died there in 1601. He bequeathed to the world, via his faithful assistant Johannes Kepler, his long and accurate series of observations.

Portrait of Galileo and Galileo's telescope. (Both: American Museum of Natural History)

Kepler's Contribution

Kepler (1571–1630), a German astronomer and mathematician, had a burning desire to discover the true cosmic system. In many respects he was a mystic—at heart a Pythagorean—who believed he could by thought alone divine the structure of the universe. However, unlike most other mystics, Kepler had a healthy respect for observation, though he also believed in and sometimes practised astrology. Above all, Kepler had faith in the accuracy of Tycho's observations. He attempted to improve the Copernican system, which he had come to accept; but as the complex of deferents, cycles, and epicycles failed to represent his observations, he turned toward other hypotheses. A wealth of observational data eventually led him to the correct answer. He abandoned the age-old theory of circular orbits with circular epicycles and so on, and he enunciated his first law—that the orbits of planets about the sun are ellipses, with the sun at one focus (fig. 4–2). One may define an ellipse as a curve where the sum of the distances of the point C from the two foci, A and B, is a constant. Thus a circle is a special kind of ellipse, where the two foci come together. The farther apart one spaces the foci, the greater the *eccentricity* of the ellipse.

Continuing his investigations, Kepler noted that as a planet moves, its *radius vector* (a line drawn from the sun at one focus of the ellipse to the planet on the boundary) sweeps out an area (fig. 4–3). What he finally discovered, as stated in his second law, was that planets sweep out equal areas in equal intervals of time. This phenomenon accounts for the fact that, as we have noted, the earth moves more rapidly during the winter when nearest the sun (*perihelion*) than during the summer, when it lies farthest from the sun (*aphelion*).

More than a dozen years of study intervened between the publication of Kepler's second law and his final work, which contained his third law. This law states in mathematical form a very simple relationship he had discovered between the orbital periods, p, of the planets and their distances from the sun, a. Since the orbits are not circular, he took a to be the mean distance or half the major axis of the ellipse. In words, the law is that the square of the periodic time (measured in years) is equal to the cube of the mean distance, expressed in units of the earth's mean distance from the sun, the so-called *astronomical unit*. Thus, the equation is: $p^2 = a^3$. We can see immediately that this equation applies to the earth, in which p equals 1 year and a equals 1 astronomical unit, so that $1 = 1$. If, say, a equals 4 astronomical units, that gives us $4^3 = 4 \times 4 \times 4 = 64$. Our equation, therefore, reduces to $p^2 = 64$. Hence, $p = 8$. We have chosen this simple example, of course, because the answer comes out in round numbers. Even so, the equation is not difficult to solve, and the important fact is that it fits the orbits of all of the planets. Many years later, the great British astronomer Sir Isaac Newton showed that all three of Kepler's laws were the direct consequence of the laws of gravitation and physics governing the forces at work between various bodies.

Kepler's studies led him into many fields: abstract mathematics, geometry, and musical harmony. By inscribing a whole series of geometrical figures,

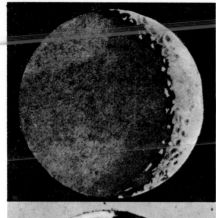

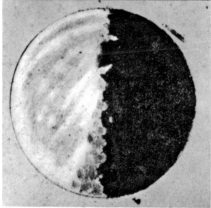

Above: Galileo's drawings of the moon.
(American Museum of Natural History)

Below: Newton's reflecting telescope
(facsimile). (Science Museum, London)

such as the pyramid, a cube, an octahedron, and so on, within one another, he thought he had found an explanation for the spacing of planets in the solar system. This agreement was only a figment of his imagination. It showed that man was still not quite ready to relinquish preconceptions about the universe and let the observations speak for themselves.

The latter principle, the basic philosophy of modern science, was just beginning to be recognized. An Englishman, Francis Bacon, in his *Novum Organum*, 1620, had clearly delineated the function of observation and experiment in the interpretation of science. Yet René Descartes, French mathematician and philosopher, some twenty years later still took issue with this point of view, asserting that one must rely wholly on thought.

The Galilean Revolution

Into this world came Galileo (1564–1642), a man whose monumental contributions to science were to shake the foundations of all that man believed. From his youth, Galileo displayed the traits that were to dominate his life. He frequently questioned the authority of his professors, refusing to accept their dogmatic statements and demanding proof with observation rather than blind acceptance of some authority.

It is well known how at the age of eighteen, while in the cathedral of Pisa, Galileo noted a lamp swinging from the roof by a long cord. As the oscillations, at first very large, slowly decreased in range, he noted that the time of an oscillation remained the same, a fact that he verified by using his own pulse as a clock. This observation led him to further experiments with a pendulum, and the discovery that the time of oscillation depended solely on the length of the pendulum and not upon the mass of the suspended object or upon the amplitude of the oscillation. He put this discovery to practical use by inventing a pendulum that the doctors could use for measuring the pulse rate of a patient.

Galileo had started to study medicine, but he gradually turned toward mathematics and experimental science. In 1589 he was appointed professor of mathematics and astronomy at Pisa, where he made numerous experiments on the laws of falling bodies. The most famous story is that of his dropping from the top of the famous Leaning Tower a number of bodies having the same diameter but different masses, and noting that they all fell to the ground simultaneously. Very light bodies that failed to conform to this law, he showed, were delayed by resistance of the air.

Like Tycho before him, Galileo's attention was drawn to astronomy by the appearance of a nova in the constellation Serpens in 1604. By observation similar to that of his predecessor, he also showed that it was an object belonging to the stellar rather than to the planetary realm.

In 1608 Galileo learned of a combination of lenses—the invention of a Dutch spectacle-maker—that enabled one to magnify distant objects. Galileo immediately grasped the basic principle of the device and constructed such a lens, which he used for astronomical observation. His earliest findings, published in a small book called *The Sidereal Messenger*, reported his observations of the moon. He had seen mountains and craters. Concerning the *terminator*, the boundary between day and night on the moon, he recorded special details, such as the long shadows cast by mountain peaks just after sunrise, or star-like points of illumination, which he identified as sunlit mountain pinnacles, with the valley deep in darkness. He ingeniously used this information to estimate the heights of the mountain peaks, arriving at a figure of about four miles—an altitude agreeing well with modern calculations. He noted the large, dark, relatively flat areas and speculated that they might be bodies of water. He was, in this respect, far more conservative than later observers who confidently dubbed them "seas," or *maria*. He also noted the absence of clouds.

The reaction to these early discoveries was immediate and violent. For, according to the philosophy of the time, the moon was supposed to be a

The mural quadrant with which Tycho Brahe accurately measured the positions of stars and planets. From *Atlas Major* by Jan Bleau, 1663. (British Museum)

Below: Figure 4–2. An ellipse is a curve, the sum of whose distances from the focal points (*A* and *B*) is constant.

perfect sphere of crystal. Undaunted by criticism, Galileo continued his survey. He resolved the Milky Way into a background of faint, twinkling stars. The telescope multiplied the seven "naked-eye stars" of the Pleiades to forty, making it a true stellar family: a star cluster. Many other nebulous patches of the Milky Way were similarly resolved.

When he looked at the wandering stars—the planets—he perceived that they were unlike the fixed stars, which remained star-like points in his telescope. The planets, on the other hand, showed up as disks. Venus, he discovered, was sometimes a crescent and at other times gibbous; whereas, according to the Ptolemaic system, Venus was always nearer than the sun and would always have to be a crescent and never gibbous. Such observations clearly supported the Copernican view of the solar system. In further proof of this concept, Galileo observed the planet Jupiter and found the four satellites revolving around it. Since these bodies were clearly circling Jupiter, their very existence proved that the sun was not the center of all motion. He regarded Jupiter's system as a micro-model of the solar system.

The world was not ready for so sweeping a revolution in thought. Most of the philosophers denied the reality of such discoveries on the grounds that Aristotle had not mentioned them. Many people refused to look through Galileo's telescope, fearing that they might themselves be bewitched and see objects that were only illusions. In the midst of this turmoil, Galileo remained calm and continued his observations. He noticed something peculiar about the planet Saturn, suggesting that it was a triple planet, with two smaller companions resting on the opposite sides of a diameter. The phenomenon he saw, of course, was merely Saturn's rings imperfectly perceived through his primitive telescope.

The discovery of sunspots, dark areas seen against the disk of the sun, con-

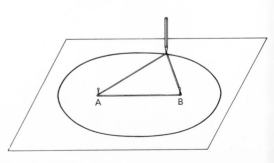

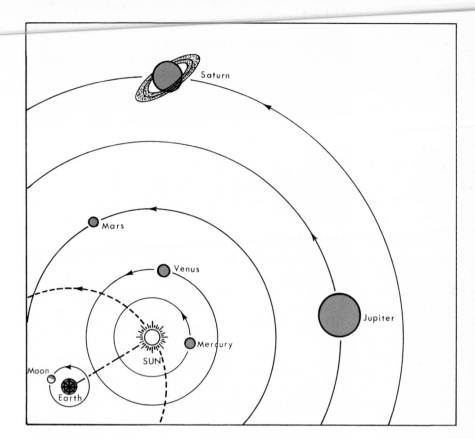

Figure 4–1. A schematic view of the solar system according to Tycho Brahe. He set the earth immobile at the center, but with all the planets revolving around the sun; this in turn revolved around the earth as a center.

Below: Figure 4–3. Kepler's law of areas. The line drawn from the planet to the sun sweeps out equal areas in equal intervals of time by moving faster when it is close to the sun.

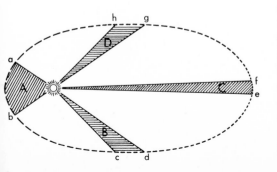

tinued to evoke criticism. Yet others confirmed the presence of these spots and, to avoid the possible criticism that the sun itself could be spotted and thus imperfect, suggested that they were small dark bodies orbiting the sun. Galileo, however, consistently maintained that they were part of the sun and lay in the surface of the sun. In proposing that they were something like clouds in the atmosphere of the sun, he was far in advance of many later astronomers. Much later, William Herschel, for example, suggested that they were holes in the shining surface through which one could see the cool surface beneath, where inhabitants of the sun might live.

Galileo Faces the Inquisition

Galileo continued his attacks on Aristotle and thereby carried the struggle into the field of theology. His doctrines were generally regarded as heretical, contrary to the Scriptures, and philosophically absurd. The church issued an injunction banning the books of Copernicus and similar works that taught or defended the heliocentric system.

In this hostile climate, Galileo struggled to be heard. He continued writing, using the form of a dialogue to expound the two systems of the world, Ptolemaic and Copernican. But the ironical character of his approach made it clear that Galileo was promoting the Copernican view rather than defending the Ptolemaic. His enemies succeeded in having him brought before the Inquisition for an examination of his writings and his beliefs. These hearings, held in 1633, convicted him of "believing and holding the doctrines—false and contrary to the Holy and Divine Scriptures—that the sun is the center of the world, and that it does not move from east to west, and that the earth does move and is not the center of the world: also that an opinion can be held in support of this, after it has been declared and decreed contrary to the Holy Scriptures." As punishment he was required to "abjure, curse, and detest the aforesaid errors, condemned to prison and required to repeat the seven penitential psalms once a week for three years." The following day, the Pope altered the imprisonment to mere confinement in a country-house near Rome. He was later allowed to return to Florence, where, broken in health and spirit, he still tried to continue his observations. But total blindness, incurred in 1636, interrupted his work, which had been devoted to studying the *librations* of the moon, a phenomenon we shall discuss later. He died in 1642, the same year (according to the old calendar) that Isaac Newton was born in England.

Although we cannot give anything like a complete account of the development of astronomy, we must mention the practical contributions of the Dutch astronomer Christian Huygens (1629–1695). He ground and polished lenses of much higher quality than any previously available, and with them he discovered the major satellite of Saturn and finally resolved the perplexing mystery of Saturn, noting that a thin ring surrounded the planet. He also invented the pendulum-clock, whose accuracy in keeping time greatly increased precision in the determination of star positions.

Newton Opens the Modern Era

Isaac Newton (1642–1727) contributed to many fields of astronomy, physics, and mathematics. Galileo had already corrected many errors inherent in Aristotelian mechanics. Where Aristotle, for example, had concluded that a force had to act continually on a body in order to keep it in motion, Galileo had shown that a body tends to remain in motion unless a force such as friction acts to stop it.

Newton expressed three fundamental laws in mathematical form, but we shall summarize their basic content in words. His first law dealt with the phenomenon we call *inertia*, as when an automobile makes a sudden stop and the occupants continue moving forward until they strike against part of the vehicle.

The second law declares that the *momentum* of a body is the product of the mass times the velocity. Momentum has direction as well as magnitude. To change the momentum of a body, we must act upon it with some force. The second law states that the rate of change of momentum is proportional to the force acting upon the body and takes place in the direction of that force.

The third law states that when two bodies exert a force on one another, there is an equal and opposite reaction. If, for example, we fire a shotgun, the gunpowder propels the shot forward and at the same time the gun "kicks" backward in such a way that the forward momentum of the bullet equals the backward momentum of the entire gun. This law, sometimes known as that of "action and reaction," applies directly to the propulsion of rockets: the backward force of the burning rocket engine propels the rocket forward.

Although many other scientists before him had speculated on the reasons why bodies fall to the earth, Newton was the first to express the law in precise, mathematical form. Previously, bodies were said to fall simply because of their "heaviness." Kepler had suggested that an actual attraction existed between the earth and the bodies. Newton theorized that this kind of attraction might extend all the way out to infinity, and he enunciated the law of universal gravitation: Every body in the universe attracts every other body with a force that is proportional to the masses of the bodies and inversely proportional to the square of the distance between them.

Combining this law with his second law of motion, Newton showed that Kepler's three laws were a consequence of the law of gravitation. This conclusion was extremely important, not merely because it confirmed Kepler's laws, but also because it introduced a new technique in science. Throughout history, the standard philosophical method had depended primarily on the imagination of the individual. The philosophers had believed in the sacred character of motion in circles and had forced this concept into their interpretations of observations. Mathematics, primarily geometry, had been used but only to interpret the observations in the light of this hypothesis.

Newton had achieved something entirely new. In this first application of mathematical physics, he even invented a new method, which we call the "calculus." One consequence of his analysis went far beyond Kepler. He

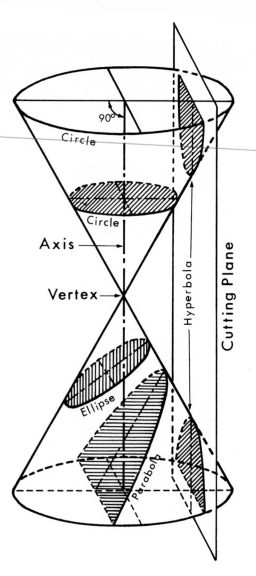

Figure 4–4. Conic sections formed by the intersection of a cutting plane with a double cone. The shape of the curve depends on the angle of the intersection.

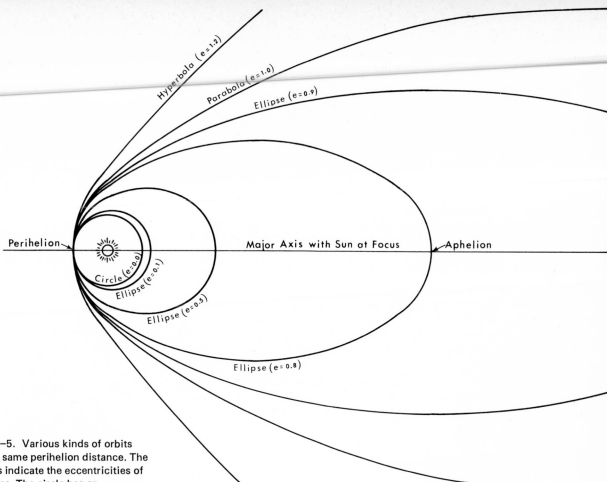

Figure 4–5. Various kinds of orbits with the same perihelion distance. The numbers indicate the eccentricities of the curves. The circle has an eccentricity of 0.00. The ellipses have eccentricities ranging between any number greater than zero and less than one. The higher the eccentricity, the longer the ellipse and the greater its aphelion distance. Eccentricity 1.0 indicates a parabola that is an open-ended curve. From the position of their orbits near the sun, it is hard to distinguish between a highly eccentric ellipse and a parabola. The hyperbola is also an open-ended curve and is even more eccentric. Most comets move in parabolic or nearly parabolic orbits.

showed that the orbits of celestial bodies need not be merely circles or ellipses. Under certain circumstances they could be parabolas or even hyperbolas, which are generally termed *conic sections* (figs. 4–4, 4–5). When the cut is perpendicular to the axis of a right, circular cone, the cross section is a circle. When the cross section is slightly oblique, the outline is an ellipse. When the cross section is parallel to the side of a cone, the curve is a parabola; at a greater angle it becomes a hyperbola.

In his study of planetary motions Newton went further. He showed that any spherically symmetrical object, such as a planet, would act as if all of the mass were concentrated at the center of the sphere. He further noted that the rotation of the earth would produce a bulge around the equator. He recognized that the pull of the sun upon this equatorial bulge was responsible for precession, the slow change of direction of the earth's axis of rotation. He further noted that the combined gravitational pull of the sun and moon would cause regular oscillations in the position of the earth's axis, a phenomenon we have referred to as nutation. He explained tides as the result of gravitational forces from the sun and moon. Newton also invented the reflecting telescope, though it was many years before opticians found a method of constructing such instruments with high optical quality. In short, he directly paved the way for modern astronomy.

Having carried the development of astronomy up to the modern era, we shall now survey the universe in the context of present-day knowledge, only occasionally pausing to review the historical background of current beliefs.

The Universe - A Panoramic View

Modern science has revealed to us a universe far more vast and magnificent than the people of antiquity could have imagined. Year by year scientific inquiry has pushed back the frontiers of knowledge, disclosing new wonders of the cosmos, the stars, planets, and nebulae, and of stellar systems complex beyond belief. Daily our own earth has become more and more insignificant—a microscopic speck floating in the illimitable ocean of space.

The possibility of leaving the earth and exploring the moon and planets has become a reality. We have learned how to break the bonds of gravitation and have explored the surface of our sister world, the moon. Interplanetary exploration is not far away.

The distances between celestial bodies are so vast that it is difficult for us to view the earth, the sun, the planets, and the stars in their true perspective. The following miniature model of the solar system, and still smaller model of the universe as a whole, may help us visualize the cosmos.

The Solar System in Miniature

Imagine, if you will, a solar system reduced in size five billion (5×10^9) times so that a million miles equals one foot. On this model, the sun will be reduced to the size of a basketball, a sphere approximately one foot in diameter. On this scale the earth appears about as large as a grain of wheat, revolving at a distance of 100 feet in a circle about the miniature sun. Within the earth's orbit lie Venus and Mercury, the size of a second grain of wheat and a mustard seed and spaced respectively at about 70 and 40 feet from the basketball sun. Mars, a trifle larger than Mercury, stands 160 feet away. We represent Jupiter, the largest of all the planets, by a sphere the size of a golf ball, and place it 500 feet away from the sun. Saturn, the size of a large cherry, encircled by its famous ring system, lies 1000 feet off. Uranus and Neptune, both as large as good-sized peas, fall 2000 and 3000 feet away respectively. Finally, Pluto, another mustard seed, fits into the picture just about a mile away. We must not forget the asteroids—more than two thousand minor planets—which are mere specks between the orbits of Mars and Jupiter. The moon is another mustard seed, revolving around the earth in an orbit whose radius is about three inches.

Of the planets, all but Mercury, Venus, and Pluto have at least one satellite. The earth's satellite, the moon, is more like a sister planet than a true satellite, because it is relatively large compared with the primary body. Mars has two satellites, Jupiter twelve, Saturn nine, Uranus five, and Neptune two. The orbital properties of planets and satellites in our solar system clearly suggest that some basic physical principle governs their arrangement. All of the planets and most of the satellites revolve around the sun in the same direction: counterclockwise, or from west to east as viewed from a station above and toward the north of the plane of the solar system. Most of the planets rotate on their axes in the same direction. With the exception of Pluto, all have orbital inclinations of 7° or less with respect to the ecliptic. Pluto has a high inclination of 17°. As we shall see, these regularities suggest that the planetary system came about through the action of some special force rather than by chance.

As we survey this model, with its tiny islands revolving at vast distances around the sun, we are impressed by the emptiness of our solar system. But if planetary distances are vast, even greater are those between our sun and

The great spiral nebula M 33 in Triangulum. This galaxy, thought to resemble our own Milky Way system, lies at a distance of slightly more than one million light-years. (Kitt Peak National Observatory)

The crescent moon. (Lick Observatory)

the stars. For on this same scale the nearest bright star is double—comparable to two small basketballs revolving about one another some four thousand miles away from our model sun. This figure is also a fair estimate of the average distance between stars. Therefore if we are to get some visual conception of our universe as a whole, we must construct a new model, one far more compressed than the one we have just discussed.

The Smallness of Solar Bodies

Mark Twain, in his story *Captain Stormfield's Visit to Heaven*, related an incident obviously intended to seem absurdly extravagant. Captain Stormfield, having died and started on his way to heaven, was unable to resist the temptation to race with a comet. He ended up, far off course, in a sort of heavenly "missing persons bureau." There an angel went up in a balloon alongside of a map of the universe about as big as the state of Rhode Island to look for our solar system, and came down three days later saying he had perhaps found it, but maybe it was just flyspecks. Mark Twain may not have intended us to take his sense of distances seriously, but nevertheless the map formed a fair model, to scale, of the universe as known in his time. Since then, modern telescopic equipment has greatly extended, and is still extending, the boundaries of the surveyed portion of the universe. Instead of Rhode Island, therefore, let us use our entire earth to represent the volume of the universe as we know it today. For the measurement of interstellar distances, the mile is a ridiculously small unit—similar to expressing the distance between New York and San Francisco in terms of the breadth of a human hair. Astronomers often use a light-year (that is, the distance that light, moving at 186,000 miles per second, travels in a year) as their unit of measurement. In a year, a flash of light will have moved approximately six million million (6,000,000,000,000) miles into space. On the scale of our new model, with the earth representing the whole universe, we shall let $1/16$ inch correspond to six million million miles, or one light-year. Alternatively, we may say that $1/100$ inch equals a million million miles. Now, let us enter this model universe and try to find the solar system.

As we enter the great volume our first impression is that the building is entirely empty. Fortunately, we have brought with us a super-microscope, for on the scale that we have used, no ordinary microscope would be able to render the stars visible. The largest are scarcely one-millionth of an inch across, and the smaller ones are about the size of atoms. When our eyes become adapted to this microscopic vision, we immediately note that the universe shows clear signs of order. Stars are by no means scattered uniformly throughout the enormous volume. They form groups, or clusters, several hundred feet in diameter, something like giant swarms of gnats. The stellar population is concentrated in these regions, with vast realms of nothingness in between. Some of these groupings of stars are irregular in shape. Others are round and flat, like a pie plate. Each group contains hundreds of millions and sometimes as many as a hundred billion stars, with the model stars spaced, on the average, a few tenths of an inch apart. Again, what impresses us most is the emptiness of space and the vast distances between the stars and groups of stars. Stellar traffic lanes are decidedly uncrowded. The chances of two stars accidentally colliding is almost infinitesimal.

There are millions of groups of clustering stars. In many clusters the stars are arranged like the coils of a watch-spring, giving the aggregation a pinwheel appearance. These are the great *spiral nebulae*. If we are to search out the sun, we must first find our Milky Way. Like many other galaxies, it has spiral arms. In our model, it is a disk-shaped aggregation of stars approximately 500 feet in diameter and 50 feet in thickness. It contains about one hundred billion stars and the task of searching out our sun from among that vast assemblage, even after we have located the Milky Way, is herculean. The task is infinitely more difficult than finding the proverbial needle in a haystack. A hundred billion small coins, spread over a 100-yard football field, would make a pile nearly 50 feet high. Mark Twain's angel who succeeded in finding the solar system only after several days of looking, had rare luck. Just to count the stars in the Milky Way at the rate of one per second would take about a thousand years. When at last we find our solar system, we discover it to be a very small "speck" indeed. The largest orbit of all, that of the planet Pluto, is invisible to the eye, and our earth is smaller than an atom.

In this universe, the stars are bodies like our own sun, self-luminous spheres of hot gas. Each star is a nuclear power plant, transforming matter into energy by processes akin to those of the H-bomb, except that the huge mass of the star controls the reaction and keeps it from escalating into a vast explosion. In the universe we find all kinds of stars: large and small, hot and cool, young and old. Part of our task will be to interpret the observational evidence in the light of known physical laws in order to try to understand how stars come into being, how they develop and mature, and finally how they decay, disappear, or otherwise pass into oblivion.

The Stars

As for the stars, we find innumerable varieties of them. We see giant stars with diameters 100 times that of our sun, glowing red because their surfaces are relatively cool. Then we find much hotter, somewhat smaller stars, but giants in luminosity, shining brilliantly white or blue because they are so very hot. At the other extreme we see stars even smaller than Jupiter and relatively cool and faint. These "red-dwarf" stars are among the most numerous of all the celestial suns, but they are so faint that we can see only the nearest ones. Our sun, though much less brilliant than the red or blue giants, is still a star of quite considerable size—midway between the brightest and the faintest.

We must classify these stars in such a way as to show their interrelationships. Then, perhaps, we may indeed be able to understand how they are born, how they live, and how they die.

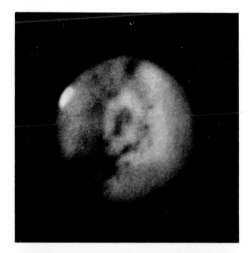

Mars, Jupiter, and Saturn as seen through a 36-inch refractor. (Lick Observatory)

Double star cluster in Perseus. (Lick Observatory)

Astronomers have often been misled by their preconceptions: thus the swollen "red-giant" stars, which astronomers once thought were the "youngsters" of our galaxy, have turned out to be elderly members of the stellar society, rapidly living out a spendthrift existence en route to extinction. Similarly, the sun's mass and supply of energy are not infinite. Its radiation into space seems to be a one-way process, and there is no indication of any compensatory process that will keep it going indefinitely. In short, the universe is running down and we see no evidence that anything will serve to wind it up again.

Our telescopes show us that about one-third of all the stars are *double stars*. The two components revolve around their common center of gravity, some swiftly, others very slowly. Many stars are multiple, some forming double-double stars or even more complex families. Next in order of complexity are the *open clusters*, comprising from perhaps a dozen to several hundred members. The most familiar of these clusters is the Pleiades, in which, as we have noted, Galileo's telescope revealed some 40 stars where only 7 were visible to the naked eye (color plate 41). Approximately 120 members are now recognized and there are undoubtedly still fainter ones. Other open clusters, visible to the naked eye as hazy patches, include the Hyades in Taurus, Praesepe in Cancer, and the double cluster in Perseus.

Still more complex are the *globular star clusters*, which contain thousands of individual members crowded toward the center and thinning out toward the edges. Stars in these regions are concentrated at least a thousand times more densely than in the neighborhood of the sun. Viewed from a planet circling a star near the center of one of these clusters, the sky would be a brilliant blaze of bright stars, far more impressive than our own Milky Way. These stars are all in motion, like gnats in a swarm. Otherwise their mutual gravitational forces would make them collapse into the center of the system.

The great star clouds of our galaxy, together with the open and globular clusters, form, as we have said, a spiral nebula, which is typical of many billions of galaxies in the universe. At one time astronomers thought that our sun was close to the center of the Milky Way, but we now realize that we are far from the center. Although it is somewhat difficult for us to discern the structure of our galaxy—simply because we are trying to do so from the inside rather than from the outside—careful studies have not only revealed the spiral structure but also have enabled us to locate clearly the direction of the galactic center. The brilliant star clouds of Sagittarius, Scorpio, and Centaurus are best seen from the southern hemisphere, where they stand directly overhead, dominating the sky during the southern winter.

Not all of the material substance of our galaxy occurs in the stars. When we survey with the naked eye the Milky Way from Cygnus down through Aquila, we discover two bright areas separated by a long, dark rift. The blackness results not from the absence of stars, but from the presence of dark nebulae—vast clouds of fine dust—that tend to obscure the brighter Milky Way that lies behind. Such dark patches, representing material that has not yet condensed into stars, are common in many galaxies. The depths of space also contain great quantities of atoms and molecules.

When the nebulosity contains hot, bright stars we can often see the structure of these regions from light reflected by the dust particles. Ultraviolet stellar radiation absorbed by the matter excites the gas and causes it to glow. Such structures we call *bright galactic* or *diffuse nebulae*, the majority of which are confined to the plane of our galaxy. Here and there, silhouetted against a bright nebula, we see an occasional concentrated dark dust cloud called a *globule*, which may be a *proto-star*, or star in the making. We see faint, highly-compressed stars, the so-called "white dwarfs." At the other extreme, we discern highly-distended stars, stars with enormous envelopes. Some of the gaseous envelopes of these are so inflated that we refer to the objects as *planetary nebulae*. Early astronomers, seeing these objects with their telescopes, often thought they had discovered a faint planet, until its lack of motion proved otherwise.

We have no direct way of ascertaining how many of the hundred billion stars of our galaxy possess planetary systems. One faint neighbor, known as Barnard's star, appears to have an invisible companion about the size of Jupiter. We conclude this from the motions of the star itself which, instead of moving precisely in a straight line, pursues a slightly wobbly path, presumably because it is revolving around the center of gravity of both the star and planet.

Many astronomers once believed that the solar system came about through the collision or near-collision of two stars, the planetary material being the wreckage of that encounter. Because interstellar space is so sparsely populated, the probability of so close an approach is almost negligible. In fact, if our solar system was formed in this manner, it might well be unique in the universe. Later we shall discuss the modified version of this theory that astronomers have adopted in recent years.

Our disk-shaped galaxy is so large that light takes about 100,000 years to travel from one rim to the other, and some 10,000 years across its shorter dimension. The galaxy rotates, and stars in the vicinity of the sun revolve around the center of the galaxy in a period of about 230 million years. This is a short time as compared with the probable lifetime of the galaxy, which must

Overleaf left: Globular star cluster M 3 (NGC 5272). (Lick Observatory)

Overleaf right: The Lagoon Nebula M 8 in the constellation of Sagittarius is an open-star cluster surrounded by a cloud of gas and dust. The black areas silhouetted against the glowing gas of the nebula are condensations. (U.S. Naval Observatory)

be counted in thousands of millions of years. Astronomers still do not completely understand the significance of the spiral structure, but clearly a combination of dynamic flow associated with rotation and gravitational forces must be responsible for it. To complicate the problem, many of the spiral galaxies possess near their center an almost straight bar of luminous material from which the sharply-curved arms emanate. One conjecture is that magnetic forces and associated electric currents may, in part, be responsible for this phenomenon.

Exploding Stars

Among the stars we find a number that vary in brightness, some doing so rapidly and regularly, others slowly and irregularly. Occasionally we encounter stars that explode—the novae. Without warning, an extremely faint, scientifically uninteresting star suddenly increases in brilliance a million or more times. If a firefly were suddenly to become as brilliant as an electric arc, the effect could be no more startling. Novae usually remain bright for a few weeks or months, and then slowly fade to invisibility. The Chinese Annals, which contain records of such apparitions over the ages, refer to them as "guest stars." The phenomenon is a true explosion, with the star ejecting a shell of gas that expands until it becomes a nebulous cloud of rarefied gas around the stellar core.

Much more rarely, explosions of an entirely different order of magnitude occur—the supernovae. These are catastrophes of tremendous import; such a nova, near maximum light, can radiate almost as much energy as an entire galaxy. The Crab Nebula in Taurus is a splendid example of the remnants of such an explosion, which occurred in the year 1054, as recorded in the Chinese Annals. In addition to sending us light, this nebula is a strong source of radio emission, which we can measure with our radio telescopes. These instruments are extremely sensitive radio receivers attached to enormous dish-shaped antennas, which collect and concentrate the weak radio noise from various celestial objects.

Tycho's "star" of 1572, as well as a similar object observed by Kepler in 1604, were undoubtedly supernovae. We sometimes observe such events in galaxies other than our Milky Way. The explosion that accompanies them is truly of cosmic proportions. Nuclear processes, analogous to those in atomic bombs, undoubtedly furnish the energy. At the same time that the outer layers of the star lift off and form a rapidly-expanding shell, the inner core appears to collapse, forming a star with the nuclei of the atoms almost in contact with one another and with densities of thousands of tons per cubic inch. These concentrated masses continue to quiver and pulse, sometimes many times in a single second. They also send out both visible and radio emissions of variable intensity, the mysterious *pulsars*.

Other Galaxies

To complete this survey we must go beyond our own Milky Way system to the vast numbers of galaxies that lie beyond. They take many forms. Like our own, some are spiral. Others are amorphous blobs, with perhaps a slight concentration of density toward the center, similar to that of a globular star cluster. Others are so irregular that they have no specific outline or shape. These objects appear to be similar to our galaxy, each consisting of billions of stars, gaseous nebulae, and extended clouds of dark dust. These galaxies are islands of light and activity, sparsely strewn through a universe that is otherwise nearly empty. The distance between galaxies is tremendous, light taking between 100,000 and 1,000,000 years to go from one galaxy to the next. The objects nearest us are two galaxies, known as the Clouds of Magellan, which look to the naked eye like segments torn loose from the Milky Way. They are approximately 100,000 light-years away from us. In effect they are dwarf companions of our galaxy. Organization in the universe does not cease with the individual galaxies. Here and there we find galaxies themselves tend-

ing to cluster together. Groups of five, dozens, or even hundreds of galaxies appear to form families or related sets. Even clusters of clusters occur.

Where does it all end? And how? Let us return to our model, where the scale is so small that an entire light-year occupies but a sixteenth of an inch. Our galaxy seems to be somewhere near the center of this system. As we look out toward the "edges" of the universe we discover the other galaxies receding from us at higher and higher velocities. This "dynamic" universe seems to be expanding rapidly. What the fundamental significance of this expansion is we shall see when we take up the complexities of Einstein's theory of relativity.

In thus depicting the universe in panoramic form, I have painted rapidly, with a broad brush. My aim has been to picture the universe as a complex structure governed by physical laws. In later chapters I shall discuss the various units and their relationship to one another and to the universe as a whole. We cannot proceed, however, without first discussing the basic blocks that make up the universe—the atoms. Further, we shall have to discuss how we have gained knowledge of the universe through observation of the various kinds of radiations emitted by heavenly bodies. Since our earth is one of the planets of the solar system, we can also learn a great deal about other bodies by studying its composition and structure.

Cluster of five galaxies, interconnected with bright streamers. NGC 6027, in the constellation of Serpens. (Hale Observatories)

6 Atoms and Radiation

Before we proceed to a more detailed look at the universe, we must understand something about the smallest units that make up the larger ones—from planet to star to galaxy. This is necessary because the forces issuing from the innermost parts of an atom can profoundly affect the birth, life, and death of a star. Furthermore, the present chemical composition of a celestial body often contains important information about its origin and evolution. And light undergoes tremendous transformations between the time of its origin in a stellar core and its escape from the surface of a star or sun.

From antiquity man has realized that some relation must exist between the nature of the universe and the matter that comprises it. We have seen how Aristotle postulated four fundamental elements in order of density: earth, water, atmosphere, and fire, signifying—in modern terms, solid, liquid, gas, and incandescent gas. Each of these elements was supposed to possess two qualities. The earth was cold and dry, water cold and wet, air hot and wet, and fire hot and dry. The ancients believed that by changing the proportions of, say, coldness and wetness they could transmute one substance into another. This concept formed the basis of alchemy and persisted well into the eighteenth century.

The ancients recognized, in part, the importance of radiation, although their concept of its nature was primitive. They associated light with the presence of fire. As for the light of the heavenly bodies, early astronomers somehow deduced that it emanated, as we have noted, from a mysterious "quintessence." In the seventeenth century, scientists believed that all combustible bodies contained a special element, to which they gave the name "phlogiston." They supposed that the process of burning released this substance. Chemists tried to explain the behavior of many chemical substances in terms of their phlogiston content.

Whatever one may say of alchemy, the hope of turning base metal into gold led people to mix nearly every substance with every other substance. The results were mostly chaotic; however, a few basic facts emerged. Alchemists discovered that when metals were heated in air, they generally lost their metallic properties and degenerated into powders, and that these metallic ashes, when heated in the presence of charcoal were reconverted into the metallic form. In the process of such experiments, they of course discovered many other reactions.

Boyle, Newton, and Lavoisier

Here and there far-thinking scientists began to question the ancient doctrines. Robert Boyle (1627–1691), self-styled "Sceptical Chymist," asserted that the world consisted of not four, but a far greater number of chemical elements. In this respect Boyle was far more advanced than his famous contemporary, Isaac Newton, who continued to support the old four-element doctrine. Newton, however, showed remarkable foresight when he speculated that "bodies could be converted into light, and light into bodies." This idea seems to presage Einstein's discovery that matter can be changed into energy and vice versa.

During the eighteenth century, chemists began to distinguish between the various basic substances. Henry Cavendish (1731–1810) discovered "inflammable air," which we know as hydrogen. Daniel Rutherford (1749–

1819) recognized nitrogen; and the great English chemist Joseph Priestley (1733–1804) found the element oxygen and a host of other important gaseous chemical compounds. These discoveries stimulated the French chemist Antoine Lavoisier (1743–1794), whose quantitative studies introduced a new era in that science. He showed that a metal that was burned in the presence of oxygen gained weight equal to the mass of the oxygen consumed. He attacked the phlogiston theory and began to recognize the relationship between compounds and basic elements. When he found that iron could decompose water into hydrogen and oxygen, he finally upset the old system by proving that water was not a fundamental element after all. Lavoisier did for chemistry what Newton had done for astronomy. He overthrew the established order and reconstructed his science on the basis of logical deductions from sound experiments.

The ancient Greeks had speculated about the existence of atoms, but the philosophical basis for their arguments is scarcely valid today. To them a pickle atom was sour and green and a sugar atom white and sweet. They invented atoms only because they found it impossible to conceive of infinite divisibility. Others pointed to the fact that water, left to itself, gradually disappears, the inference being that water atoms leave the surface, flying off like

Various vibrational patterns of the hydrogen atom, in terms of an electronic cloud surrounding the invisible nucleus at the center. The atom radiates energy as it changes from one vibrational state to another. (H. E. White)

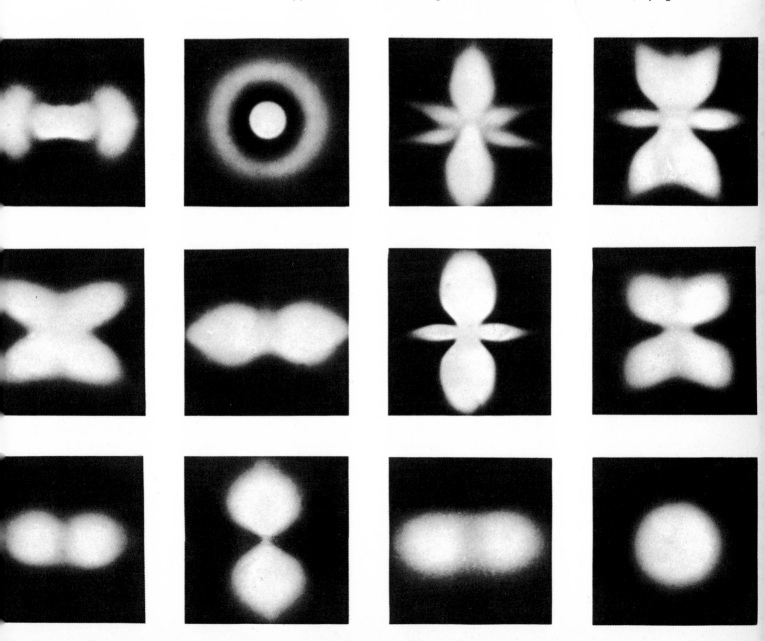

tiny bullets. In expressing this view, Lucretius (ca. 96–55 B.C.) adopted a view that is singularly modern. We must remember, however, that this conclusion was completely unsupported by any experimental evidence.

Weighing an Atom

Continued laboratory experimentation provided quantitative data on the existence of atoms. John Dalton (1766–1844) enunciated a very important law after he had noted that every chemical compound contains the same proportion of basic elements by weight. Thus 18 grams of water, when decomposed into its elements, always gave 16 grams of oxygen and 2 of hydrogen. Similarly, 34 grams of hydrogen sulfide always broke up into 32 of sulphur and 2 of hydrogen. Dalton clearly saw that these laws of constant proportion, which every chemical substance appeared to follow, could be explained if one assigned specific relative weights to the different atoms. For example, if one assigned to hydrogen the weight 1 and to oxygen the weight 16, then water would be a compound, a molecule consisting of two atoms of hydrogen and one of oxygen, or, as we call it, H_2O. Analogously, with a weight of 32 assigned to sulphur, hydrogen sulphide became H_2S of molecular weight 34, and sulphur dioxide became SO_2 of molecular weight 64. This principle could be extended to many other elements and compounds.

Hence, chemists gradually learned to distinguish between elements and molecules, and they built up an ever-lengthening table of chemical elements, ordered in terms of their atomic weight, as shown in Table I. Hydrogen, the lightest element, comes first in the table; helium, the next lightest, comes second, and so on. Using this table, one can calculate the molecular weight of any substance if one knows its composition. For example, a molecule of calcium carbonate, $CaCO_3$, would have a weight of $40+12+(3\times16)$, or 100.

William Prout (1785–1850), an English physician and chemist, noted that many of these atomic weights were very nearly integers and surmised that they were themselves compounds of hydrogen rather than true elements. Prout's hypothesis, as we shall see, agrees in many ways with modern views of atomic structure. By adding hydrogen nuclei, known as *protons*, to the nuclei of other atoms we can change their chemical nature. However, such processes require the use of very high energies not available in ordinary chemical reactions. Thus, as far as chemistry is concerned, the elements are invariable—as is suggested by the original Greek sense of the word "atom," derived from *a*, not, and *temno*, cut, that is, the uncuttable.

The Periodic Table

John A. R. Newlands (1838–1898), another English chemist, was the first person to tabulate the elements in such a way as to show the similarity in the properties of different atoms. The Russian chemist Dmitri I. Mendeleev (1834–1907) greatly extended this concept in his basic Periodic Table of the Elements in modern form. Mendeleev's original table had many gaps at points where elements remained undiscovered. In fact, he knew nothing about the entire column, headed by helium, that contains chemically inactive gases. The remarkable thing about Mendeleev's arrangement is the chemical similarity among the atoms in each column. For example, sodium, potassium, rubidium, and cesium are all soft metals that burn in air to form the oxide, or react with water to release hydrogen gas. The chlorides of all these substances have a single atom of chlorine bound into each molecule, so that the formulas are, respectively, NaCl, KCl, RbCl, and CsCl. The atoms of the second column, magnesium, calcium, strontium, and barium, are also similar chemically and they often occur together in nature. Their chlorides have the formulas, $MgCl_2$, $CaCl_2$, $SrCl_2$, and $BaCl_2$. In other words, these stable molecules each had *two* atoms of chlorine bound into them. Chemists expressed this property by saying that these atoms of the second column of the Periodic Table have a *valence* (or chemical combining power) of 2.

Not surprisingly, the chlorides of atoms in the third column have three

Table I. The Chemical Elements

Z	Name	Symbol	Atomic Weight	Z	Name	Symbol	Atomic Weight
1	Hydrogen	H	1.00797	52	Tellurium	Te	127.60
2	Helium	He	4.0026	53	Iodine	I	126.9044
3	Lithium	Li	6.939	54	Xenon	Xe	131.30
4	Beryllium	Be	9.0122	55	Cesium	Cs	132.905
5	Boron	B	10.811	56	Barium	Ba	137.34
6	Carbon	C	12.01115	57	Lanthanum	La	138.91
7	Nitrogen	N	14.0067	58	Cerium	Ce	140.12
8	Oxygen	O	15.9994	59	Praseodymium	Pr	140.907
9	Fluorine	F	18.9984	60	Neodymium	Nd	144.24
10	Neon	Ne	20.183	61	Promethium	Pm	—
11	Sodium	Na	22.9898	62	Samarium	Sm	150.35
12	Magnesium	Mg	24.312	63	Europium	Eu	151.96
13	Aluminum	Al	26.9815	64	Gadolinium	Gd	157.25
14	Silicon	Si	28.086	65	Terbium	Tb	158.925
15	Phosphorus	P	30.9738	66	Dysprosium	Dy	162.50
16	Sulphur	S	32.064	67	Holmium	Ho	164.930
17	Chlorine	Cl	35.453	68	Erbium	Er	167.26
18	Argon	Ar	39.948	69	Thulium	Tm	168.934
19	Potassium	K	39.102	70	Ytterbium	Yb	173.04
20	Calcium	Ca	40.08	71	Lutetium	Lu	174.97
21	Scandium	Sc	44.956	72	Hafnium	Hf	178.49
22	Titanium	Ti	47.90	73	Tantalum	Ta	180.948
23	Vanadium	V	50.942	74	Tungsten	W	183.85
24	Chromium	Cr	51.996	75	Rhenium	Re	186.2
25	Manganese	Mn	54.9380	76	Osmium	Os	190.2
26	Iron	Fe	55.847	77	Iridium	In	192.2
27	Cobalt	Co	58.9332	78	Platinum	Pt	195.09
28	Nickel	Ni	58.71	79	Gold	Au	196.967
29	Copper	Cu	63.54	80	Mercury	Hg	200.59
30	Zinc	Zn	65.37	81	Thallium	Tl	204.37
31	Gallium	Ga	69.72	82	Lead	Pb	207.19
32	Germanium	Ge	72.59	83	Bismuth	Bi	208.980
33	Arsenic	As	74.921	84	Polonium	Po	—
34	Selenium	Se	78.96	85	Astatine	At	—
35	Bromine	Br	79.909	86	Radon	Rn	—
36	Krypton	Kr	83.80	87	Francium	Fr	—
37	Rubidium	Rb	85.47	88	Radium	Ra	226.0254
38	Strontium	Sr	87.62	89	Actinium	Ac	—
39	Yttrium	Y	88.906	90	Thorium	Th	232.038
40	Zirconium	Zr	91.22	91	Protactinium	Pa	231.0359
41	Niobium	Nb	92.906	92	Uranium	U	238.03
42	Molybdenum	Mo	95.94	93	Neptunium	Np	237.0480
43	Technetium	Tc	—	94	Plutonium	Pu	239.0522
44	Ruthenium	Ru	101.07	95	Americium	Am	—
45	Rhodium	Rh	102.905	96	Curium	Cm	—
46	Palladium	Pd	106.4	97	Berkelium	Bk	—
47	Silver	Ag	107.870	98	Californium	Cf	—
48	Cadmium	Cd	112.40	99	Einsteinium	Es	—
49	Indium	In	114.82	100	Fermium	Fm	—
50	Tin	Sn	118.69	101	Mendelevium	Md	—
51	Antimony	Sb	121.75	102	Nobelium	No	—
				103	Lawrencium	Lw	—

chlorine atoms apiece. Thus we have: BCl_3, $AlCl_3$, and so on. Atoms in the fourth column have a valence of 4. Here we encounter the familiar cleaning fluid, carbon tetrachloride, CCl_4, and silicon tetrachloride, $SiCl_4$. The next element in this column was still unknown, but Mendeleev confidently predicted its approximate atomic weight, density, metallic appearance, the color of its oxide, and even that the chloride would boil at a temperature lower than 100°C. Chemists finally isolated this element and called it germanium.

Atoms in the fifth column can have a valence of 5, but ordinarily they have a valence of only 3. Thus we find that nitrogen trichloride, an unstable or even explosive compound, is NCl_3. A more familiar nitrogen compound, ammonia, is NH_3. The elements of the sixth column have a valence of 2, and those of the seventh column a valence of 1, as indicated by the formula for hydrochloric acid, HCl, and so on. Helium, neon, argon, and the other gases of the eighth column have a valence of 0, which means that they do not combine with other substances. The Table also includes the transition elements, the Lanthanides (often referred to as "rare earths") and the Actinides. Although the elements in this Table may appear unrelated, those in the same columns possess, chemically, a remarkable resemblance to one another. But the fundamental reason behind these similarities remained unexplained for a long time. Chemists and physicists assigned to each atom a so-called atomic number, according to its order in the table: thus hydrogen was 1, helium 2, lithium 3, and so on (Column Z in Table I). With the exception of hydrogen, the atomic weights of the substances near the beginning of the Table are approximately twice the atomic number. However, by the time we pass calcium, the ratio begins to exceed 2, and climbs higher and higher toward the end of the table.

The Role of the Electron

Meanwhile, man had made a tremendous advance in his understanding of the world around him. At last he knew what the elements were, even though he did not understand their origin. The chemical similarity of atoms in each column of the Periodic Table indicated the need for a revision in scientific thought. Where original atomic theory had emphasized the differences between the elements, the presence of similarities suggested that atoms must contain some features in common. Otherwise, why should sodium and potassium, for example, show such similar behavior?

Joseph J. Thomson (1856–1940), experimenting in the Cavendish Physical Laboratory at Cambridge, England, became interested in certain emanations, then called "cathode rays"—a form of electrical discharge. He found that electric and magnetic fields would deflect these rays and he concluded that they were material particles rather than some form of "ether waves." Above all, each electron possessed a definite negative electric charge. Thomson's experiments enabled him to measure the ratio of the mass to the charge of individual particles; he found that their nature was completely independent of the chemical nature of the source. Here at last was evidence pointing toward an ultimate constituent of matter, with a mass that seemed to be almost two thousand times smaller than that of the individual hydrogen atom. Thomson referred to these particles as "corpuscles," but they later became known as *electrons*.

Atomic Nuclei

We cannot cover in detail the development of man's knowledge of atoms. However, we must mention Ernest Rutherford (1871–1937), who succeeded Thomson as director at Cavendish, for a series of critical experiments that showed that atoms, far from being solid pellets, were—like our solar system—mostly empty space. Rutherford's experiments were simple and convincing. He bombarded thin sheets of gold foil with fragments from exploding, radioactive atoms. These tiny projectiles, known as *alpha particles*, themselves possessed a positive electric charge. Physicists eventually recognized that these particles were themselves nuclei of helium atoms. Most of these alpha particles passed through metal almost as if it were full of holes. And that, indeed, proved to be the answer. From the small proportion of particles that were sharply deflected, Rutherford concluded that most of the mass of the atom was concentrated in a nucleus whose diameter was about $1/10000$ of the whole atom. He visualized the atom as a sort of miniature solar system, with the nucleus at the center and the tiny electrons revolving around it like planets around the sun.

The forces holding the atom together are electrical, not gravitational. Like charges repel and unlike charges attract one another. The positively-charged nucleus can attract to it a number of negative electrons to balance its positive charge. In fact, this principle determines the chemical nature of the atom. Hydrogen, the simplest and lightest of all the atoms, has one electron, helium has two electrons, lithium three, and so on down the list of chemical elements. Uranium, the last element that occurs naturally, possesses ninety-two electrons.

These electrons do not arrange themselves haphazardly in an atom. They form a regular and precise pattern in a series of separate layers, generally referred to as "shells." The innermost shell can accommodate only two electrons, the second shell can hold as many as eight electrons, the third eighteen, the fourth thirty-two, and so on.

Atoms that do not combine with other atoms to form compounds (listed in the eighth column of Table II) have their electrons arranged in shells, as shown in Table III. The sum of the number of electrons in the shells of any row equals the total number of electrons, as stated in the second column, which in turn equals Z, the atomic number or numbers of the atom in Table I. For example, the eighteen electrons of argon are arranged two in shell 1, eight in shell 2, and eight in shell 3. These atoms, with the exception of helium, all resemble one another in that each has eight electrons in the outer shell. That is why, from a chemical point of view, they behave in much the same way.

To represent atoms of the first column of the Periodic Table, we may start with sets of electrons identical with those we have just considered and add a single electron in the next higher shell. Thus again, all these atoms possess a similar structure, with the extra electron outside the symmetrical inner shells.

II. Periodic Table of the Elements

Transition Elements

Metal Triads

1	2	3	4	5	6	7	0											
1 H							2 He											
3 Li	4 Be	5 B	6 C	7 N	8 O	9 F	10 Ne											
11 Na	12 Mg	13 Al	14 Si	15 P	16 S	17 Cl	18 A											
19 K	20 Ca							21 Sc	22 Ti	23 V	24 Cr	25 Mn	26 Fe	27 Co	28 Ni	29 Cu	30 Zn	
		31 Ga	32 Ge	33 As	34 Se	35 Br	36 Kr											
37 Rb	38 Sr							39 Y	40 Zr	41 Nb	42 Mo	43 Tc	44 Ru	45 Rh	46 Pd	47 Ag	48 Cd	
		49 In	50 Sn	51 Sb	52 Te	53 I	54 Xe											
55 Cs	56 Ba						*	71 Lu	72 Hf	73 Ta	74 W	75 Re	76 Os	77 Ir	78 Pt	79 Au	80 Hg	
		81 Tl	82 Pb	83 Bi	84 Po	85 At	86 Rn											
87 Fr	88 Ra					+	103 Lw											

* Lanthanide Series →

57 La	58 Ce	59 Pr	60 Nd	61 Pm	62 Sm	63 Eu	64 Gd	65 Tb	66 Dy	67 Ho	68 Er	69 Tm	70 Yb

+ Actinide Series →

89 Ac	90 Th	91 Pa	92 U	93 Np	94 Pu	95 Am	96 Cm	97 Bk	98 Cf	99 Es	100 Fm	101 Md	102 No

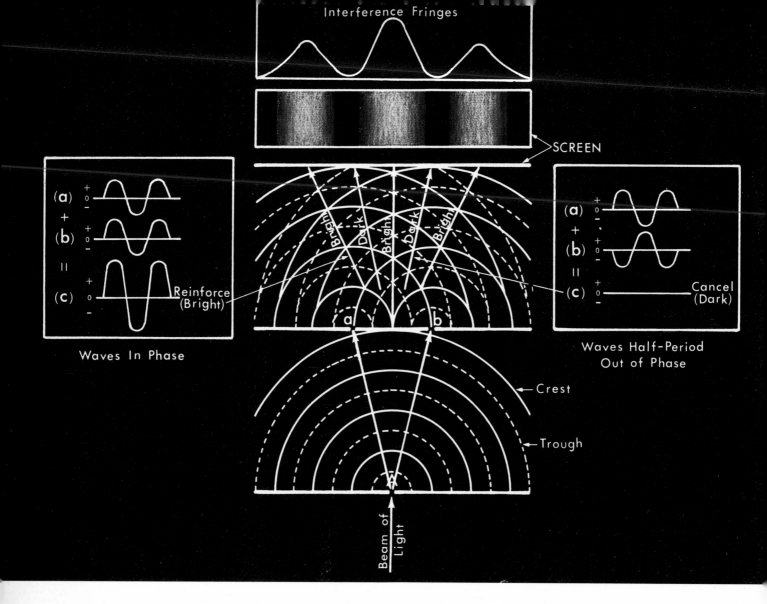

Figure 6–2. The interference of light. A beam of light passed through hole *A* forms two identical beams when the light spreads out and passes through holes *a* and *b*. Because these holes are sources of waves, alternate bright and dark stripes called "fringes" are formed when the light falls upon a card. Depending on the distance from the holes, the waves either vibrate in phase (b) and form a bright line, or out of phase (c), canceling each other and forming a dark line. Young's discovery of this phenomena strengthened his views concerning the wave theory of light.

To achieve the symmetry that seems to indicate stability, these atoms often "share" this outer electron with other atoms and form molecules. This characteristic accounts for the fact that these atoms have a valence or chemical combining power of 1. They have only one electron to share.

We could continue to illustrate the close connection between various other columns of the Periodic Table. For example, to represent the atoms Be, Mg, Ca, Sr, Ba of the second column, we merely change the 1's of Table IV to 2. These atoms are bivalent because they all have two outer electrons to share. But we need go no further for the purpose of this book. The basic fact is that each chemical element possesses a distinctive electronic structure that governs its chemical behavior and how it can build into crystals.

Table III

Atom	Symbol	No. of Electrons	Shells					
			1	2	3	4	5	6
Helium	He	2	2					
Neon	Ne	10	2	8				
Argon	A	18	2	8	8			
Krypton	Kr	36	2	8	18	8		
Xenon	Xe	54	2	8	18	18	8	
Radon	Rn	86	2	8	18	32	18	8

Figure 6–3. The spectrum of electro-magnetic radiations ranges from very long radio waves through infrared, visible (shaded), ultraviolet, and X-rays, to the waves of highest energy known as gamma (γ) rays. The range of these vibrations is about 67 octaves; by comparison, the human eye can record only about one octave. There are no distinct boundaries between the various types of radiations.

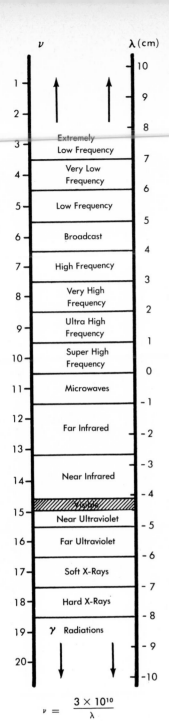

$$\nu = \frac{3 \times 10^{10}}{\lambda}$$

Log $\nu = 10.5 -$ Log λ

Radiations	Range (cm)
VLF	$10^6 - 10^7$
LF	$10^5 - 10^6$
BC	$10^4 - 10^5$
HF	$10^3 - 10^4$
VHF	$100 - 1000$
UHF	$10 - 100$
SHF	$1 - 10$
Microwaves	$10^{-1} - 1$
Far Infrared	$2 \times 10^{-3} - 10^{-1}$
Near Infrared	$7 \times 10^{-5} - 2 \times 10^{-3}$
Visible	$4 \times 10^{-5} - 7 \times 10^{-5}$
Near UV	$2.9 \times 10^{-5} - 4 \times 10^{-5}$
Far UV	$10^{-6} - 2.9 \times 10^{-5}$
X-Rays	$10^{-9} - 10^{-6}$
γ-Rays	$10^{-12} - 1.4 \times 10^{-9}$

Table IV

Atom	Symbol	No. of Electrons	Shells					
			1	2	3	4	5	6
Lithium	Li	3	2	1				
Sodium	Na	11	2	8	1			
Potassium	K	19	2	8	8	1		
Rubidium	Rb	37	2	8	18	8	1	
Cesium	Cs	55	2	8	18	18	8	1

Light and Radiation

The early Greeks were aware of many of the properties of light and radiation. They used lenses as magnifying glasses and burning glasses. They also used concave mirrors to concentrate the heat of the sun, although the often-repeated story that Archimedes used such mirrors to focus sunlight on an attacking Roman fleet and set the ships on fire, is undoubtedly apocryphal. Most of the Greek scientists recognized that light was something emitted by a luminous body, which caused the sense of vision as it entered the eye. A few of the ancients, among them Euclid, theorized that the sensation of light was akin to that of touch, that invisible tentacles from the eye reached out and "touched" the luminous object in much the way fingers feel whether a body is rough or smooth.

Passing white light through a prism of glass, Newton broke it up into its component colors, that is, into the spectrum. And when this spectrum went through a second prism with its angles reversed, the colors recombined to yield the original white light. Newton thought that radiation consisted of tiny particles or corpuscles. Christian Huygens, a Dutch contemporary of Newton who later moved to Paris, had expounded a wave theory of light, but so great was the authority of Newton that this concept found little support for more than a century. During this era one great achievement stands out, the discovery by astronomer William Herschel (1738–1822) of infrared radiation. Using a thermometer as a detector, he found that the temperature rose when he placed the bulb in the region just beyond the last visible trace of red. Later on, scientists found invisible ultraviolet by means of photographic plates.

The Wave Theory of Light

When he tried to revive the wave theory of light, Thomas Young (1773–1829) encountered opposition and derision. He strengthened his view by discovering an important phenomenon known as the "interference" of light. As shown in Figure 6–2a, Young passed light from a bright source through a small hole, A, in a card; this light spread out to illuminate a circle on a second card that contained two small holes, a and b. Light passing through these two holes fell upon a third card, with part of the illumination overlapping. In this region appeared a series of horizontal stripes, alternatively bright and dark, usually called "fringes." Young deduced that holes a and b were sources of wave motion. Along the central line, midway on the overlap, the waves from the two sources vibrate together (fig. 6–2b) and a bright fringe results from this cooperation. A short distance above or below the center strip, the difference in distance to the holes a and b is equal to half a wave, so that overlapping waves occur, as in Figure 6–2c. The vibrations, being equal and opposite, cancel one another and a dark fringe appears. The two beams have "interfered" with one another, causing darkness. This alternation of bright and dark fringes continues indefinitely along the overlapping patches of light from the two holes. This phenomenon seems to give clear support to the wave theory of light. Other brilliant experiments by Young and later scientists seemingly established the wave theory beyond all question.

The Electromagnetic Spectrum

It was Scottish physicist James Clerk Maxwell (1831–1879) who analyzed the accumulated knowledge concerning electricity and magnetism and developed the idea that radiation consisted of electromagnetic waves caused by oscillations of electrons within the atom. The oscillations were supposed to be extremely rapid and the waves very small. Those of ordinary green light, for example, are of the order of 20-millionths of an inch, so that some 50,000 waves, spread side by side, occupy only one inch. The waves of red light are longer and those of blue light shorter. In the region of still longer waves, Maxwell boldly predicted that electromagnetic oscillations could be produced with wavelengths of the order of inches, feet, yards, or even miles.

That such waves could be made by electrical discharges through a spark coil was discovered by Heinrich Hertz (1857–1894), a German experimenter, in 1888. He proved, moreover, that the waves had electromagnetic characteristics identical with those predicted by Maxwell. In this way was born the theory that later developed into the stupendous complex that comprises radio, television, and other electronic communications.

The electromagnetic spectrum extends all the way from the long radio waves through the short radio waves, the infrared, the visual spectrum, the ultraviolet, into the still shorter wavelengths that we identify as soft X-rays, hard X-rays, and finally gamma-rays (γ-rays) (fig. 6–3). The gamma-rays result from the highly-energetic transitions that often accompany the disruption or reorganization of an atomic nucleus during radioactive decay. Perhaps the most striking fact here is how small a range visible light occupies; our eyes are blind to the rest of the electromagnetic spectrum.

Radiations from the sun, stars, and other heavenly bodies are not at all limited to the visible spectrum, the near infrared, and the ultraviolet. Various astronomical objects also radiate radio waves, which we can pick up with huge dish-shaped antennas that focus the feeble radio energy into receivers of extremely high sensitivity. Other objects radiate X-rays under conditions of extremely high temperature and excitation. Our sun, in no way a remarkable star, sends us radiation over almost the entire electromagnetic spectrum.

The Doppler Effect

In a vacuum, the velocity of light as measured by any observer is a constant, c, independent of the velocity of the source. Hence, if a star were rushing at us with a speed of one-half that of light, the velocity of its light would still be c, rather than $1.5c$. There would, however, be one marked result of the relative motion. An atom in stellar atmosphere, emitting, say, 10^{15} vibrations per second would move toward an observer a distance of v in one second, where v is the velocity of the source. The train of 10^{15} waves emitted per second would ordinarily occupy a distance equal to c, but now the same number of waves will lie in the space c minus v. The spacing between the waves is less, which is to say that the wavelengths are shorter. Similarly, the wavelengths will increase if the object is receding.

This relationship, first proved for sound waves by the Austrian physicist Christian Doppler (1803–1853), is known as the *Doppler effect*. A familiar example of this is that of a whistle: when approaching rapidly it has a higher pitch than when it is receding. By measuring the shift in wavelength, astronomers can determine the relative motion of an object toward or away from the observer. Since motion across the line of sight does not affect the wavelength, we refer to the relative motion in the line of sight as "radial velocity." By measuring the displacement of the spectral lines of a heavenly body, astronomers can measure the velocity of approach or recession. Such knowledge is very important for studies of the dynamics of our universe.

The Quantum Theory

About the turn of the century, the wave theory of radiation suffered a severe setback. The German physicist, Max Planck (1858–1947), studying the rela-

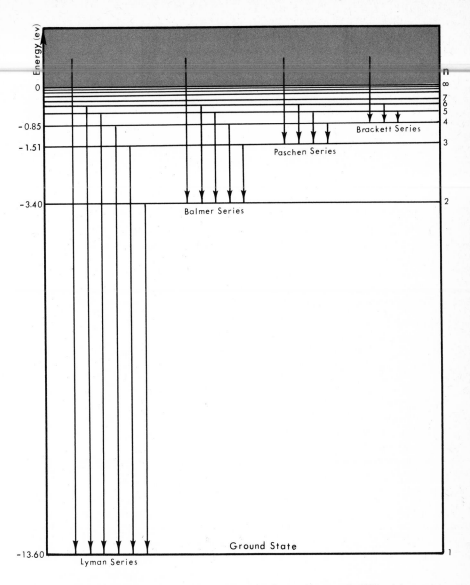

Figure 6–4. The energy level diagram for hydrogen. As an electron cascades from an upper to a lower level, it radiates electromagnetic energy. The greater the energy released, the shorter will be the wavelength of the emitted radiation.

tion between radiation and temperature, had encountered difficulties with the wave theory. To reconcile theory with experiment, Planck found it necessary to postulate that atoms absorb and emit energy in units, which he called "quanta." As a result of this, the corpuscular theory of radiation appeared to gain new life. But the wave theory was not entirely abandoned. For the energy of a quantum was equal to a constant (called "Planck's constant") multiplied by the frequency; and frequency depends on the wavelength, which we measure only in terms of wave theory. Hence radiation came to possess a dual "personality." Sometimes it behaved like waves; at other times, like corpuscles.

We have seen how electrons tend to arrange themselves in shells or layers around the atomic nucleus. The specific patterns previously discussed represent the most stable arrangement. This is what we would expect to find in most atoms on earth, where temperatures are generally quite low. At the high temperatures of stellar atmospheres, however, atoms are continually jostling one another. They often collide at high speed, sometimes, as previously noted, even tearing away one or more of the outer electrons and producing ions.

For a moment, let us consider the simplest of all atoms, hydrogen. Its single electron will normally occupy shell number 1, the position of lowest energy. But when a hydrogen atom collides with another, the electron can be knocked into shells 2, 3, 4, and so on, of successively higher energy content. It will then drop back, by some random path, ending up again in the shell number 1.

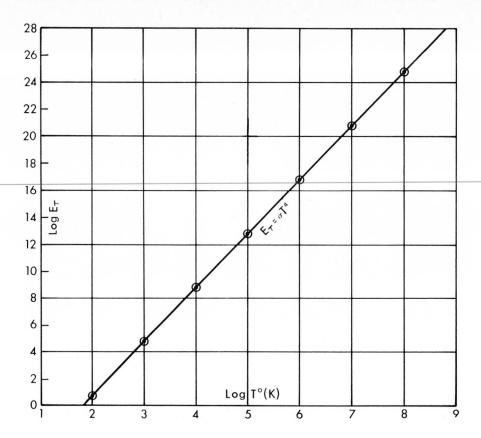

Figure 6–5. Knowing the radiation emitted from a square centimeter of any object, we can use the Stefan-Boltzmann law—the intensity of radiation (vertical scale) increases with increasing temperature (horizontal scale)—to calculate its temperature. This is known as the black-body temperature.

In falling to a shell of lower energy, the electron must emit the difference in the form of radiation. In Figure 6–4, showing the relative energies of the different shells, note how the energy levels crowd together more and more closely for shells of successively higher numbers.

Just what are these shells of electrons and how does an atom radiate? In one theory, proposed by the well-known Danish physicist Niels Bohr (1885–1962), the "shells" represent the different sizes of orbits of electrons revolving about the nucleus. A small jump means a release of less energy than a large jump. According to quantum theory, the higher the energy released, the greater the frequency of emitted radiation. A quantum of blue light carries more energy than one of red light. However, Bohr's atom, with its electron jumping from orbit to orbit, raised certain problems that a newer theory, proposed by Erwin Schrödinger, an Austrian physicist (1887–1961), circumvented. His theory, known as "wave mechanics," regards the electron as a pulsing cloud of electricity around an atomic nucleus. The atom radiates when the electrons change their vibrational patterns. Each atom radiates its own characteristic vibrations, producing a spectrum so distinctive that a spectro-analyst can determine the chemical composition of the luminous material. The spectra of molecules are equally distinctive.

The Meanings of Temperature

Several scales are in use to designate temperature. The one most widely employed around the world is the Celsius, or Centigrade (C), scale. On this scale, water freezes at 0° and boils at 100°. The scale can be extended upward indefinitely or downward to absolute zero, which lies at 273° below zero or —273°C. On the Fahrenheit scale (F), still used in the United States, water freezes at 32° F and boils at 212° F. This system is cumbersome and rarely used by scientists. Still a third system, called the Kelvin scale (K), is the one most useful in astronomy. On it, 0° K is the absolute zero. The scale is otherwise basically Centigrade, with water freezing at 273° K and boiling at 373° K. For high temperatures, of several thousand degrees K or more, the

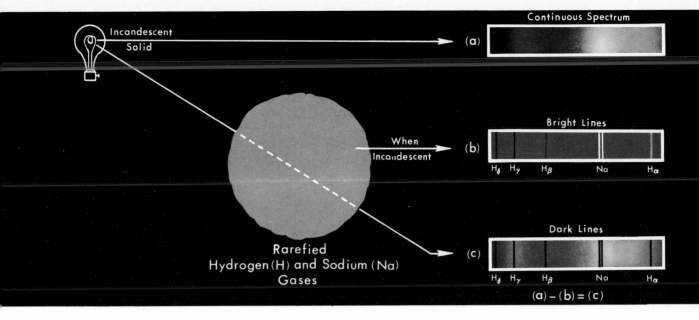

Continuous Spectrum

(a)

Incandescent Solid

When Incandescent (b)

H_δ H_γ H_β Na H_α

Bright Lines

Rarefied
Hydrogen (H) and Sodium (Na)
Gases

Dark Lines

(c)

H_δ H_γ H_β Na H_α

(a) – (b) = (c)

Fahrenheit temperature is very roughly about twice that given by the Kelvin scale.

The temperature of a medium is important since it exerts a profound influence on the spectrum. It is generally assumed that the term temperature has only one meaning; actually it has many definitions, each applicable in its own area. The most familiar concept relates to the sensation of heat or cold as quantitatively measured by a thermometer. The molecules of any solid, liquid, or gas are in a state of continual agitation. The more energy possessed by the substance, the faster the molecules will move, and the higher will be the "kinetic temperature." If the atoms are motionless, the kinetic temperature of the medium is said to be at absolute zero.

As we have seen, we can employ radiation flowing through a medium as a measure of "radiation temperature" (fig. 6–5). Out in the depths of interstellar space far from any star, the temperature resulting from the total amount of radiation present may be very low, perhaps only a degree or two above absolute zero K. We say that such radiation is very "dilute." However, the temperature, as defined in terms of the spectral distribution of the radiation rather than as total energy content, may be very high. We would, in fact, usually obtain a different temperature for each wavelength. An incandescent solid gives a continuous spectrum with a wide range of colors. An incandescent gas emits bright lines. The same rarefied gas will absorb from white light those colors it would emit if incandescent (fig. 6–6).

Figure 6–6. The Draper-Kirchoff laws. An incandescent solid, such as the filaments of a lamp, produces a continuous spectrum. An incandescent rarefied gas produces a discontinuous or bright-line spectrum characteristic of the gas. Light from an incandescent solid, passing through rarefied gas, undergoes absorption. The lines that previously appeared bright appear as dark, or absorption, lines in the spectrum.

Table V. Elementary Particles

Name	Electric Charge	No. of Neutrons	Symbol	Atomic Weight
Proton	+1	0	p or H 1	1.007276
Neutron	0	1	n	1.008665
Deuteron	+1	1	d or H 2	2.01355
Alpha particle	+2	2	a or He 4	4.00150
Electron	−1	0	β—	.000549
Positron	+1	0	β+	.000549
Neutrino	0	0		0
Antineutrino	0	0		0

The Microworld of Atomic Nuclei

Thus far we have referred to the atomic nucleus only as a minute, positively-charged body carrying most of the mass of the atom. We have noted that the nucleus of hydrogen carries a single unit of charge, that of helium two units, that of lithium three, and so on. But we have given no attention to the internal structure of the nucleus. That internal structure is very important if we are to understand how nuclei may interact with one another. For in such nuclear reactions we expect to find the explanation of the chemical composition of the sun or a star and of the evolution of heavier atoms from lighter ones, with the release of immense quantities of energy.

Atomic nuclei have a structure as well defined as that of a house, and, like a house, a nucleus is built up from what we may term "atomic bricks." We do not know what these bricks look like, but we can fairly well define their properties. Quite a few varieties of atomic bricks are known. We are already familiar with two of these: first, the proton, or positively-charged nucleus of the hydrogen atom; and second, the negatively-charged electron, whose weight or mass is about 1800 times smaller than that of the proton. The third type of brick, the *positron*, has a mass identical with that of the electron, but the charge is positive instead of negative. In other words, its electric charge is the same as that of the proton.

Free positrons are relatively rare because they are incompatible with the negative electrons, which, we have seen, abound as the orbital companions of atomic nuclei. When a positron collides with an ordinary electron, both disappear as material objects and are converted into two quanta or flashes of high-frequency gamma radiation moving in opposite directions. Positrons are often released during certain atom-building processes.

If we subject a mass of hydrogen gas to pressures that will crush the atoms enough to free the electrons from their nuclei, and if we then further increase the pressure, the negative electrons will unite with the positive protons, producing particles with no residual electric charge at all. Such particles, called *neutrons*, commonly exist as one of the stable components of an atomic nucleus. But, if a neutron happens to escape, as neutrons often do, it decays in about 12 minutes on the average into its parent materials—a proton and an electron.

With these four bricks—protons, neutrons, electrons, and positrons—we can explain most of the properties of atomic nuclei relevant for understanding the stars. Although we use these bricks to build up more complex nuclei, the surprising fact is that the total mass of the composite nucleus is generally less than that of its component parts. The explanation of this is that a certain amount of matter has vanished during the atom building. As Einstein originally showed, this lost matter of mass (m) reappears as energy (E), as set forth in the familiar equation, $E = mc^2$, where c is the velocity of light. This source of energy is truly enormous. According to this formula, a single pound of matter, completely converted, will yield ten billion (10^{10}) kilowatts of energy, as much as is supplied by the combustion of about four million tons of coal! Such processes furnish the energy that keep the stars shining for billions of years. They also make possible the H-bomb.

The Atom-Building Process

Let us trace some elementary steps in atom-building. In the hot core of a star two protons collide with sufficient energy to cling together momentarily, even though their identical electric charges would ordinarily cause them to repel each other. If we say that the proton has mass 1, this nucleus has mass 2 and charge 2. Since the charge determines the chemical nature of the substance, this nucleus would be helium. However, it is very unstable and within less than a billionth of a second one of two things may happen. First, the two protons may disengage themselves and go their independent ways, leaving the original situation unchanged. Or second, the proton pair may eject a positron, leaving a nucleus of weight 2 but charge 1, since one unit of positive charge departed with the positron. A nucleus of charge 1 must be hydrogen, but the mass weighs twice as much as ordinary hydrogen. This nucleus is stable and occurs naturally, though with an abundance some 500 times smaller than that of normal hydrogen.

This double-weight nucleus is called a *deuteron* to distinguish it from its lighter-weight brother, the proton. The chemical properties of heavy hydrogen, which will ordinarily possess a single orbital electron, will be like those of ordinary hydrogen. Although they have very different nuclei, the two substances occupy the same place in the Periodic Table and are therefore called *isotopes*, a term meaning "same place." One other significant fact is that the deuteron weighs less than the two protons that united to produce it. This difference in mass escaped in the form of energy when the deuteron was formed.

Now suppose that the deuteron encounters and engorges another proton. The product will increase one unit in both charge and mass. It will therefore be an isotope of helium, having mass 3, which is also stable although some energy is released by the conversion. Now suppose that this particle of charge 2 and mass 3 meets and unites with another of the same kind. The temporary nucleus of charge 4 and mass 6 will be very unstable, but it quickly ejects two protons each of charge 1 and mass 1, leaving a nucleus of charge 2 and mass 4. We thus recover two of the six original protons and find ourselves with a helium nucleus—called an alpha particle—of charge 2 and mass 4. About one per cent of the original mass has been converted into energy by this process.

We can continue to follow this atom-building process although we will encounter difficulties in getting beyond beryllium. Frustratingly, every time we try to build up a more complex atom, the structure collapses into helium. The process releases energy, but how can we account for the existence of elements of intermediate or heavy atomic weights? There is, however, one way of circumventing the difficulty in building a more complex nucleus. Three helium nuclei, simultaneously colliding, can unite to form a carbon nucleus, with the release of energy as follows: He 4 + He 4 + He 4 = C 12. But our calculations indicate that this process will occur only at temperatures and densities that are much higher than those that are present anywhere in the sun.

With carbon present, the atom-building process could continue in another manner, the so-called "helium-burning" process, with consequent liberation of energy. In this way we add alpha particles (α) to carbon 12, getting oxygen 16; then successive additions of α particles produce, in turn, neon, magnesium, silicon, and so forth. It is possible to trace this process as central in building atoms up to and even beyond the abundant isotope of iron, of atomic weight 56.

Some of the various reactions, produced at super-high temperatures and densities, release neutrons that also enter into the production of still more complex nuclei. But it must again be emphasized that the temperatures and densities that are required far exceed those existing in the cores of our sun or in the average star.

Of the first 83 elements, through bismuth, all but two have at least one stable isotope. The exceptions are technetium, Tc, element number 43, and prometheum, Pm, element number 61 in the Periodic Table. Tc is the more important. Of its 16 isotopes, only three have mean lifetimes longer than a few days: Tc 97 with 2.6×10^6 years, Tc 98 with 1.5×10^6 years, and Tc 99 with 2.1×10^5 years. These lifetimes are so much smaller than the age of the universe, or even of most of the stars, that we could scarcely expect to find it occurring naturally. Indeed, we do not find any of it on earth, except as prepared in atomic incubators. But it does appear in the spectrum of certain stars, from which we deduce that the substance must have been manufactured there sometime during the last few million years. However, it is certain that technetium could not possibly be made in any ordinary, stable star.

Table VI. The Uranium-238 Series

Atomic Number	Name	Atomic Weight	Half Life
92	U	238	4.51×10^9 y
90	Th	234	24.1 d
91	Pa	234	1.17 m
92	U	234	2.48×10^5 y
90	Th	230	76,000 y
88	Ra	226	1,620 y
86	Rn	222	3.823 d
84	Po	218	3.05 m
82	Pb	214	26.8 m
83	Bi	214	19.7 m
84	Po	214	.164 ms
82	Pb	210	22 y
83	Bi	210	5 d
84	Po	210	138.4 d
82	Pb	206	stable

m = minutes; d = days; y = years; ms = milliseconds

Radioactivity and Isotopes

Where the lighter atoms can be built up into heavier atoms, many of the heaviest—including such substances as uranium, thorium, and radium—possess nuclei that are unstable. Such substances are said to be radioactive. Their nuclei naturally tend to explode and eject various fragments. As early as 1896, Antoine H. Becquerel (1852–1908), French physicist, found that certain salts of uranium emitted unfamiliar rays that could penetrate black paper or thin sheets of aluminum. Studies by the Curies, Marie (1867–1934) and Pierre (1859–1906), and others finally solved this phenomenon. The nuclei of atoms were truly exploding, sometimes ejecting helium nuclei or alpha particles and sometimes electrons, processes that changed the electrical charge of the nucleus and the chemical nature of the atom involved.

The study of atomic structure was confronted by a new problem when T. W. Richards (1868–1928) of Harvard University noted that the atomic weights of lead from different sources were not identical. Ordinary lead weighs 207.19, but lead from radioactive sources weighs 206.08. Were these two different elements or simply different forms of the same element? They had essentially identical chemical properties and thus occupied the same place in the Periodic Table, which made them, as we have said previously, isotopes. The measured chemical atomic weight is therefore the average of the weights of the naturally occurring isotopes. Every element has at least several isotopes, and toward the end of the Periodic Table some substances have as many as 35. Of these, only 280 isotopes of 81 elements are stable and occur in nature. The remaining isotopes, produced when we "incubate" various substances in an atomic reactor, are unstable. Their nuclei tend to explode, some quickly and some more slowly, ejecting various kinds of atomic fragments and reverting to other elements.

On earth we do find a number of unstable substances occurring naturally, chiefly among elements 81 to 92. Most of the isotopes are descended from three long-lived but unstable parents: U-238 with a lifetime of 4.51×10^9 years; U-235 with 7.13×10^8 years; Th-232 with 1.39×10^{10} years. Table VI depicts the successive stages in the decay of U-238 to Pb-206. Alternate paths exist, but the end product is the same. The mere presence of these radioactive substances on earth poses some complex questions and also points to several important conclusions. Certainly they are relics from some event long past, for they are no longer being formed on earth. In the earth's crust, the amounts of U-238 and Pb-206 are roughly equal. If all of this lead came originally from the decay of uranium, the age of the earth would be about 4.5 billion (4.5×10^9) years. But some separation of the lead from the uranium may well have occurred during the early history of the earth, so that the atoms could be much, much older.

Where did the uranium originate? Our knowledge of nuclear processes convinces us that even the center of our sun is not hot enough or dense enough to form the heavier atoms, including those of radioactive character. And when Sir James Jeans (1877–1946), a British astronomer, objected that the stars were not hot enough, his fellow astronomer Sir Arthur Eddington (1882–1944) suggested that he "try and find a hotter place." That is precisely what modern astrophysicists are doing.

The primordial universe, evidence indicates, probably consisted of pure hydrogen. Somewhere, somehow, some of this original material condensed to form a mass far greater than that of an average star. Some scientists have suggested that perhaps all the atoms in the universe were compressed into a single huge ball, which broke up into millions of millions of fragments when it exploded.

The pressures and temperatures inside a star that is a thousand or more times more massive than our sun would favor the production of the heavier atoms, up to and including uranium. Such a star, however, would be precariously unstable. It could explode violently, spewing its material into space, where fragments now containing radioactive matter could recondense into the more normal stars, including our sun. We shall later return to the subject of exploding stars.

Meanwhile, we must keep in mind that the key to understanding our universe lies in the nuclei of its component atoms.

Neutrinos and Antineutrinos

Most of the atomic building-blocks appear to possess some form of spin. When two such particles unite and, as they sometimes do, annihilate each other, giving off radiation in the process, the spin must also somehow be "conserved," because atoms are not exempt from the basic law of conservation of angular momentum. To carry off the spin momentum of the original positive and negative electrons, physicists found it necessary to postulate the existence of two additional particles: the *neutrino* and the *antineutrino*. These particles have unusual properties. Almost paradoxically, they are weightless, that is, they possess zero mass. As it moves away, the former is spinning like the advance of a left-handed screw; the latter like a right-handed screw. Neutrinos and antineutrinos are much smaller than most other atomic particles. Many neutrinos and antineutrinos originating deep in stellar interiors such as the sun are able to penetrate the outer layers of the sun and escape into space. Exactly how many neutrinos thus leave the sun is a matter of conjecture, because we do not know precisely how opaque the sun is to their flow. We surmise that a constant hail of neutrinos bombards us from the sun: every second, millions of such particles beat down on every square inch of the sunlit earth. Yet we are completely unaware of them because they rarely interact with atoms of the human body. They go through us and right on through the earth and come out on the other side of the earth.

To capture neutrinos and antineutrinos physicists have built huge tanks far underground in the deepest mines to shield their experiment from other kinds of penetrating radiation and particles. They have filled these huge vats with special chemicals, hoping to trap and detect their unimaginably small quarry—the smallest and most elusive quarry in the universe. Absorption of a neutrino will alter the nature of the chemical substance in the tank. One substance used in the tank is carbon tetrachloride. Absorption of an antineutrino changes the chlorine atom in this substance into a form of argon, which can be detected by special techniques. Four such events a day would be a large number. We might term the device a "neutrino net." Neutrino astronomy is in its infancy, but it could prove to be one of the most exciting branches of the science.

7 The Instruments of Astronomy

Until three centuries ago, only the unaided eye was available to reveal the wonders of the heavens. With the invention of the telescope in the seventeenth century, man began to see multitudes of objects for the first time and to discover fine details on bodies that had previously appeared featureless or as mere points of light.

Since then, increases in telescopic magnification and resolution have continued to take place. The spectrograph has made it possible to disperse light and analyze its component colors. The development of the photographic process has enabled man to make lasting records of the heavens, including some of the faintest astronomical objects. Just within the past few decades, new types of sensors have been designed that allow us access to parts of the spectrum well beyond the visible range. For example, various kinds of photocells and imaging devices can detect light whose wavelength lies anywhere between the extreme ultraviolet and the far-infrared. These instruments are most effective when put aboard rockets and satellites, thus enabling them to operate beyond the point where light is absorbed in the earth's atmosphere.

In addition to exploring the visible range, astronomers are exploiting another relatively transparent atmospheric "window" by means of radio wavelengths. Radio studies are leading to a better understanding of the solar atmosphere, the planets, the structure of the galaxy, cosmological processes, and the electromagnetic radiation we receive from celestial objects. It is the task of the astronomer to organize the data obtained into an intelligible and coherent picture of the universe around us.

Left: Herschel's 40-foot telescope at Slough, England, was one of the wonders of its time. However, control of the mounting was a great problem. The mirror, four feet in diameter and made of metal, did not retain its reflectivity, and the instrument eventually fell into disuse. (Yerkes Observatory)

Right: Both reflecting and refracting telescopes were used in early days to study the sun, the stars, and other heavenly bodies. The lenses of the long-focus telescopes were set on top of obelisks. The lower diagram shows how solar features such as sunspots appear on the solar image projected upon a screen. (Science Museum, London)

VERVM ITA SVBTILI ARGVMENTATIONE COMPREHENSVM

VT
PVDEAT NON CREDERE

C
Telioscopio

Immiſſione naturali.

Trans.
miſſione Refractoria ſimplici

Heliaſcopio

G

R

Reflexione.

D

V

Immiſſione Refractoria compoſita.

Maculæ et Faculæ ex uariis obſeruandi modis, ſtabiliuntur.

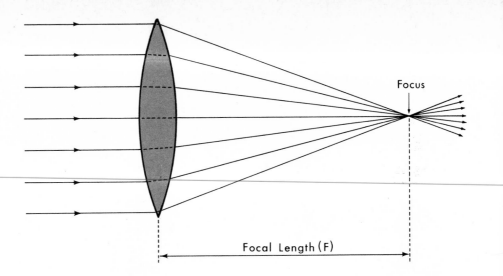

Figure 7–1. Formation of an image by a simple convex lens. Parallel light entering from the left comes to a focus at right.

Focus

Focal Length (F)

Light Waves and Lenses

The principal function of a telescope is to gather and concentrate the incoming electromagnetic radiation. In a simple optical telescope, lenses and mirrors accomplish this task. Light can be so manipulated because of three of its very remarkable properties. First, a ray of light travels in a straight line when moving through a homogeneous medium. In interstellar space, where the medium is almost a vacuum, light travels linearly and at a speed of 186,300 miles per second. Second, the law of reflection declares that when a ray of light falls at an angle upon a plane surface, part of the beam bounces like an elastic ball, and returns into the medium from which it came at the same angle on the opposite side of the perpendicular to the surface. The incident ray, the reflected ray, and the perpendicular to the surface all lie in the same plane. Third, the law of refraction tells us that when a beam of incident light passes into a medium that is optically more dense, the ray bends closer to the perpendicular (fig. 7–1).

Prior to the invention of the telescope, astronomers designed and used instruments for measuring the positions of the stars and planets. These devices were, like gun sights, pointers that the observer could direct skyward and use in estimating positions with his eye. The more sophisticated instruments often had circles engraved with angels, along with indices to measure precise directions. Still more advanced instruments had special scales engraved on their faces that simplified the calculations of triangles on the celestial sphere. These devices were a forerunner of certain types of computers.

The telescope greatly extended the range of astronomical observation, because the magnification allowed a greater accuracy both in pointing the instrument and in measuring the position of stars. In the telescope's field of

Figure 7–2. Formation of the image of an extended celestial object. The image is inverted.

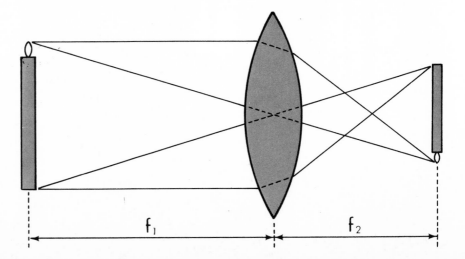

f_1

f_2

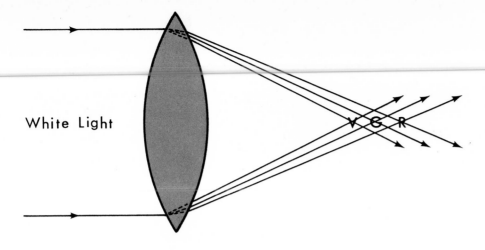

White Light

V G R

Figure 7–3. In a simple lens, as in a prism, the violet rays are bent more sharply than the red and hence come to a focus nearer the lens. This phenomenon, termed chromatic aberration, severely limited refracting telescopes until scientists learned how to correct for it.

view, fine hairlines, made from a spider's web, provided a sensitive reference pointer. The image of a star could be set on the crosshairs with very high precision.

The operation of a telescope is in principle very simple. A lens forms an image of the object toward which it is pointed—in the same way that the lens of a camera focuses an image on a film. The image is real and readily visible (but upside down) on a ground-glass screen (fig. 7–2). To examine the image more carefully one may use an ordinary magnifier. In theory a telescope consists of two lenses: one to form an image, called the *objective*, and the other to look at and magnify the image, called the *eyepiece*. The longer the focus of the objective and the stronger the eyepiece, the higher will be the magnifying power of the telescope.

The early astronomers soon learned that telescopes possess inherent defects that limit their performance. The curved outer edge of the lens acts somewhat like a glass prism, bending—that is, refracting—the blue light more than the red. As a result the blue light comes to a focus nearer the lens and the red farther away (fig. 7–3). If one looks at the blue image of a star he will see a red blur surrounding it; similarly the red image possesses a blue border. Scientists, including Sir Isaac Newton, decided that this phenomenon, called *chromatic aberration*, was impossible to circumvent, although some early astronomers tried to do so by making objectives of extremely long focal lengths. However, these were extremely unwieldy and were not widely used.

Achromatic Telescopes

Newton himself conceived of one way of solving the problem caused by the failure of the glass objective to bring all of the colors of light to the same focus. In a letter to the Royal Society in 1672, Newton pointed out that a

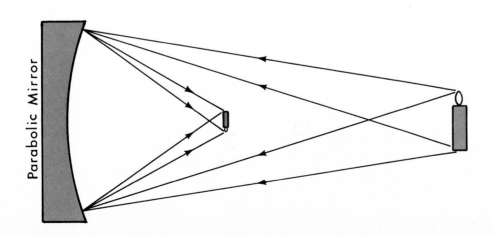

Parabolic Mirror

Figure 7–4. A parabolic mirror can serve as well as a lens to form an image. The image will also be inverted.

concave mirror can form an image; and since the angle of reflection—unlike that of refraction—does not depend upon the color of the light, all of the different rays will come to the same focus. The telescope will be *achromatic*, that is, without color. Using a concave metal mirror, he succeeded in constructing a small instrument of this kind (fig. 7–4). To get the image outside of the telescope, where he could see it with his eye, he fitted a small flat mirror into the tube at an angle of 45° in order to reflect the light to one side. This type of telescope is known as the Newtonian system. Newton's telescope (on view at the Royal Society in London) was extremely small, with a mirror slightly over an inch in diameter and a focal length of only six inches. It reportedly showed, however, details similar to those revealed by a refracting telescope three or four feet long and with a magnifying power of 40 times.

The reflecting telescope did not become practical, however, until about 1730, when James Short (1710–1768), a Scottish optician, developed new ways of grinding and polishing sizable metal mirrors in his machine shop. These mirrors proved to be very popular, especially with amateurs, because of the brightness and sharpness of the images. For some reason, however, it was difficult to put cross-wires into the instrument; and so many professional astronomers, concerned with determining the positions of stars, continued to use the simple refracting telescopes despite their blurred images.

This practice persisted until 1757, when a London optician, John Dollond (1706–1761), found that he could overcome the difficulties of the simple lens by combining two lenses of different kinds of glass. The first, a double-convex lens, was made of crown glass, a material similar to ordinary window glass. The second lens was concave and, had it been made of crown glass, would merely have put the different colors of light together, restoring the original direction so that the light would have been unfocused. But by using flint glass, a much denser material, Dollond forced the spectral colors to recombine, but still form an image (fig. 7–5). For this invention of an achromatic lens Dollond received a special award from the Royal Society. It was later established that an English inventor, Chester Moor Hall (1703–1771), had invented such a lens much earlier—in 1733. But it did not receive much publicity, probably because Hall did not try to stimulate its manufacture. There was some argument over patent rights, but the judge who presided over the court awarded the license for fabricating the lenses to Dollond on the grounds that "it was not the person who locked his invention in his scrutoire that ought to profit from such invention, but he who brought it forth for the benefit of the public." The Dollond instruments became very popular and scientists around the world eagerly sought them.

There were many other makers of telescopes, but none more famous than Alvan Clark (1804–1887) and his son Alvan G. (1832–1897), of Cambridge, Massachusetts. They produced the lenses for most of the world's greatest refracting telescopes, including the 36-inch lens for the Lick Observatory and the 40-inch lens for the Yerkes Observatory. The latter is still the world's largest lens of this type.

Figure 7–5. By using two kinds of glass with different dispersive effects, as shown here, one can correct for chromatic aberration sufficiently to bring two colors of light to the same focus. The denser flint glass causes the rays to bend in the opposite direction and reunite at a common focus. This lens is termed "achromatic," that is, without color. To achieve even greater spectral purity in the image, astronomers often use compound lenses embodying six or more components.

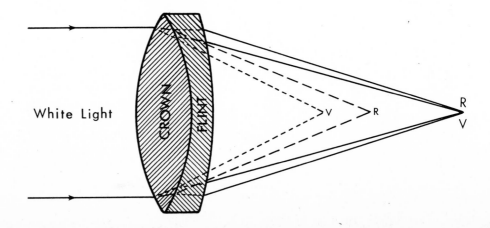

Large, achromatic refracting telescopes became the vogue in the late nineteenth century. They reached their limit with the 40-inch telescope of the Yerkes Observatory and the 36-inch telescope of the Lick Observatory, shown here. (Lick Observatory)

Overleaf left and top right: Most modern telescopes are reflectors, using large, concave mirrors to focus the light. Such is the 84-inch reflector of the Kitt Peak National Observatory in Arizona. Starlight enters from the retracted shutter of the dome, falls on the 84-inch mirror, and is reflected to a secondary mirror that may reflect it down to the Cassegrain platform. There an observer can study the light. An additional mirror can reflect the light diagonally down the polar axis to the Coudé spectrograph, below and to the left. (Both: Kitt Peak National Observatory)

Overleaf bottom: The Robert R. McMath Solar Telescope of the Kitt Peak Observatory. A coelostat (double-mirror system) reflects sunlight down the inclined shaft to another mirror that focuses a large solar image in an underground laboratory. The inclined shaft in the telescope shows the beam of sunlight enroute to the laboratory. (Both: Kitt Peak National Observatory)

William Herschel was an English astronomer of German ancestry who had achieved considerable fame as a musician, conductor, and composer. He was keenly interested in science and experimented first with small and then with larger telescopes. He successfully ground and polished a number of metal mirrors, the largest 19 inches in diameter and 20 feet in focal length. We shall see later how William Herschel and his son John (1792–1871) made astronomical history with these instruments, contributing much to our knowledge of the universe. His use of the reflecting telescope placed it on a level with the achromatic refractor. With the passage of time and the construction of larger instruments, larger refracting telescopes became more difficult to build and proportionately far more costly, for several reasons. A refractor requires two essentially perfect pieces of glass, free from bubbles and internal striations. There are four surfaces to grind and polish, each requiring painstaking care. Also, the lens must be hung from its very edges, and in a cell that supports—at least in the larger refractors—an immense weight of glass. In addition, glass is not completely free from strains and stresses: it will bend under its own weight. Hence the 40-inch lens at Yerkes Observatory, completed in 1897, represents about the ultimate in refractors and probably no larger lenses of this type will be constructed.

In comparison, the great reflecting telescopes are models of simplicity (fig. 7–6). The glass does not have to be of high quality. It need not even be transparent. It may contain internal bubbles and other small defects as long as the surface is relatively free from them, and even there a few bubbles will

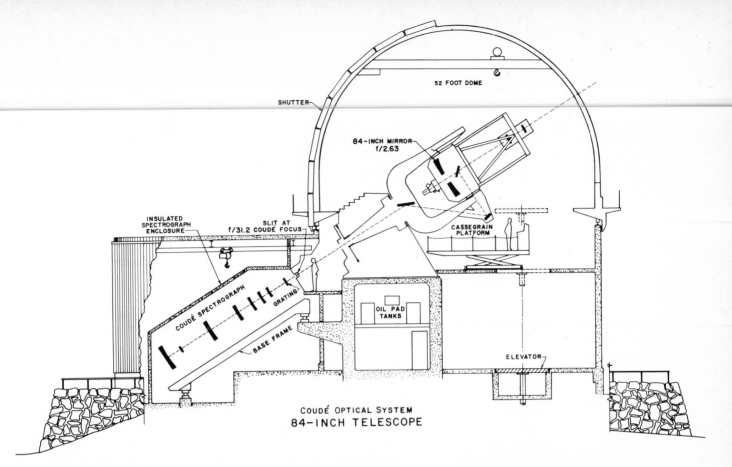

SHUTTER

52 FOOT DOME

84-INCH MIRROR
f/2.63

INSULATED
SPECTROGRAPH
ENCLOSURE

SLIT AT
f/31.2 COUDÉ FOCUS

CASSEGRAIN
PLATFORM

COUDÉ SPECTROGRAPH

GRATING

BASE FRAME

OIL PAD
TANKS

ELEVATOR

COUDÉ OPTICAL SYSTEM
84-INCH TELESCOPE

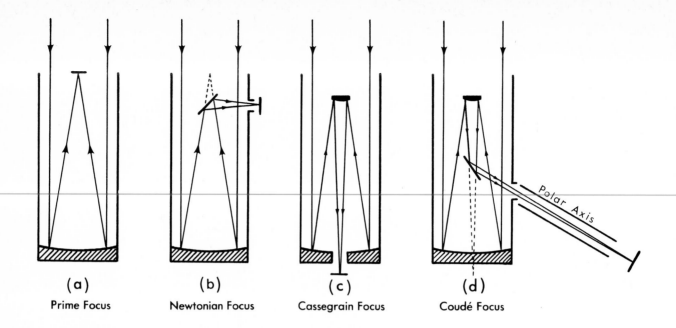

(a)	(b)	(c)	(d)
Prime Focus	Newtonian Focus	Cassegrain Focus	Coudé Focus

Figure 7–6. The reflector telescope has the advantage of being achromatic because the angle of reflection does not depend on the color of the light. Four widely-used types of telescopes are shown here. In (a) the rays focus at a point where the photographic plate or other measuring equipment can be inserted. Except for very large telescopes, where the observer can sit in the middle of the instrument without blocking too much light, the prime focus is somewhat difficult to use. Some instruments use (b) a 45° plane mirror to bring the image outside the telescope, a mounting known as the Newtonian type. One may also introduce a hyperbolic convex mirror, which brings the focus back to (c) through a hole in the mirror. Or one may use another flat, placed at 45° in front of the hole, to bring the image outside the telescope, as with the Newtonian focus. These are known as Cassegrain types. Since it is sometimes awkward to attach heavy instruments to a telescope, astronomers often use a Coudé focus (d), which sends images down the polar axis.

not be a serious deficiency. The fact that only one surface, instead of four, need be ground and polished represents an enormous saving in time and cost. In addition, the mirror can be made quite thick, thus improving its rigidity; and it can be completely supported from the back, since light does not have to pass through it. The modern telescope, which employs glass instead of metal, has the additional advantage that when the mirror's surface becomes tarnished or defective in any way, the layer of silver or aluminum can be dissolved and a new layer put on without damage to the expensive and delicate glass surface. Whereas the old metal mirrors made by Herschel still have their original figures preserved, they have long since lost their luster and cannot be used as telescopes. The Schmidt Optical System (fig. 7–7), which combines a correcting plate (a form of lens) with a concave mirror, is in common use today for astronomical photography over a wide field.

With the advance of technology still other improvements have been possible. Glass proved to be superior to metal in that it was less affected by temperature changes, which cause material to expand or contract. The invention of pyrex further reduced the effect of temperature; and still later, it became possible to make mirrors of pure quartz. Today many of the mirrors are constructed from highly-sophisticated ceramic materials, such as Cer-vit, wherein temperature changes are minimal. For example, a mirror made of Cer-vit that has been heated almost red-hot can be plunged into ice water without damage to the surface.

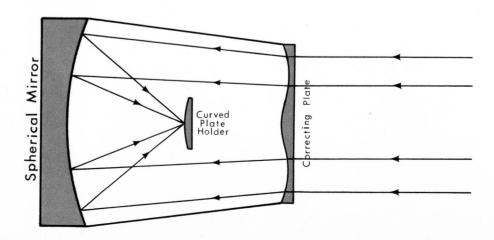

92

Metal reflector of the Kitt Peak National Observatory, used for detecting heat from the sun and planets. (Kitt Peak National Observatory)

Left: Figure 7–7. The Schmidt Optical System. Large parabolic mirrors are not beset by the lack of achromatism that limits reflectors, but they have other aberrations: rays that are off the axis do not come to a sharp focus. Star images appear fuzzy and exhibit a "tail," which increases the farther it is from the axis. The Schmidt Optical System combines the best features of reflectors and refractors. Light enters through a curved correcting plate, falls on a spherical mirror and reaches a plate-holder strictly in focus, thus permitting sharply-focused photography of large areas of the sky.

Telescope Supports

Amateur astronomers usually mount their small telescopes on a tripod. These can be turned up and down through a horizontal axis or rotated from side to side on a vertical axis. Such a support is known as an *altazimuth* mounting because astronomers term the angle of a star above the horizon its "altitude" and its compass direction its "azimuth." This mounting would be ideal if only stars moved strictly up and down or in circles parallel to the horizon. The diurnal motion of the earth causes the stars to rotate on an axis parallel to the earth's axis of rotation. Following a star with a telescope is much simpler, therefore, if we set one axis of the support system parallel to the earth's axis of rotation. Moving the telescope either north or south will point the instrument toward the celestial object under observation. And a clockwork drive will turn the telescope toward the west to keep it pointed toward the star. This axis is usually called the *polar axis*, because it points toward the two celestial poles, around which the celestial sphere appears to rotate. Such a system, which almost all large telescopes use, is known as an *equatorial* mounting (fig. 7–8).

With an equatorially-mounted telescope, the observer who is taking a long-exposure photograph merely checks the telescope every minute or two to see if it is following correctly. If the clock is off, the observer can move the telescope slightly with one of the "slow motions" that govern the position of the telescope in the two coordinates. He can also compensate for the effect of atmospheric refraction—the bending of light by the earth's atmosphere, which makes a star appear somewhat above the position it would occupy as seen from an airless earth. This refraction is zero for the zenith and increases toward the horizon, where it amounts to about one-half of a degree.

The equatorial mount has, I believe, about reached the limit of its usefulness. If we are ever to build larger telescopes, we shall probably return to the more stable altazimuth mount, with its vertical axis and a horizontal axis

Spectacular mountain observatory, Pic du Midi, in the high Pyrenees of southern France, provides some of the finest observing conditions in the world. (L'Observatoire du Pic du Midi)

supported from opposite ends of a U-shaped support. With such a mounting, the weight of the telescope is directed vertically through the center of the upright axis, and does not hang unsupported in space, as it does for most of the equatorial mountings. We can use altazimuth mountings today because high-speed computers can readily transform the changing position of the star into the coordinates of altitude and azimuth needed for the instrument. Of course, if one were to take a long-exposure photograph with such an instrument, he would find that all of the star images were drawn out into arcs of circles on the plate. But the computer can remedy even that difficulty by making the plate itself rotate at the proper rate. One of the most sophisticated solar telescopes, the one at the Sacramento Peak Observatory, uses the altazimuth system. The whole very heavy instrument floats in a pool of mercury and rotates about a vertical axis in such a way as to compensate for the rotation of the image.

The Clock

Time-keeping is essential to astronomical observation, just as astronomical observation is essential to keeping correct time. The first clock was undoubtedly a gnomon: a "sundial" in the form of a vertical post. It was set in the ground and its moving shadow recorded the passing hours. However, the motion was slow and it was complicated by the changing altitude of the sun according to the seasons. Even so, sundials served man long and faithfully. and before modern watches were invented, men carried miniature folding sundials, fitted with compasses to help the user orient the dial north and south. Stars served as a clock at night, but stars are not always visible or easy to use.

Various other devices were used, such as dripping water, or flowing sand as in an hourglass, but all of these were inaccurate and cumbersome. Galileo discovered the basic principle that led to the pendulum clock when he observed that the duration of the swing of a lamp hanging from the ceiling of a cathedral was independent of the amplitude of the swing. But friction soon stopped his crude pendulums, and it was not until 1656 that Huygens, using weights, invented a method of keeping a pendulum swinging.

Sensors of Radiation

In the previous chapter we noted the vast extent of the electromagnetic spectrum from the long, medium, and short radio waves, through microwaves, infrared, the visual, ultraviolet, soft X-rays, hard X-rays, and gamma rays. Despite the fact that the human eye is literally blind to all but a minute octave of the magnificent band of the electromagnetic spectrum, still it is one of the most important sensors of radiation. For, even if we rarely observe celestial objects directly with the eye, as did the earlier astronomers, we nevertheless use it effectively in analyzing astronomical records of every type.

The invention of photography was a tremendous boon to the astronomer. The photographic plate was a permanent record that could be studied again and again. A single plate might have the images of thousands of stars recorded on it. The earliest experimenters in photographic techniques were the French inventors Louis J. M. Daguerre (1789–1851) and his partner Joseph N. Niepce (1765–1833). The former discovered the action of light upon copper plates coated with a salt of silver and developed what is known as the "daguerrotype" process. In the 1850's George P. Bond (1825–1865), then director of Harvard College Observatory, successfully used this process to photograph the moon, Jupiter, and the bright star Vega. He foresaw how valuable photography would be to astronomy. During the next few decades, copper plates gave way to glass plates coated with silver salts suspended in albumen. Then came the wet-plate process, with coatings of collodion; and finally, the modern dry plate, with the sensitive silver salts supported in a gelatine emulsion. Over the years the sensitivity of photographic materials has

Figure 7–8. Most telescopes are mounted equatorially, that is, with an axis parallel to that of the earth and pointing to the north celestial pole. Thus, as the earth rotates or moves in orbit the polar axis always points in the same direction. The telescope is mounted on the declination axis perpendicular to the polar axis, so that the telescope can move north or south to reach the declination circle of the stars. When the telescope is set on a star, with the polar axis rotating counter to the earth's rotation, the telescope will remain on the star.

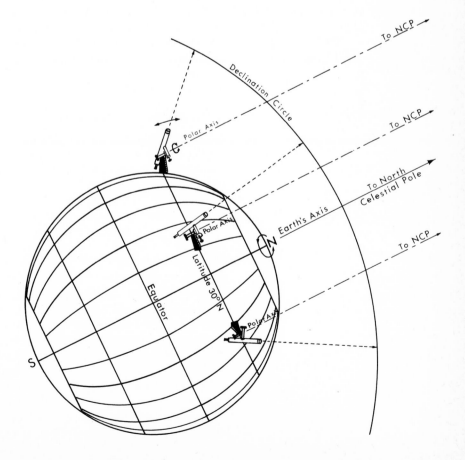

95

Left: The 200-inch Hale telescope of the Hale Observatories (formerly Mount Wilson and Palomar) is the largest operating telescope in the world. (Hale Observatories)

Right: An unusual mounting of the 15-inch refractor at the Pic du Midi Observatory gives protection from high winds that might make the telescope vibrate. (L'Observatoire du Pic du Midi)

been increased considerably. Where previously ordinary photographic plates were sensitive only in the range from blue to ultraviolet, plates have been made sensitive to the red and even the infrared through the incorporation of various dyes in the emulsion.

Astronomers invented still other sensors. The photoelectric cell, which in form resembles a small electric light, generates an electric current when light falls upon its sensitive surface. The magnitude of the current provides a very accurate measurement of the brightness of the star—one far more precise than an estimate based on the darkening in the image of a star on a photographic plate. Devices using this principle are now basic in the field of stellar photometry.

Astronomers have increased the sensitivity of the photographic plate by using what is generally called an "image tube" at the focus of the telescope. This device, like a television camera, amplifies the incident light, which, in turn, is recorded on a photographic plate or film.

Thermocouples, formed by the junction of two dissimilar metals, respond similarly when heat falls on one of the metals. By means of these, astronomers extend the range of their studies into the far-infrared. They use highly-sensitive radio receivers that amplify and register the energy concentrated by one enormous antenna or by dozens or even hundreds of small antennas. The small antennas are arranged in a special pattern, such as a cross, in order to improve the accuracy of the measurements.

The Spectrum

The spectroscope, or spectrograph, is another very important tool of the astronomer. This instrument spreads light out into its component colors. If we place a glass prism in front of a telescope, the point images of the stars diverge to form a line, with violet at one end and red at the other. Thus, one may record the spectra of thousands of stars on a single photograph. Alternatively, one may use a powerful telescope to concentrate the light from a star upon a narrow slit and then focus that slit, through a prism, on a photographic plate. The images of the slit in the various colors provide an accurate rendition of the full spectrum (fig. 7—9). One can record on the same photograph the spectrum of some substance such as iron and, by comparing the difference in wavelengths between the laboratory and stellar sources, determine through the Doppler effect whether the star is receding or approaching the observer, and at what speed. The spectrum also provides a means of determining the chemical and physical nature of the object that is under investigation.

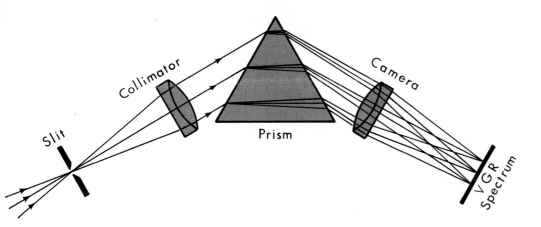

Collimator

Camera

Slit

Prism

V G R
Spectrum

Among the important instrumental accessories, one must also list the artificial satellites and space probes that have done so much to provide information about our universe. Above all, satellites have provided data about the far-ultraviolet and the X-ray region, information that we could obtain in no other way, because these wavelengths are so heavily absorbed by our earth's atmosphere.

There are, of course, many instruments and accessories designed for special purposes. We shall encounter a few of these elsewhere in the book. One new device must be mentioned here because, although it was originally designed for other purposes, it has completely revolutionized astronomy: the high-speed digital computer. Within minutes, or even seconds, this device can perform complicated calculations that would have taken a lifetime by the older methods.

Figure 7–9. The spectrograph is a primary accessory of the telescope. In one common type, light from a celestial body is focused on a slit at the focus of a collimator lens. This lens delivers parallel light to a prism, which disperses it. As shown here, a camera lens then focuses the various colors of light. Instead of prisms, many types of spectrographs employ diffraction gratings as the dispersive medium; such gratings have thousands of parallel lines per inch ruled on a flat (or sometimes curved) surface.

Below: A radio dish 38 feet in diameter, built especially for recording very short radio waves, that is, from one millimeter to one centimeter. Built by the National Radio Astronomy Observatory, it stands on top of Kitt Peak in Arizona. (National Radio Astronomy Observatory)

8

The Earth as a Planet

The flights into space and to the moon have made us more aware than ever that our earth is just one of the planets of our solar system (color plates 7, 8, 11). Although we regard the earth as *terra firma*, symbol of stability, it is in reality a great space vehicle, slightly less than 8000 miles in diameter, moving in its orbit at a speed of about 18.5 miles per second. It is also drifting, along with the sun and other planets of our solar system, at about 12 miles per second toward the constellation of Hercules (fig. 8–2). As a result of the rotation of earth on its axis, the equator—that is, any point on it—is, moreover, whirling at a speed of about 1000 miles per hour.

We also know that the earth rotates once every 24 hours. The centrifugal force produced by this rotation causes the earth to bulge at the equator, so that the equatorial radius is about $13^1/_3$ miles greater than the polar radius. Thus the mouth of the Mississippi River is farther from the center of the earth than its source. If the earth stopped rotating, the Mississippi would reverse its flow; in fact, water would then flow into the polar regions until it equalized the polar and equatorial diameters.

I should also add that the pole of the earth's rotation is not a fixed point on the surface of the earth. The earth wobbles slightly about this axis, an effect that is probably attributable to the varying load of ice in different latitudes and longitudes. The actual wobble is small, however, amounting to an oval-shaped path 60 feet or so in its longest dimension. The phenomenon is known as variation of latitude, since it was discovered by accurate determinations of latitude, which in turn depend on the distance of the point of observation from the pole. If the pole of the body moves, the latitude will correspondingly change. From accurate measures of latitude, astronomers have deduced the extent of the wandering of the earth's pole.

Inside the Earth

Although man has scarcely made a dent in the earth's surface—the deepest mines extend only about two miles down—he has nevertheless found out a great deal about the earth's interior. As we all know, from time to time intense earthquakes occur, caused by the breaking and slipping of parts of the earth's crust. Such land-slips produce vibrations as well as several distinct kinds of waves that travel great distances. First there are the longitudinal, or "push-pull," waves, which travel through the interior of the earth at a speed of 5 miles per second. Seismologists call these P-waves (from the Latin *prima*, first) because they are the first waves to arrive at any given distance from the quake. The second type, "shake" waves, consists of oscillations perpendicular to the direction of flow—like the waves along a rope when one shakes it from side to side. These are called S-waves (from the Latin *secunda*, second) because they travel more slowly—at about 2.7 miles per second—and arrive later. From the interval between the arrival of the P- and S-waves, a seismologist can generally gauge quite accurately the distance of the earthquake. There are also important waves, called the R-waves (after Lord Rayleigh who first discussed them), which travel around the earth's crust.

The speed of these waves depends on the nature and density of the rocks through which they move. By comparing the records of a given quake from hundreds of stations around the world seismologists have been able to assemble much information about the earth beneath us. They have determined

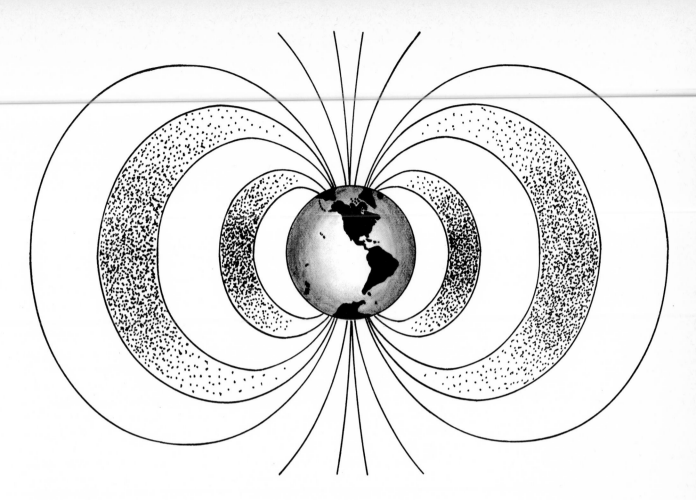

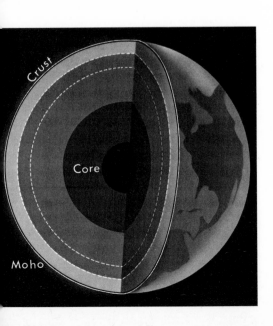

Above: Figure 8–1. The Van Allen radiation belts consist of charged ions and electrons trapped in the earth's magnetic field.

Cutaway diagram of the earth's interior, showing the core, the shell of molten nickel and iron, the mantle, and the "Moho."

that the earth's interior contains at its center a solid core of nickel-iron about 800 miles in radius. On top of this core lies a shell of molten nickel-iron, about 1400 miles thick. Next comes the "mantle," which extends almost to the surface of the earth. The mantle itself consists of several distinct layers. At the top of the mantle there occurs a sharp discontinuity (discovered in 1910 by the Yugoslav, Mohorovičić) generally referred to as the "Moho," consisting of an abrupt change in density. Under the ocean floors it lies at a depth of approximately five miles, but under the continents it can be as much as twenty miles down. The layer on top of the Moho is the earth's crust, on whose surface we live. A few years ago man made an attempt to drill a hole through the crust into the Moho's discontinuity. The task proved to be too difficult and expensive and it remains a major challenge to scientific exploration in the future.

Intense electric currents flow in the nickel-iron core of the earth, producing a magnetic field that we can detect at the earth's surface. Indeed, this field extends well out into space, where it traps electrons and ions to form the concentrations known as the Van Allen radiation belt, which was discovered by observations from orbiting satellites (fig. 8–1). Inside the earth the density ranges from 3.3 near the surface to 5.5 at a depth of about 1800 miles. It reaches 9.5 in the outer core and as high as 14 at the center. These figures are given as grams per cubic centimeter or, simply, in terms of the density as compared with water, whose density is 1.

The earth is somewhat elastic and tends to yield under the strain. In fact, the continents seem to float on the lower strata in such a way that, for any given latitude, about the same amount of mass lies along a radius to the earth's center, whether it is over a continent or over the ocean. The material under the continent is simply less dense than that under the ocean.

The earth's continents, or the lithosphere, occupy about 30 per cent of the earth's surface. The oceans, or the hydrosphere, comprise the remaining 70 per cent. Since its origin the earth has been subject to evolution and

99

change. We see evidence of this continuing change everywhere. Of the two types of rocks that comprise the crust—igneous and sedimentary—the igneous came first, the result of lava flow through cracks and fissures in the earth's crust. In many places these formed distinctive volcanic cones and other rugged features.

Volcanism and Crater Formation

Volcanism and associated lava flows assume many forms. Molten magma, rising to the surface, may simply ooze out and produce an enormous lava flow. Often, the molten material hardens and builds up a cone that may reach altitudes of 20,000 feet or more. During an eruption, smoke, ashes, and lava pour out of a crater at the top of the cone. Sometimes the volcano may eject glowing masses of superheated steam and red-hot dust and ashes. These clouds, known as *nuées ardentes*, can move at hurricane speeds, enveloping and destroying everything in their path.

Occasionally the lava may solidify and plug up the central vent. If the internal pressure continues, there will be a violent explosion accompanied by earthquakes and the break-up of the entire volcanic cone, with fiery clouds of dust ashes, huge fragments, and live steam flying into the air. Such a catastrophe can wipe out an entire island. It can initiate a tidal wave, or tsunami, that may start as a mountain of water half a mile high and rush outward over the ocean as a vast ring of water.

Such a disaster destroyed the volcanic island of Thera, in the Aegean Sea, about 1500 B.C. The central part of the island exploded and collapsed, leaving a crescent-shaped fragment surrounding a circular basin, called a caldera, some six miles in diameter. Near the center of the island—known today as Santorini—lies a new cone with a central vent from which steam and sulphur fumes still escape. The explosion also had a tremendous effect on the island of Crete 90 miles south. Huge clouds of wind-borne dust and ashes rained down upon the island and the tsunami from Thera was perhaps 1000 feet high when it struck the Cretan coast. The disaster completely buried the Minoan civilization—including the famed palace at Knossos—that had developed there.

The formation of calderas is still going on. Among the destructive explosions that have occurred in modern times is the eruption that obliterated the South Pacific island of Krakatoa in 1883 and the one that killed forty thousand people on the island of Mount Pelée in the Caribbean in 1902.

Two cinder cones (top left) and part of McDougal Crater (bottom left), both in the Pincante Volcanic field, Mexico. Some types of terrestrial craters, known as caldera, bear some similarity to the larger lunar craters. Though most astronomers concur with the theory that the craters were caused by lunar impact, a few scientists still consider the volcanic-caldera theory distinctly possible.

Right: Schematic diagram showing rotation of earth and resolution around the sun. The angle of 1° is highly exaggerated. The earth, starting at E_1 lies at E_2 a day later. Sidereal noon occurs when the vernal equinox (sign of Aries) lies directly overhead. But the sun will not be overhead until four more minutes have elapsed.

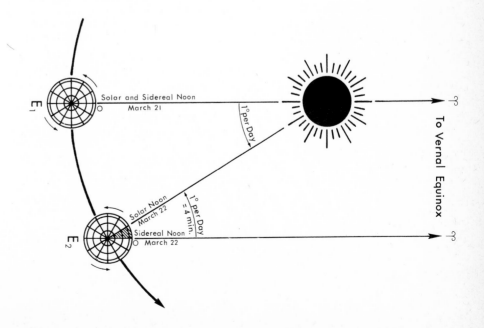

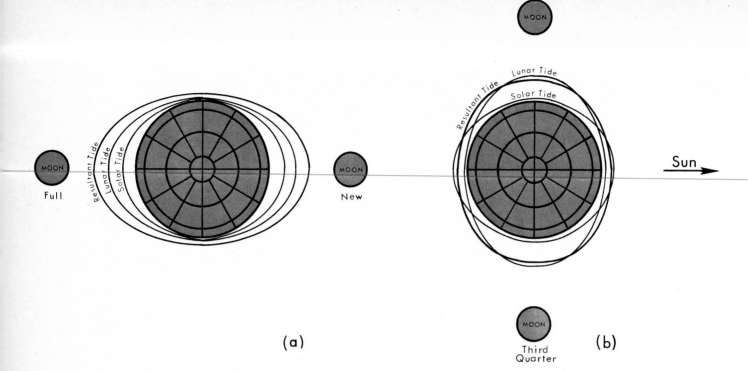

First
Quarter

MOON

Resultant Tide
Lunar Tide
Solar Tide

Lunar Tide
Solar Tide

MOON
Full

MOON
New

Resultant Tide
Lunar Tide
Solar Tide

Lunar Tide
Solar Tide

Sun →

(a)

MOON
Third
Quarter

(b)

Figure 8–3. When the moon and sun lie in the same straight line (a) their combined gravitational pull makes the tides higher than when they are at right angles (b). The former are called spring tides; the latter neap tides.

Forces other than volcanism can also produce craters. Most significant is the impact of giant meteors, such as the one that landed in Arizona 5000 or more years ago and created a crater more than a mile across and 500 feet deep. Many other astroblemes, as meteor craters are called, have been found on the earth. The largest of these, the Vredevoort Dam in South Africa, is about 50 miles across. As we shall see, craters, whether meteoric or volcanic, can tell us much about physical processes on celestial objects.

Erosion

The phrase "the eternal mountains" is a common expression. But mountains are eternal only according to a human time scale. Over the ages our earth has heaved, cracked, and buckled. Mountains have thrust up from the ocean depths, lifting thick layers of sedimentary rock, breaking and folding them into weird patterns. Huge layers of sedimentary rock, which lay flat on the ocean floor at the time of their formation, now stand almost vertical. Melted lava has occasionally welled up to fill some of the cracks, so that igneous intrusions often occur along with sedimentary formations.

Ever battling the tectonic forces that build mountains are erosive forces that can reduce great peaks to mere scars on the earth's surface. Of the various erosive forces, water is by far the most important. Clouds tend to form over elevations, causing rain and snow. Water, seeking the lowest level, runs down hillsides, wearing rills that collect into brooks, streams, and eventually huge rivers flowing into the sea. Viewed from the air, we see rivers as a vast circulatory system, with a characteristic branching structure, the smaller branches joining the larger ones and all eventually uniting to form the main stream (color plate 10).

Streams carry enormous quantities of mud and silt into the oceans every day. Geologists have estimated that the Colorado River—which is not among the greatest rivers—transports about half a million tons of such material every 24 hours. The weight of these vast quantities of eroded material, accumulating over long intervals of geologic time, causes the particles to adhere to one another and form solid rock. Slight changes in the composition of the accumulating silt impart different colors to the layers of deposit, clearly revealing how it was laid down.

In arctic zones or at very high altitudes the water freezes into glaciers, which slowly flow to lower levels, grinding the surface beneath them and carving out huge U-shaped valleys. Along the shores the wind-driven waves and ocean tides remodel the coastline continuously. The wind is a very important earth-altering agent, sometimes piling up layers of sand, or loess, to form huge drifts or dunes, which may slowly creep over the land and reshape the surface (color plate 9). Even temperature changes can have an erosive and disintegrating effect through the cracking and crumbling caused when rocks expand with heat or contract with cold.

Rivers carve deep channels and canyons. The combined forces of the flowing water and the earth's rotation can cause a river bed to shift and flow in sinuous curves rather than in straight lines. We term this process meandering and, as we shall see, scientists have found evidence that it may also be important on the moon.

The temperature increases as one digs down into the earth. We have already noted the existence of a liquid shell around the solid nickel-iron core, where the temperature may rise as high as 14,000° K (25,000° F). Although most of the evidence indicates that the early earth was probably quite cold, the internal layer contained some radioactive material, such as uranium, thorium, and an isotope of potassium. The heat generated by the radioactive decay of these materials leaks out very slowly from the interior, serving in the course of many millions of years to heat up the earth's interior until some of the material was even liquefied. It is this heat that produces all such phenomena as volcanos and geysers.

The Tides

The gravitational pull of the moon and the sun, with the former being the stronger, causes tides in the oceans. When the sun and moon lie in the same straight line, their pulls cooperate to produce very high tides called spring tides. When the sun and moon lie at right angles to one another, their pulls partially cancel each other out and produce weaker high tides, known as neap tides (fig. 8–3). When the moon is considerably north or south of the earth's equator, successive high tides, at twelve-hour intervals, are often very unequal (fig. 8–4).

The moon drags the earth's tidal bulge over the surface in such a way as to oppose the earth's normal rotation. Therefore, the day is constantly being lengthened by about $1/1000$ of a second per century. This amount may seem negligible, but over the course of many centuries, the total accumulation is

Figure 8–4. Two successive high tides for a given latitude may have very unequal heights. For example, the one in the northern hemisphere on the side toward the moon is appreciably higher than the one at the same latitude on the opposite side.

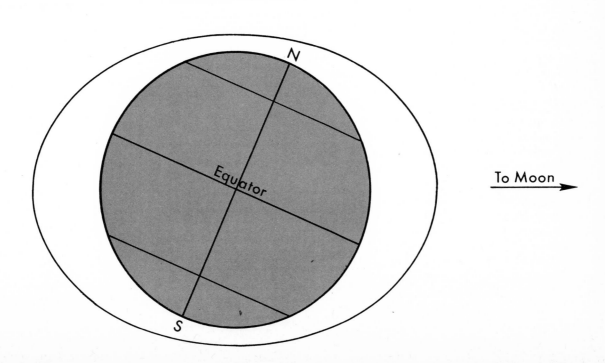

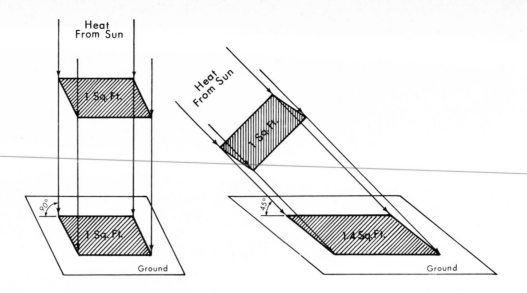

Figure 8–5. Differences in insolation caused by the inclination of the sun's rays. When sunlight falls vertically, its energy is distributed over a smaller area and produces greater heat than when the beam falls obliquely. This effect explains the difference between winter and summer in the opposite hemisphere.

sufficient to be detected. If, for example, we compare the predicted paths of total solar eclipses with the actual locations of eclipses in a certain area, we find discrepancies in excess of an hour. This very fact adds to our knowledge of the earth's past history. Scientists have worked out the whole theory of tidal friction, including the fact that the greatest friction takes place on the relatively shallow continental shelves, and find that it is consistent with observations.

If, moreover, the earth is slowing down, the moon must accordingly be speeding up. Paradoxically, an acceleration of the moon causes it to move slightly farther from the earth and thus take longer to complete its orbit. Our study shows that the moon is moving away from the earth at a rate of about one inch per year. Again, this figure may seem altogether negligible compared with the present distance of the moon, which is about 15 billion inches. But we find that, since tidal friction would have been much greater in the past, when the moon was very much closer to the earth, a billion or so years ago the two bodies would have had to be nearly in contact with one another. Evidently something has served to reduce the amount of tidal friction. Scientists suspect that this reduction may have come about through the continental drift. When all of the continents were nearly touching, the total tidal friction would have been much less than it is today because the total perimeter of the continental shelf would have been much smaller.

Figure 8–6. Atmospheric refraction. A ray of light entering the earth's atmosphere is bent toward the perpendicular as it descends into denser layers. The apparent direction of the star is thus different from the true direction insofar as refraction makes it appear higher in the sky. Similarly, when the sun appears to touch the horizon, it is actually completely below the geometrical horizon.

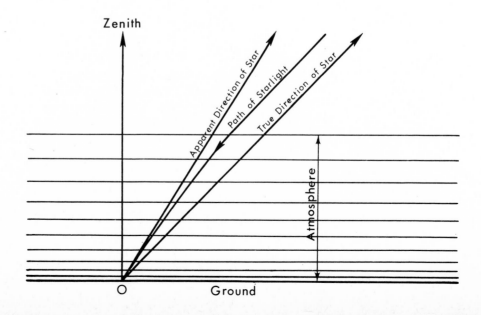

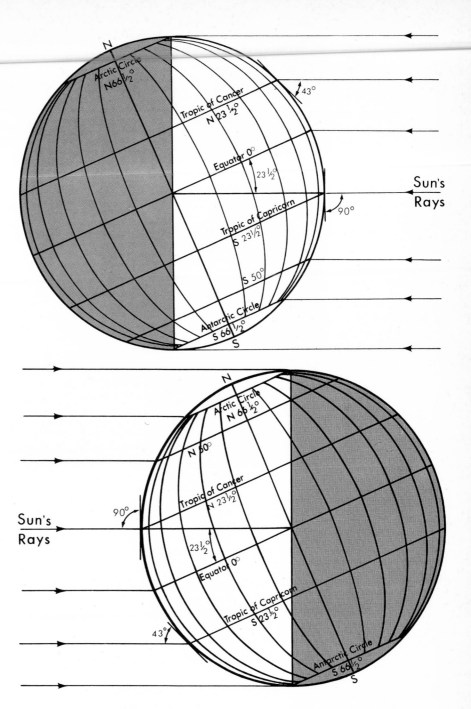

Top: Figure 8–7. The earth at winter solstice (December 21), showing the North Pole tilted away from the sun and therefore in darkness, and the South Pole tilted toward the sun.

Bottom: Figure 8–8. The earth at summer solstice (June 21). It is now on the opposite side of the sun, its axis still parallel to the position it had at the winter solstice. However, now the North Pole receives the sunshine and the South Pole is in darkness.

Atmosphere and Climate

The earth has a very distinctive atmosphere, consisting of about 78 per cent nitrogen, 21 per cent oxygen, and a little less than 1 per cent argon, with carbon dioxide, neon, helium, methane (marsh gas), krypton, and a few other still rarer substances making up the remainder. Air also normally contains a certain amount of water vapor. If one were to lower the temperature of the atmosphere to —195° C (—320° F), the whole atmosphere would condense and form a layer of liquid air about 44 feet thick over the surface of the earth. About 15 pounds of atmosphere lie above every square inch of the earth.

The chemical composition of the earth's atmosphere must have changed many times since it was first formed. Both the water of the earth's oceans and the atmosphere are probably a secondary formation, having been released from the rock through the long-continued action of volcanism and by the process known as liquidation. Nor has the chemical composition of the atmosphere remained constant over geologic time. The primitive atmosphere must

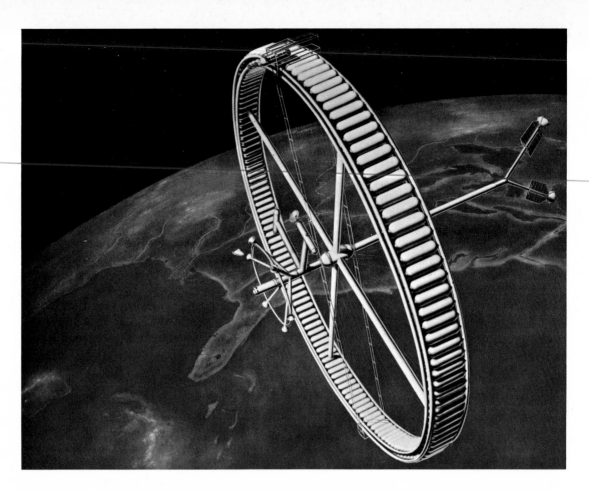

have consisted largely of such substances as methane, ammonia, and water vapor; later, carbon dioxide became a major constituent. Primitive forms of life appeared on the surface of the earth and great forests in warm prehistoric bogs permitted the growth of trees, giant ferns, and other organisms that eventually produced huge deposits of fossil fuel, such as coal, oil, and gas.

Since extensive coal deposits have been found in such cold areas as Greenland and major oil reserves in northern Alaska, we must infer that the climate of the earth has changed significantly over geologic time. There are several possible reasons for this change. First, the sun may somehow have altered its flow of radiation. Second, chemical changes in the earth's atmosphere may have sharply increased the amount of heat trapped by the lower atmosphere, a phenomenon known as "the greenhouse effect." This works as follows: the earth's atmosphere is relatively transparent to short-wave radiation from the sun. The absorbed energy warms the earth's surface, which tries to radiate energy back into space. But this energy lies in the far-infrared, where water vapor and carbon dioxide, for example, hinder its escape. Like the glass of a greenhouse, the atmosphere traps this radiation and thus tends to raise the temperature of the earth. Something like this has also happened, it seems, on the planet Venus. There is one other way in which the earth's temperature may have been changed: the continents may not be fixed but may be drifting over the earth's surface, affecting climate as they drift.

The average chemical composition of the earth is probably not very different from that of the sun, except that the two lightest elements, hydrogen and helium, appear to have largely escaped from the terrestrial environment. But the distribution of the elements over the earth is far from uniform. In certain places we find large concentrations of iron; in others, concentrations of silver, copper, or zinc. Scientists do not fully understand how this differentiation occurred, and they speak rather vaguely of mineral-rich "solutions" that flowed through the soil and left veins of various substances in the cracks and

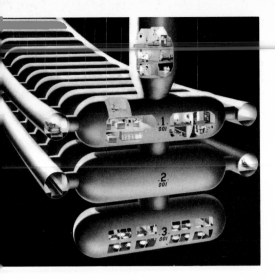

Left: An artist's conception of a space city of the 1990's: an enormous wheel containing offices, laboratories, living quarters, and even a hotel. A ferry system would transport men and supplies from home base.

Above: Detail of the space city, showing laboratories, offices, living quarters, and even the transportation system enclosed in the giant tube along the rim of the wheel. (Both: Lockheed Missiles and Space Company)

crevices between faulted rocks. Whether we understand it or not, the process was an important part of the evolution of the earth.

Living organisms such as coral polyps and various kinds of algae have certainly had a tremendous effect on the earth. Most of the carbon once found in the atmosphere as carbon dioxide was used by various living forms and converted into such substances as limestone, or calcium carbonate. If all the carbon dioxide thus stored in the rocks were released, the amount in our atmosphere would be increased many times.

The earth's atmosphere absorbs great quantities of solar radiation (figs. 8–5, 8–7, 8–8). This has several effects on us, some beneficial and some otherwise; it does, for example, remove a large part of the radiation in the far-ultraviolet, energy that would be lethal to most forms of life. Inequalities of temperature and pressure provide motive power for the winds that drive the clouds and control precipitation.

In the upper atmosphere, ultraviolet absorption leads to the production of O_3, a special type of oxygen molecule known as ozone, which causes a high amount of absorption in the ultraviolet. Then, at still higher levels, absorption of X-radiation tears electrons away from the molecules and atoms, producing ions. Several such regions of highly electrified material exist in the upper atmosphere, known as the D, E, F layers of the ionosphere. They play an extremely important role in radio communication, reflecting, like a mirror, the longer radio waves around the earth and allowing the shorter ones to penetrate. Ions and electrons, trapped in the Van Allen radiation belt, occasionally spill over into the upper atmosphere, especially in zones not too far from the magnetic poles of the earth. These particles, guided by the earth's magnetic field, collide with the molecules of the earth's upper atmosphere; they emit radiation, which appears in beautiful forms and colors as the Aurora Polaris.

The atmosphere also protects us from the many meteors, small and large, that strike the earth in the course of a day. It also greatly weakens the cosmic radiation coming in from the depths of space—energy that could have some malignant biological effects on our bodies.

The atmosphere, especially the lower atmosphere, also affects astronomical observations (fig. 8–6). Ascending and descending currents of air deflect the rays of light from a star or other heavenly body. The resulting atmospheric shimmer blurs images and makes it impossible to see the finest details. The image of a star may even appear to dance and change in both color and intensity. To obtain better images, with higher resolutions, astronomers have sent telescopes up in balloons to heights of nearly 100,000 feet. One of the great advantages of observations from orbiting satellites is the fact that the equipment lies completely above the earth's atmosphere. Stars do not twinkle in interstellar space. There one can observe the far-ultraviolet and other radiations that do not penetrate to the earth.

The molecules of the earth's atmosphere scatter the sunlight that falls upon them. The blue light is scattered more than the red; hence the blue of the sky. Particles of dust or smoke, which are usually somewhat larger than the wavelengths of the incident light, do not show selective scattering. They scatter all kinds of radiation equally; moreover, they tend to scatter more toward the observer than to the side or away from him, a phenomenon called "Mie scattering." This is responsible for the halo of white light around the sun visible near large cities, especially those distant from western coasts. In the United States, for example, one usually finds the dark blue sky only in the clean, rain-washed atmospheres of the far West. That is why the best observatories have generally been located on mountain tops in the West.

As orbiting astronauts have frequently noted, this blueness is a characteristic feature of the planet earth. So are the distinctive patterns of white clouds, whose curved fringes mark cyclonic movements. Cyclones and hurricanes derive their energy in part from the earth's rotation. In the northern hemisphere they rotate in a counterclockwise direction: in the southern hemisphere the motion is clockwise.

9

The Moon as a Planet

What a long, historic vista we have, looking backward from the Apollo landings (color plates 12 to 17) to that prehistoric period when man first began to contemplate the moon, to note its changes of shape through the month, and to wonder what it all signified. To many of the ancients, the moon was a goddess, Silver Artemis to the Greeks, and to the Romans, Diana, lover of the woods and the wild chase. She had a triple personality, divided between Selene as the true moon-goddess, Artemis for earthly adventure, and Hecate as goddess of the underworld, when the moon lies below the horizon and the earth is dark.

Other ancients, more discerning, recognized that the variations in shape from crescent to full and back to crescent again resulted from sunlight falling upon a sphere from different directions. The vague, shadowy markings, popularly called "the man in the moon," remain the same despite the changing illumination. It was clear, at least, that the moon always kept the same face turned toward the earth. Some people even thought of the moon as a mirror and the dark areas as reflections of the earth.

The telescope changed all such speculations, for it clearly revealed the moon as an independent world with mountains and lowlands. The early observers, with their imperfect instruments, had reasoned by analogy that the dark areas were bodies of water, and so they are known to this day as *mare* (plural *maria*), the Latin word for sea: for example, Mare Tranquillitatis, the Sea of Tranquility. Other smaller, dark areas bear such names as *sinus* (bay), *lacus* (lake), and *palus* (swamp). But the truly outstanding and unique

Figure 9–1. The moon, rotating as it revolves around the earth, keeps one side facing toward the earth.

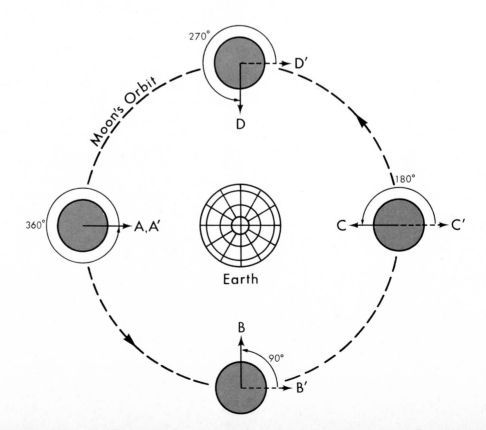

Lunar Orbiter II photograph showing the moon's Marius Hills; the surrounding plateau, Oceanus Procellarum; and many volcanic domes and cones. The crater Marius, about 30 miles wide, appears at upper right. (NASA)

features of lunar topography, as Galileo himself recognized, were the mountains and the large and small craters that mark the surface. These craters have diameters ranging from five or six hundred miles—such as Mare Orientale—to mere depressions only a few feet across.

The total number of lunar craters exceeding a given diameter increases with their decreasing size, as shown in the following table:

Diameter	Number of craters with diameters exceeding width in first column
10 kilometers	4,000
1 kilometer	60,000
100 meters	40 million (4×10^7)
10 meters	4 billion (4×10^9)
1 meter	4 trillion (4×10^{12})
10 centimeters	400 trillion (4×10^{14})

Depressions smaller than 10 centimeters exist, but are generally indistinguishable from ordinary surface irregularities.

There are two main schools of thought concerning the origin of these craters. The majority of astronomers favor the view that the pits and holes are astroblemes arising from the impact of meteoric bodies upon the lunar surface. We have already noted that such craters are found on the earth's sur-

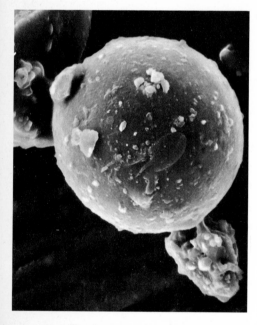

Top: Moon fragment (shown enlarged 1100 times) among the lunar material collected by Apollo XI astronauts. Scientists are analyzing age, structure, and cosmic ray damage in such materials.

Bottom: A glassy spherule (here enlarged 2200 times) also found among Apollo XI lunar rocks. Its shape indicates that it underwent melting, perhaps when a meteorite crashed into the moon, melting lunar material and splashing it long distances. (Both photographs taken with a scanning electron microscope by General Electric Research and Development Center)

face. A minority attribute the craters to some form of volcanism akin to the terrestrial tectonic forces that produced the great calderas.

The lunar maria, although heavily cratered, are relatively flat and smooth. They are clearly lowlands and not bodies of water at all, although they would become true seas if large quantities of water were to become available on the moon. There are several large chains of mountains named for terrestrial counterparts—such as the Alps, the Caucasus, and the Apennines—and also a number of mountain peaks. The moon is comparatively much more rugged than the earth, for some of the peaks rise to heights of more than 25,000 feet. Astronomers determine the altitudes of such features by measuring the length of the shadows they cast upon the lunar surface.

Since the moon possesses no appreciable water or atmosphere, the lunar sky is completely black. To an astronaut standing on the surface of the moon the stars are plainly visible in the daytime, right up to the edge of the sun. The shadows are black and sharp because there is no blue skylight to illuminate them, as there is on earth.

Earth-Shine on the Moon

The planet earth, rich blue in color and streaked with layers of clouds, shines brightly in the lunar sky. First of all, the earth seen from the moon appears about four times larger in diameter than the moon appears to us on earth. Furthermore, the reflectivity of the earth is four or five times greater than that of the moon. Hence, altogether, the "full earth" sends to the moon about eighty times as much light as the full moon sends to us. We can best perceive the result of this earth-light when the moon is a slender crescent; the light from earth falling on the moon's dark hemisphere illuminates it enough for us to see the complete circle. The phenomenon is commonly referred to as "the old moon in the new moon's arms." Seen from the moon in the course of a synodic month of 29 days, the earth also exhibits phases, from new earth to full and back to new earth again.

The Moon's Rotation

As noted earlier, the moon rotates on its axis in such a way as to keep one face turned toward the earth. The sun shines, in turn, on every part of the moon, rising and setting with the full lunar day, which is equal to 29 of our days (figs. 9–1 and 9–2). The moon rotates uniformly but, since the orbit is appreciably elliptical, it moves more rapidly when nearest the earth and more slowly when farthest away, in accordance with Kepler's second law. As a result, rotation and revolution coincide only on the average. At times we can perceive some distance around the eastern, and at other times around the western edges of the moon. Since the axis of rotation is slightly inclined with respect to the moon's orbital plane, we look beyond either pole. This apparent shifting of the moon is known as *libration*. Because of it, from the earth's surface we are able to view, not one-half, but about five-ninths of the lunar surface. The remaining four-ninths would have been forever inaccessible except for the American and Soviet space programs.

The Lunar Maria

A decade of lunar research conducted from space vehicles began with the Soviet "Lunik" of 1961, which orbited the moon and transmitted to earth television pictures of the moon's far side, never before seen by man. To everyone's surprise the far side showed many differences from the familiar near side. For example, only one major mare appears on the far side, the Sea of Moscow; whereas the near side contains fifteen or more, several of which encroach up on the edges of the far side. The reason for this marked difference is not immediately evident. One possible explanation is that a large comet crashed into the near side, leaving the maria as scars of the event.

The floors of these maria are relatively smooth as compared with the highlands. The evidence is clear that something has flowed into them, deeply burying prior formations—the tops of which project above the level of the seas. Faint, circular rings, clearly the ghosts of old craters, mark the floors of the maria. The boundaries of the seas exhibit sharp discontinuities of both slope and composition, facts also supporting the idea that the seas are low regions, partially filled with some material: the basic question is with what? The appearance strongly suggests that lava flows were generally responsible, and most astronomers support this view. A few, however, prefer the hypothesis first proposed by the British-American scientist Thomas Gold, of Cornell University, suggesting that the transported material is dust rather than lava. The dust, he argues, is the result of the continual plowing of the lunar surface by meteoric fragments crashing down from outer space. If the individual dust grains were to become electrically charged, Dr. Gold points out, they could flow downhill in jumps like a grasshopper, ending up on the lowlands, where the layer could eventually build up to depths as great as several miles.

British science-fiction writer Arthur C. Clarke, elaborating on Gold's ideas, suggested that the thick dust layer might be hazardous to astronauts in a lunar landing. If the dust were only lightly compacted, it might not be able to support the spacecraft, or the astronauts; they would then sink to the bottom of the dust-heap like a lead weight in a drift of fine snow. This possibility was seriously considered by many scientists of the Apollo program. However, the successful Apollo landings removed all doubt about the ability of the lunar soil to support heavy weights. And the second landing, in particular, revealed the existence of quantities of dust. The two astronauts, covered with the fine, dark material, looked as if they had been cavorting in a coal bin.

Although I am inclined to favor Gold's idea that the maria are filled with dust, his suggestion that this was transported by electrostatic forces seems rather unconvincing. A simpler explanation, I believe, and one that works well on earth, is that the dust has been washed down with water. No one has previously considered this possibility, because the moon has neither oceans nor atmosphere. In addition, because of its small mass and low surface gravity, (respectively only $1/81$ and $1/6$ that of the earth), scientists have generally followed the British astronomer Sir James Jeans, who tried to demonstrate that the moon could never have possessed an appreciable atmosphere. I recently found a serious error in his work, which appears to reverse his conclusion. I believe that a fairly extensive lunar atmosphere could have existed on the moon for as long as 100 million or perhaps even a billion years.

The excellent photographs of the lunar surface taken by the various spacecraft of the NASA Lunar Orbiter series and returned to earth by radio techniques reveal details previously unsuspected on both the near and far sides of the moon. The maria surfaces are rough and uneven. Numerous crevasses exist, known as *clefts* or *rilles*. Some are jagged cracks, often with many branches, such as the Huyginus Cleft. Some are clearly faults, such as the Straight Wall, where one side of the crack has fallen, leaving an almost perpendicular cliff. Many of the maria contain sinuous ridges, whose origin is not yet understood. Many of the rilles are sinuous in form. An example is Schroeter's Valley. The rilles there so closely resemble terrestrial meandering valleys that a number of astronomers have argued that they must have been produced by flowing water. The first astronomer to make this suggestion was William H. Pickering. Recently, Nobel Prize winner Harold Urey suggested that the moon may have temporarily acquired water and atmosphere by collision with a comet. And, as noted earlier, I alternatively indicated that the moon could have retained an original atmosphere much longer than scientists previously believed.

The Problem of Sinuous Rilles

The lunar orbiters have discovered dozens of sinuous rilles, possessing a typical structure. Their source is usually a pear-shaped crater a few miles in

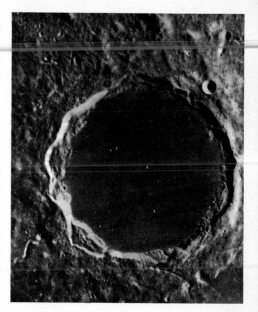

Top: The mare-filled crater Plato, 60 miles in diameter, north of Mare Imbrium. The lack of connection between the mare material in Plato and similar material surrounding the rim suggests local subsurface sources for the materials or a subsurface duct connecting the two. The sharp, sinuous features to the left and below are called rilles.

Bottom: The crater Tycho, 50 miles wide, is an excellent example of a fresh, young lunar crater with typical high central peak, slumped walls, and hummocky rim deposits. In addition, the floor is extremely rough with mounds and fissures, and the rim has prominent flow structures and a strong concentric texture. (Both: NASA)

diameter. The stem leads into a valley that meanders irregularly over the surface, finally disappearing into a low-level mare. Their appearance has led some astronomers to call them "cobra valleys." They are evidently the result of some form of erosion, the flow of some kind of matter. I have suggested that the cobra heads—the pear-shaped depressions—were a type of artesian lake from which water flowed out and downward. As alternatives to water, suggestions include lava, volcanic ash, *nuées ardentes*, and subsurface ice or permafrost. The absence of a veined or tree-like structure formed on the earth by most terrestrial river systems in regions of heavy rainfall has led certain astronomers to reject the water hypothesis. On the other hand, aerial views of terrestrial rivers, such as the Kuiseb in Southwest Africa (color plate 9), flowing intermittently through the rain-free Namib Desert, show a meandering structure similar to that of the lunar sinuous rilles. Some of these rilles, chiefly the deepest and most rugged, may be described as canyons with narrow, tortuous secondary rilles at the bottom. The Alpine Valley is a notable example of this formation. This secondary rille was first revealed in lunar orbiter photographs.

Lunar Craters and Rays

The lunar craters are varied in form, size, and structure. Clearly, they were not all formed simultaneously but over a long period of time. Newer craters have partly obliterated the walls of older ones and these in turn overlie the scars of still older craters. The floors of some of the older craters, such as Plato, are smooth. Like the maria, a substance—lava perhaps—has filled in their originally rugged interior. They are sometimes referred to as "walled plains." The walls of the more recent craters are rugged and terraced and the interiors have pronounced central peaks, which in turn—as in the case of Eratosthenes—may also possess a central *craterlet*. The inner walls of the great crater Copernicus have suffered slumping, or giant land slides. The smooth, gaping mouth of the keyhole-shaped depression known as Fauth strongly suggests that some form of volcanism was responsible for its formation.

Systems of craterlets, forming chains, occur in the neighborhood of some of the larger craters. These are so regular in their appearance and so clearly related to the parent crater, that they could not be the result of random meteor impact. What probably happened was that as the original large meteor hit the lunar surface, the resulting explosion ejected huge masses of lunar rocks,

The far side of the moon. Near the top is the spectacular rayed crater Giordano Bruno. Below it, with the dark center, is the crater Lomonosov, and below Lomonosov to the right is the dark crater Edison. The large, dark, oval feature in the lower left is the crater Joliot Curie. (NASA)

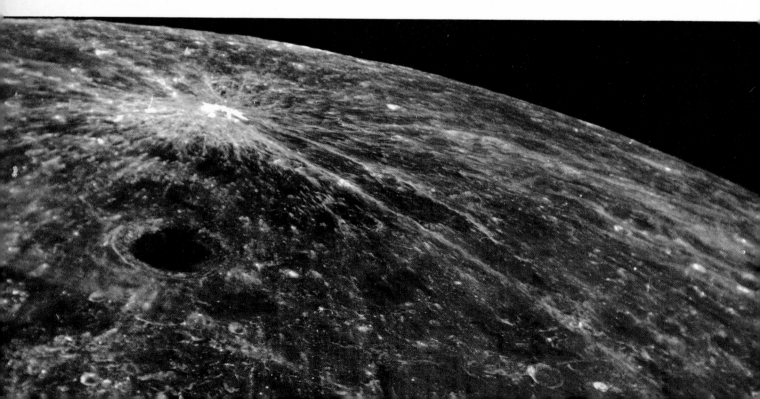

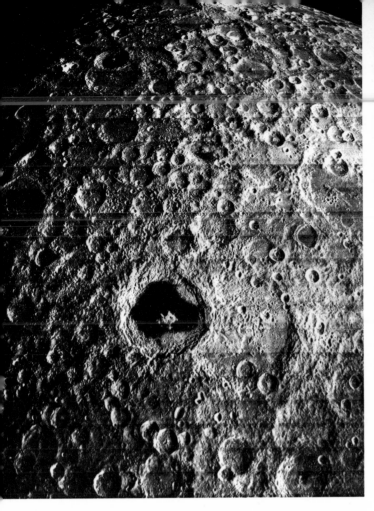

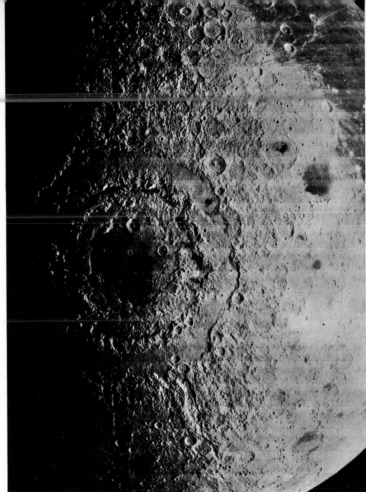

Above left: The dark-floored crater Tsiolkovsky, named for an early Russian rocket scientist, with its jagged central peak and very rugged surrounding region. (NASA)

Above right: The large, multiringed crater known as Mare Orientale. This complex formation contains three circular mountain ranges of which the outermost, the Cordillera Mountains, has a diameter of more than 540 miles. (NASA)

which crashed in turn to form a pattern of secondary craters around the primary crater. The impact also produced great quantities of fine dust, which streamed out to form long splashes stretching radially from the crater. The powdery material has the property of reflecting light back in the direction of the sun. Hence these so-called *lunar rays* are conspicuous near full moon but otherwise nearly invisible. The ray system of Tycho makes the full moon look something like a peeled orange, with the rays radiating from the crater at the stem end. The crater Giordano Bruno, on the moon's far side, also has a ray system almost equally prominent. Many other newer craters also have significant ray systems. Apparently they darken with time or disappear with their continual bombardment by meteors.

The Temperature of the Moon

On earth, large bodies of water, an extensive atmosphere with vast clouded areas, and the shortness of the day all combine to temper the climate. On the other hand, the airless, waterless moon becomes extremely hot, reaching a temperature somewhat greater than that of boiling water when the sun is at the zenith. During the long lunar night, which lasts more than fourteen terrestrial days, the temperature plummets downward to about —250° F (—150 °C).

These extremes of temperature, however, are only surface deep. The surface layers of the moon consist of lightly-compacted dust or fine sand. The individual particles, barely touching one another and surrounded by an almost perfect vacuum, form the best possible thermal insulation. Fifteen centimeters, or six inches, below the surface, the temperature varies only slightly throughout the lunar month, staying not far from the freezing point of water. Short wavelength radio emission of thermal origin coming from these layers is likewise nearly constant. Very long radio waves escaping from depths of several kilometers have such exceptionally low intensity that

Oblique view of the Valley of the Alps, a well-delineated feature about 90 miles long by 5 miles wide. This Orbiter photo reveals, near the center, an unexpected formation—what appears to be a meandering terrestrial valley produced by water erosion. This is a notable example of a sinuous rille. (NASA)

Smithsonian scientist Winfield W. Salisbury has concluded that the sub-surface temperature of the moon—unlike that of the earth—decreases inward for at least a short distance. From this effect, Salisbury concludes that a deep layer of ice may exist far below the surface.

In 1958 and 1959, the Soviet scientist Kozyrev reported seeing an unusual reddish glow in the crater Alphonsus. The spectrum he took resembled that of molecular carbon. Perhaps he recorded the escape of some gaseous matter that the sun's ultraviolet radiation had excited to luminescence. But a number of years of careful observation on a worldwide basis have shown no definite repetition, nor have similar events occurred elsewhere. In any event, the eruption—if it existed—could not have been volcanic in nature, as originally reported.

Mascons

The various vehicles still orbiting the moon have provided unsuspected information about the moon's interior. Although the lunar satellites them-selves are silent, their positions can be measured with high accuracy by means of radar. The surprising fact is that they do not move uniformly. They speed up over the maria and slow down elsewhere. The conclusion seems inescapable that dense concentrations of mass, called *mascons*, lie under the maria and have a gravitational pull that accelerates the orbiting vehicle. No one knowns precisely what these mascons are. One school of thought regards them as huge iron or stone meteorites whose impact produced the maria originally. Another school proposes that the mountainous regions may be composed of semi-porous or "vesicular" rock, whose density is less than that of the maria and are composed of highly-compacted fine sand and dust.

Moonquakes

Perhaps bearing on this question and tending to favor the former theory was a remarkable experiment occasioned by the second lunar landing. The astro-nauts of Apollo 12 set up a working seismograph on the lunar surface, designed to detect moonquakes and vibrations of the lunar surface, and to transmit the data back to earth by radio. After the astronauts reboarded the command ship, they fired the engines of the abandoned lunar module and sent it crashing into the moon. The surprising fact is that the vibrations continued for almost an hour before they finally died away.

Nothing similar has ever been detected on earth, where friction between rocks and loosely-compacted layers causes an unsustained vibration to die away quickly—in a few minutes if not in seconds. The moon, on the contrary, reverberated like an enormous bell. Such vibrations are not unusual and they occur naturally; this is demonstrated by the fact that many other similar events, probably triggered by meteoric impact, have also been observed. It has been suggested that large masses of rock, welded together to form a rigid structure, could act in such a vibratory manner. The seismic waves would resound back and forth between the individual rock boundaries as in a giant echo chamber. Alternatively, a huge iron-nickel meteorite might continue to ring literally like a bell. Some quantitative calculations appear to support this idea. When an array of seismographs has been established on the moon we may hope to find answers to such questions about the moon's interior.

Measuring the Distance to the Moon

Figure 9–2. The phases of the moon in its revolution around the earth.

The space program devised a method for measuring the distance to the moon within about one foot. The device for achieving this spectacular result

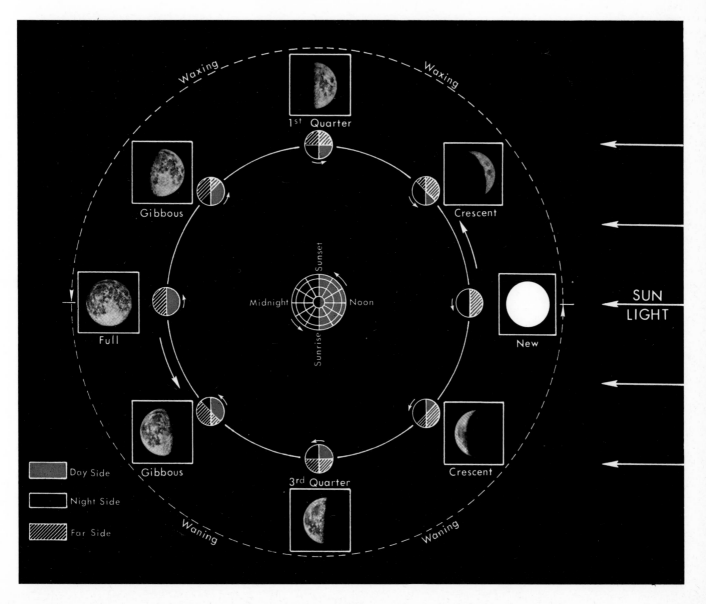

The crater Copernicus. Above it lies Mare Imbrium; to the northeast, along a chain of craters, lies the crater Eratosthenes, whose central peak also appears to possess a crater. Just below Copernicus, and resembling a keyhole, is the crater Fauth. Between Copernicus and Eratosthenes, lies a chain of craters probably produced by material splashed from Copernicus or from secondary volcanic activity induced by the impact. (Lick Observatory)

Facing page: An Orbiter I photograph showing the crater Taruntius, about 35 miles across. The linear, rope-like features are probably splash craters formed when the major impact occurred. The inside of Taruntius is marked with concentric rilles and ridges. (NASA)

is known as a "corner reflector" and is, in effect, a corner cut from a cube of glass. A beam of light entering a mirror built up of such glass prisms bounces three times, once from each face of the cube, and then returns precisely in the direction from which it came. Measurements of the time required for a sharp pulse of light from a laser beam to reach the moon and return provide the basic data for the accurate determination of distance. These studies should also yield new values for the rotation period of the earth, the motion of the earth's pole, the east-west continental drift, and the suspected drift of Hawaii toward Japan—which is estimated to be about 4 inches (10 centimeters) per year.

The Chemical Nature of Lunar Rocks

The rock samples returned to earth from Tranquility Base by Apollo 11 were chiefly basaltic igneous in character mixed with soil and small rock fragments and compacted into coherent rock. The soil consisted of glassy beads and crystalline fragments. The surfaces of the rocks and crystals were generally scarred and pitted as the result of high-velocity impacts by micro-meteorites. Experiments showed that most of the crystals must have solidified from a magma at temperatures between 1000° and 1200°C. The more common minerals, which do have terrestrial counterparts, were pyroxene, olivine, and ilmenite. Several complex crystals were found that do not occur naturally on earth.

There were many surprises. The chemical elements titanium, scandium, and zirconium occurred in exceptionally high concentration. Sodium was unusually rare in the rocky components as were some of the more volatile substances, such as bismuth, mercury, zinc, lead, chlorine, and bromine. On the other hand, the lunar soil was enriched with these volatile elements, as well as with copper, silver, and gold, apparently the result of meteoric

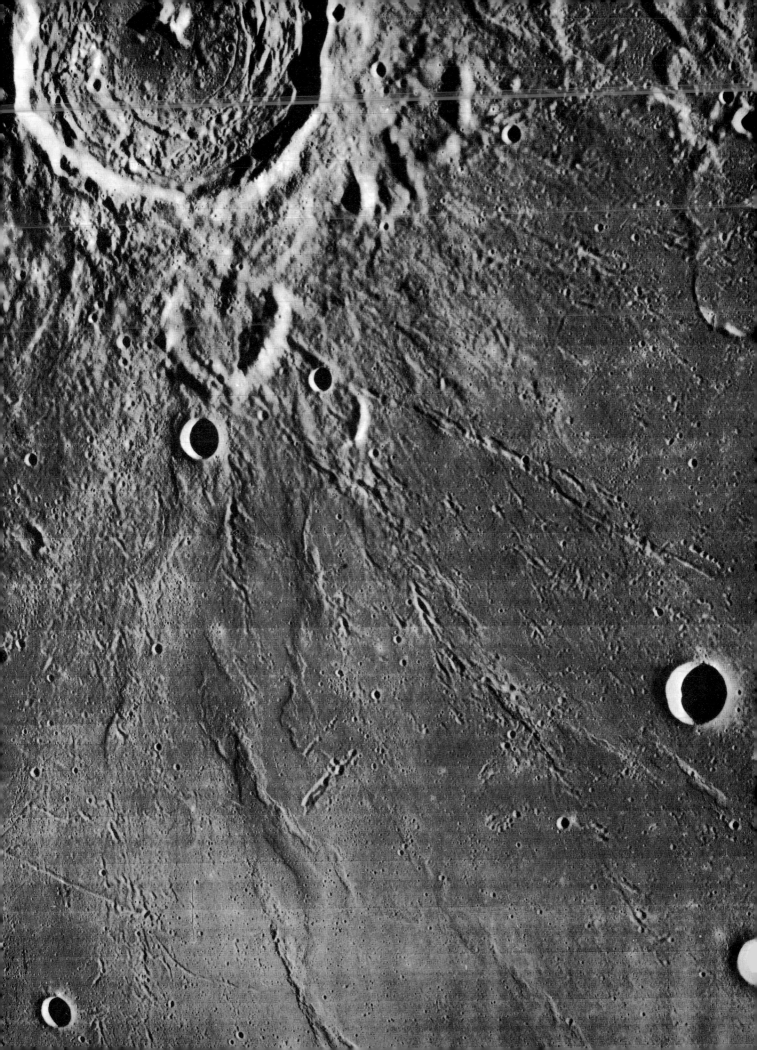

Close-up of the large crater Copernicus showing the central mountains and northern wall. The sharp escarpment in the distance, with the secondary ridge that slumps to the crater floor, is fully twice the depth of the Grand Canyon of the Colorado. Large blocks clutter the slopes of the central mountains, which rise about 1200 feet above the crater floor. (NASA)

material present in the soil. This peculiar chemical composition clearly suggests that the moon itself did not originate from the gradual accretion of meteoric material. Instead, the main body of the moon solidified and crystallized from a molten magma that was deficient in the volatile substances listed above. Furthermore, remarkable chemical differences between the rocks from Tranquility Base and those from the Apollo 12 mission indicate that some sort of magmatic separation may have taken place on the moon analogous to what occurred on earth in the distant past. Some scientists still adhere to the "cold moon" theory, affirming that the body never liquefied, but this concept is becoming harder to defend.

Isotopic analysis has set the ages of the lunar rocks at almost five billion (4.6×10^9) years, with variations downward to somewhat less than four billion years. Lunar rocks are generally older than corresponding rocks on earth. The earth, of course, has been subject to much greater erosion than the moon. Study of lunar material will therefore in the long run throw considerable light on the early history of the moon. Lunar samples from highland areas, from deeper crustal levels, as well as from different regions in the maria should prove invaluable. It is too early to make any definite comment on the age-old idea that the moon was somehow torn from the planet earth. However, the once popular notion that the Pacific Ocean is the scar left by a "Caesarian" type of birth can be dismissed. If such separation did occur, it must have taken place more than 4.3 billion (4.3×10^9) years ago. The Australian geophysicist D. W. Ringwood has recently suggested that the moon may have formed during an early stage when the earth possessed an extensive primitive atmosphere containing large amounts of dust and solids, which precipitated out to form the satellite

The lunar rocks show evidence of continual bombardment by cosmic rays of galactic origin. This evidence is particularly important in that the intensity of cosmic radiation appears to have remained sensibly constant since the moon was formed. The sun, as the result of flares and other forms of solar activity, continues to eject into space energetic puffs of atoms, ions, and electrons, which constitute the *solar wind*. The earth's magnetic field deflects the particles into the Van Allen belts, but they strike the surface of the non-magnetic moon directly and become imbedded in the structure of the rocks. However, a few of the rocks exhibit traces of magnetism, a fact that has led some scientists to speculate that the moon may once have possessed a definite, though small, magnetic field. The relatively high concentration on the moon of atoms of the rarer gases, such as hydrogen, helium, neon, argon, krypton, and xenon, indicates that this bombardment has continued throughout the ages—which provides indirect evidence of the sun's relative constancy over this period. Since the proportion of these gases does not vary appreciably with depth, we further conclude that the lunar rocks have been tumbled about, buried, and uncovered by meteoric plowing of the surface.

Water and Organic Compounds

Another surprising revelation is the relatively low abundance of water and of carbon compounds on the moon. Most earth rocks contain a considerable quantity of water bound into them as water of crystallization, which a gentle heat can release—although the source material usually crumbles to a powder during the process. Other rocks have their water content more firmly bound into them so that only high temperature will release the liquid. The lunar rocks

Large-scale photograph of the surface of the moon taken from Orbiter IV, showing a remarkable meandering, sinuous rille. Most astronomers believe that such features were produced by lava flow or similar volcanic activity. A few observers suggest that they may result from the flow of water; however, the branching pattern characteristic of terrestrial water erosion (see the formation around the Kuiseb River of Southwest Africa shown in color plate 9) is completely absent on the moon. (NASA)

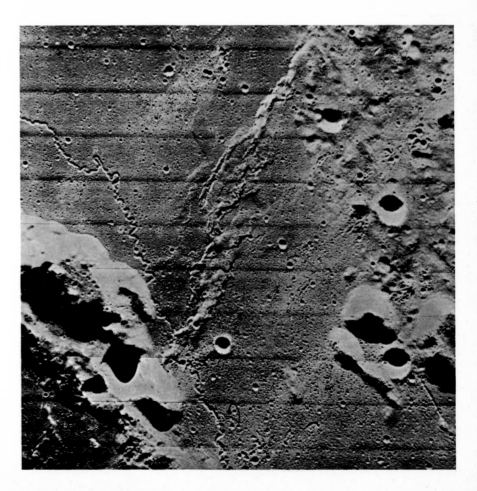

appear to be of this second variety, but even so the amount of water recovered from them has been disappointingly small. I say "disappointing" because I and other scientists had harbored the hope that future manned expeditions to the moon might become self-sufficient by using solar heat to obtain water from the rocks, which could then be processed to obtain vital oxygen. That hope now appears to have been vain, though subsurface layers of ice that can be tapped by deep mining may very well exist.

As for carbon, a very careful analysis for the most elementary of organic compounds, such as purines, pyramidines, and amino acids, proved completely negative at extremely low levels of detection—usually less than one-millionth of one per cent. Carbon is present in small quantities, either in the form of pure carbon (graphite), mineral carbides, carbon monoxide, or carbon dioxide. But chemists consider none of these substances organic material, since many meteors—the so-called carbon chondrules—contain sizable amounts of pure graphite. The only truly organic substance recognized in the analysis was methane or marsh gas. A search with optical and electron microscopes for viable organisms also proved to be negative, as did the quarantine periods for astronauts of Apollo 11 and 12. Similarly, extracts of moon dust injected into germ-free mice also gave negative results. The moon appears to be absolutely free from all contamination or pollution, and except for the debris and equipment left by lunar landings, everything possible has been done to minimize biological contamination of the lunar environment.

Lunar eclipses due during one complete Saros of 18 years, 11⅓ days, from August 17, 1970 to August 27, 1988. The second column indicates whether the eclipse is partial or total. The last two columns locate the point on the earth where the moon will be directly overhead at maximum eclipse. Minus longitude is west of the Greenwich meridian; plus longitude is east. The plus and minus signs in latitude indicate north and south of the equator respectively.

The Saros relationship can be used to predict eclipses beyond this limit. By adding 18 years and 11⅓ days to any eclipse date (10⅓ days, if 5 leap days intervene), the date of another similar eclipse can be predicted.

Eclipses of the Moon

Date		Type	Moon in Zenith	
			longitude	latitude
1970	Aug. 17	p	—50°	—14°
1971	Feb. 10	t	—112°	+14°
1971	Aug. 6	t	+65°	—17°
1972	Jan. 30	t	—160°	+18°
1972	July 26	p	—108°	—20°
1973	Dec. 10	p	—29°	+23°
1974	June 4	p	+26°	—22°
1974	Nov. 29	t	+128°	+21°
1975	May 25	t	—87°	—21°
1975	Nov. 18	t	+20°	+19°
1976	May 13	p	+62°	—18°
1977	Apr. 4	p	—64°	—6°
1978	Mar. 24	t	+115°	—2°
1978	Sept. 16	t	+73°	—3°
1979	Mar. 13	p	+45°	+3°
1979	Sept. 6	t	—164°	—7°
1981	July 17	p	—71°	—21°
1982	Jan. 9	t	+63°	+22°
1982	July 6	t	—112°	—23°
1982	Dec. 30	t	—171°	+23°
1983	June 25	p	—126°	—23°
1985	May 4	t	+60°	—16°
1985	Oct. 28	t	+90°	+13°
1986	Apr. 24	t	+168°	—13°
1986	Oct. 17	t	+67°	+10°
1987	Oct. 7	p	—13°	+5°
1988	Aug. 27	p	—166°	—10°

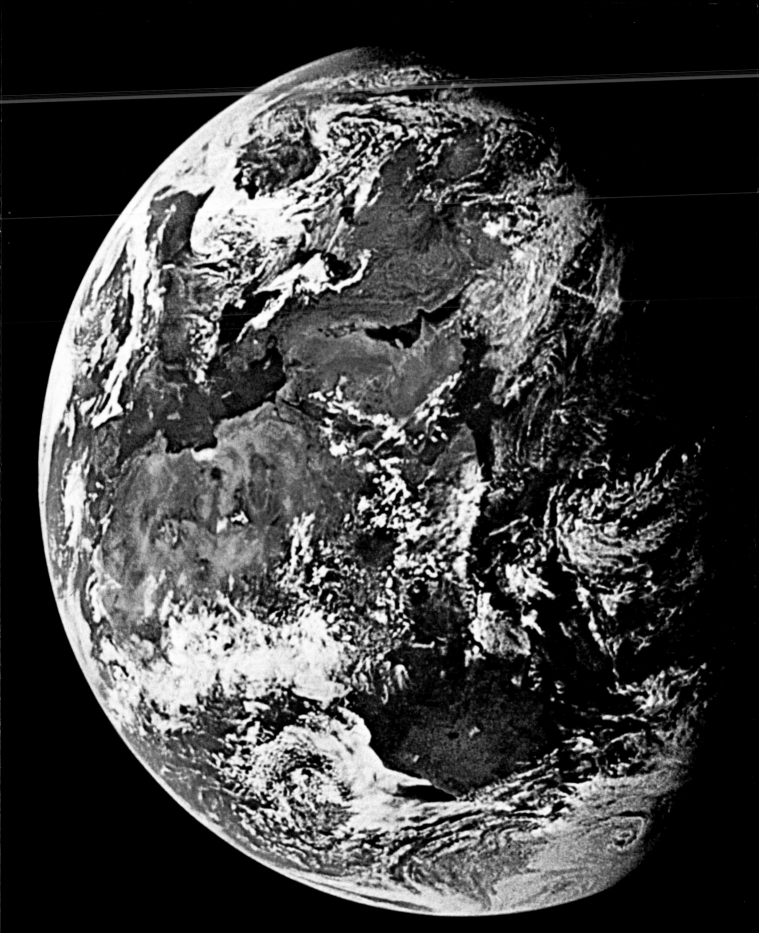

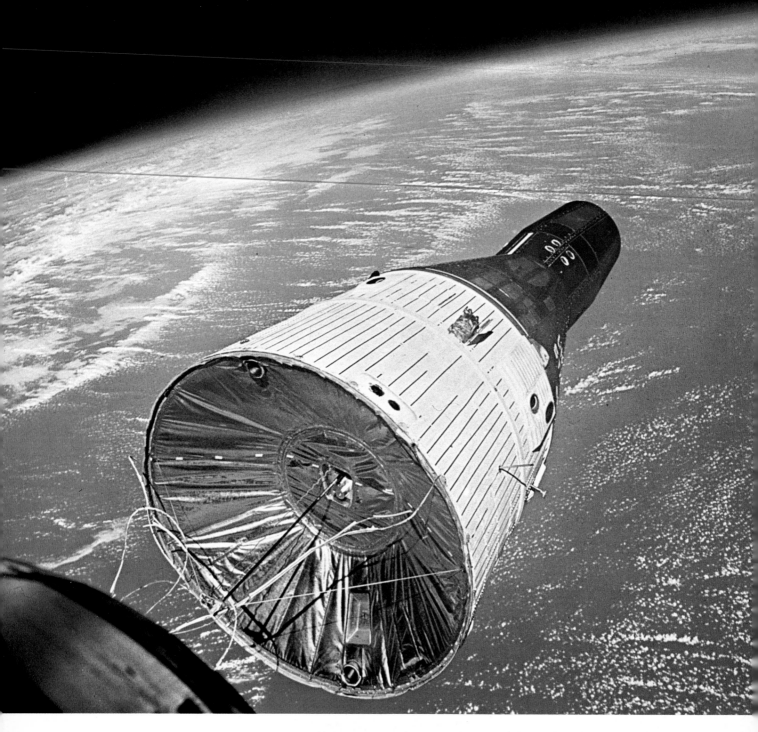

8. Above: Photograph from Gemini VI of the orbiting Gemini VII during historic rendezvous in space in December 1965. (NASA)

9. Right: Gemini V photo of southwest Africa with port of Walvis Bay to the left and vast sand dunes of the Namib desert in the lower third of the picture. The Kuiseb River, upper boundary of the dunes, meanders, but the branching structure of most terrestrial rivers, perhaps here obliterated by drifting sand, is noticeably absent. (NASA)

12. Overleaf: The earth as seen from the command module of Apollo XI while orbiting the moon. At bottom is the characteristic gray-brown color of the rugged lunar surface. (NASA)

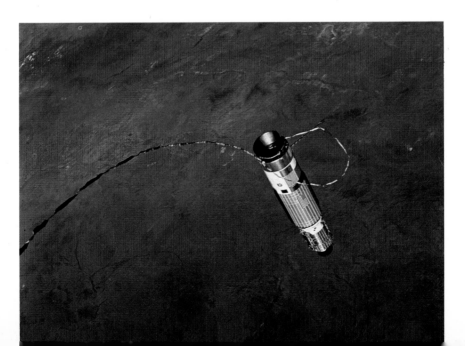

10. Above: The Hadra-maut Plateau of the southern Arabian penin-sula seen from Gemini IV spacecraft, June 1965. The branching surface markings are character-istic of terrestrial water erosion. (NASA)

11. Left: The view from Gemini XII of Sonora, Mexico, southeastern Arizona and south-western New Mexico. A 100-foot tether line connects the Agena target docking vehicle with the Gemini XII spacecraft. (November 1966, NASA)

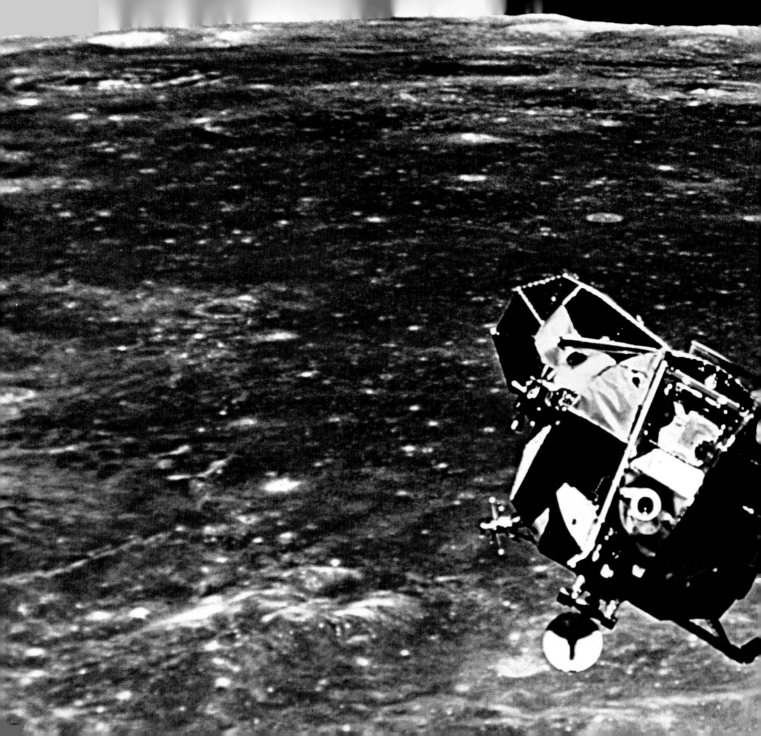

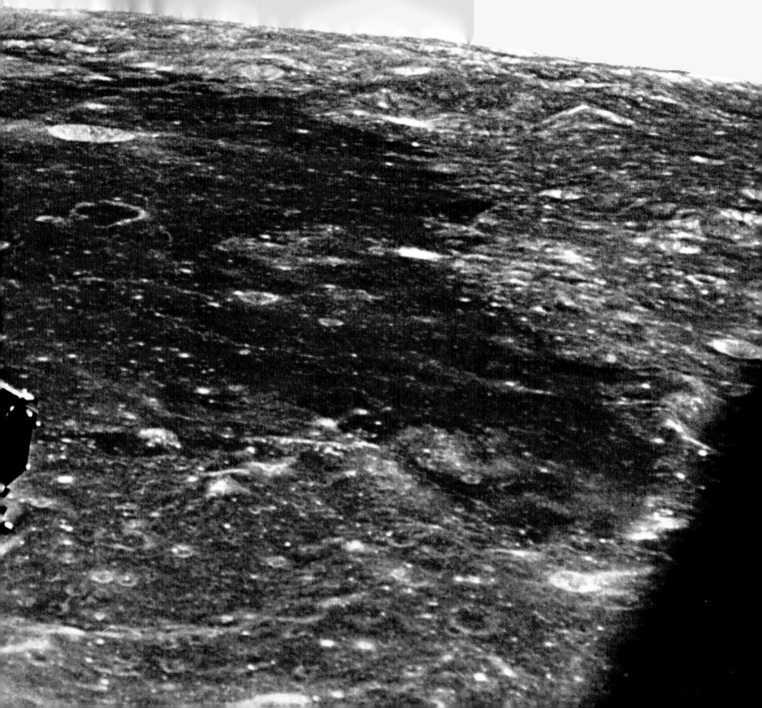

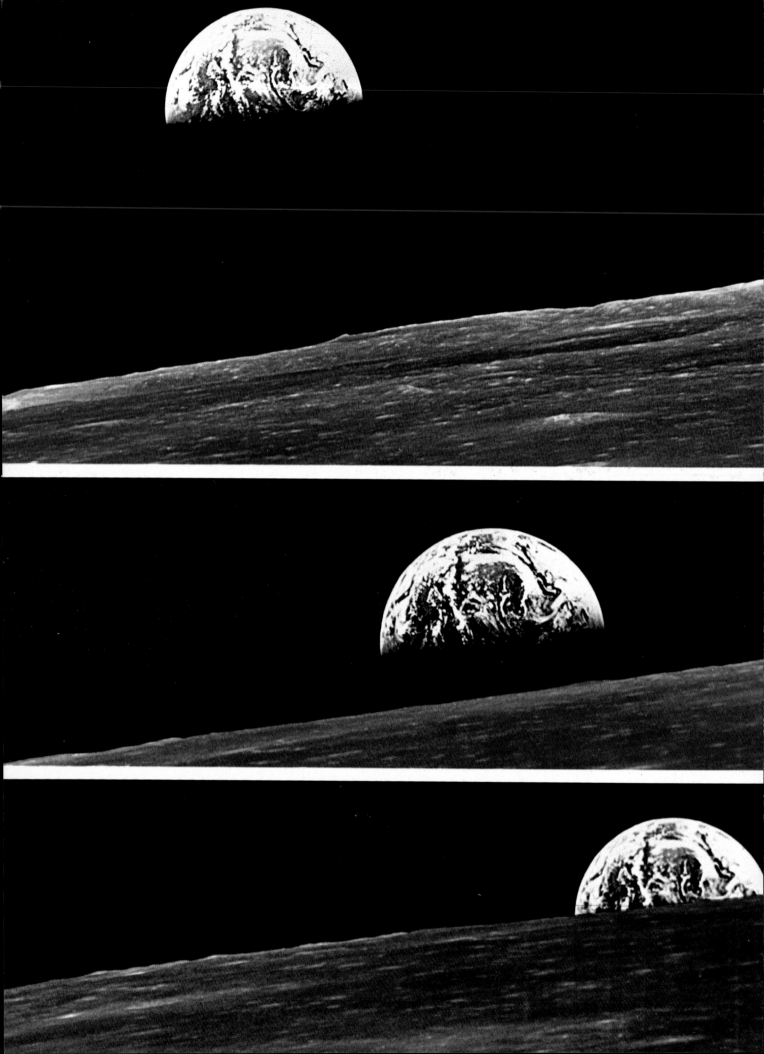

13. Left: Earth-rise on the moon. A complex pattern of clouds partially veils the earth. (NASA)

14. Right: Apollo XI, man's first landing on the moon. Astronaut Edwin Aldrin beside the Lunar Module, with his footprints clearly visible in the lunar foreground. (NASA)

15, 16. Below: Remarkable stereoscopic photographs taken by Apollo XI astronauts at 17 inches from the lunar surface. The area, about the size of a postcard, reveals an abundance of glass-like beads or splashes. The reader can get a three-dimensional view without a stereoscope if he looks at the left picture with his left eye and the right picture with his right eye while relaxing the focus of both eyes. (NASA)

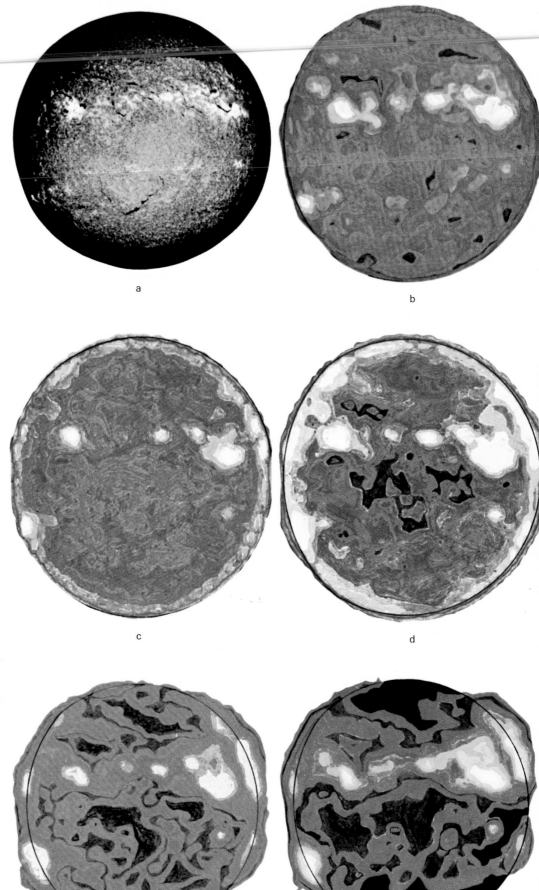

a

b

c

d

e

f

17. Left: The full moon as photographed by the Apollo VIII astronauts. (NASA)

18. Right: The active sun photographed from an orbiting solar observatory far above the earth's atmosphere. The first photograph (a) is a ground-based record from Sacramento Peak Observatory showing the sun in hydrogen light. In (b), taken in the light of the Lyman continuum of hydrogen, the excited regions appear much brighter. This radiation is in the far-ultraviolet part of the spectrum. The next zone (c), in doubly-ionized nitrogen, begins to show the effects of the hot corona, providing the sun with a bright rim. In (d) the intensity of the rim continues to grow with higher excitation, as in five-times ionized oxygen. Next, in the light of nine-times ionized magnesium (e), the corona has grown in size. In the next level of excitation (f), in eleven-times ionized silicon, the active regions continue to increase both in size and in intensity. (Photographs directed by Leo Goldberg and staff of Harvard College Observatory, under NASA contract)

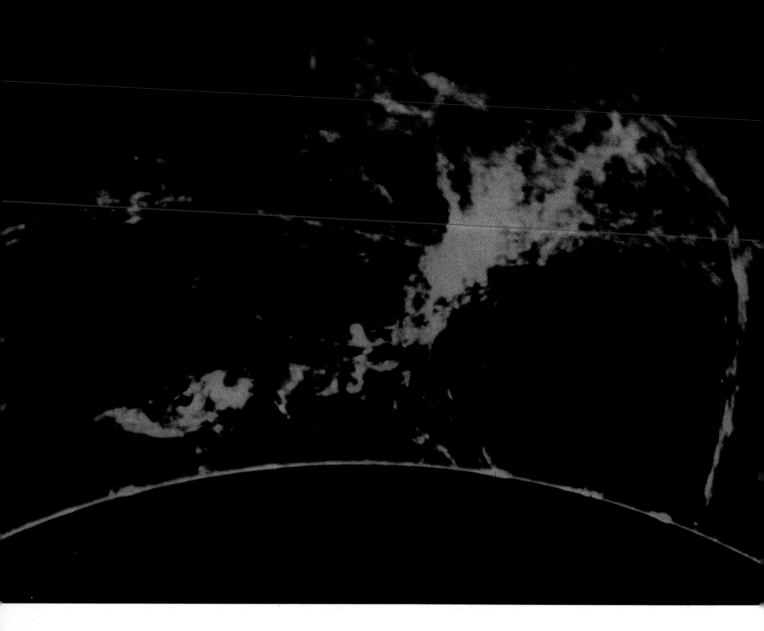

19. Above: Ascending
prominence arch photographed
in hydrogen light.

20. Above right: The solar
corona, photographed in green
light from thirteen-times
ionized iron atoms. (Both:
Sacramento Peak Observatory,
Air Force Cambridge Research
Laboratories)

21, 22. Right and far right:
Active solar region, March 24,
1963. An active solar flare; and
a surge prominence above an
active region. A special photographic technique imparts a
reddish color to gases receding
from, and a greenish hue to
gases approaching, the
observer. (Harry Ramsey,
Lockheed Solar Observatory)

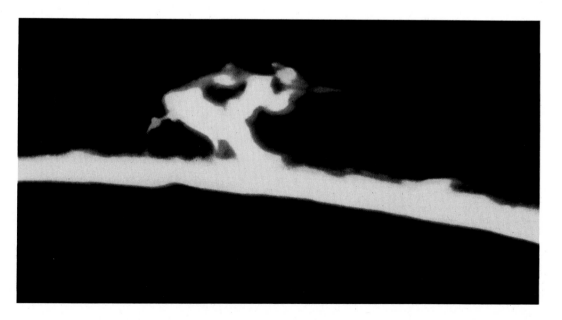

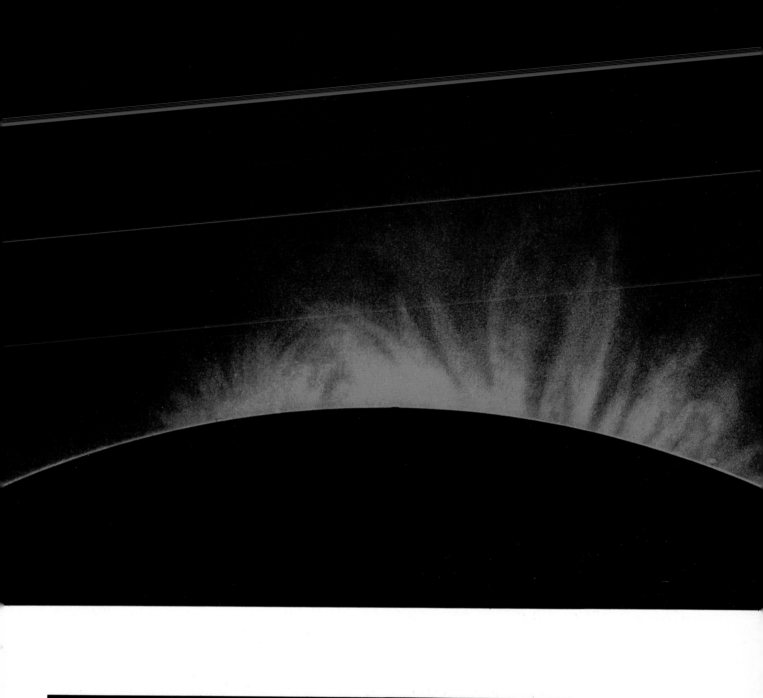

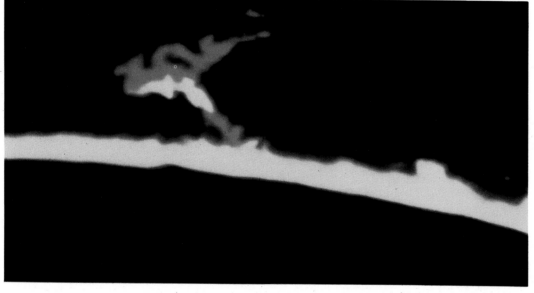

23. Above: Polar Aurora. The marked curvature often comes from the interaction of moving particles with the earth's magnetic field.

24. Right: Aurora Borealis. Produced by the interaction of fast solar ions and electrons colliding with atoms and molecules in the upper atmosphere, the aurora can sometimes be seen from latitudes far from the polar regions. (Both: Geophysical Institute, University of Alaska)

25. Below: Active solar region, May 23, 1967. This photograph has been double printed, so that masses of gas approaching the observer have a greenish tinge, while those receding appear red. (Harry Ramsey, Lockheed Solar Observatory)

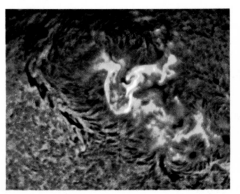
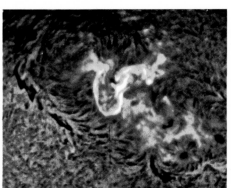
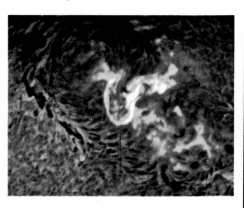

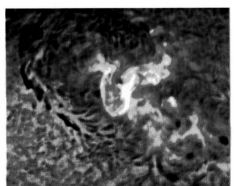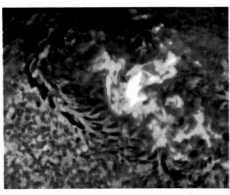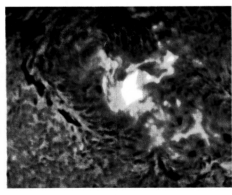

26. Above: Solar eclipse in the USSR,
September 22, 1968. The landscape is
dimly visible in the foreground. (M.
Laffineur, Institut d'Astrophysique, Paris)

27. Right: Bright aurorae, especially in
lower latitudes, indicate major sunspot
activity. (Geophysical Institute,
University of Alaska)

28. Above right: Solar corona at the
total eclipse, September 22, 1968. (M.
Laffineur, Institut d'Astrophysique, Paris)

29. Far right: The solar spectrum shows
the dark Fraunhofer lines produced by
various chemical elements in the sun's
atmosphere. The strong pair of dark lines
in the violet, at the top, are H and K,
from singly-ionized calcium. (Sacramento
Peak Observatory, Air Force Cambridge
Research Laboratories)

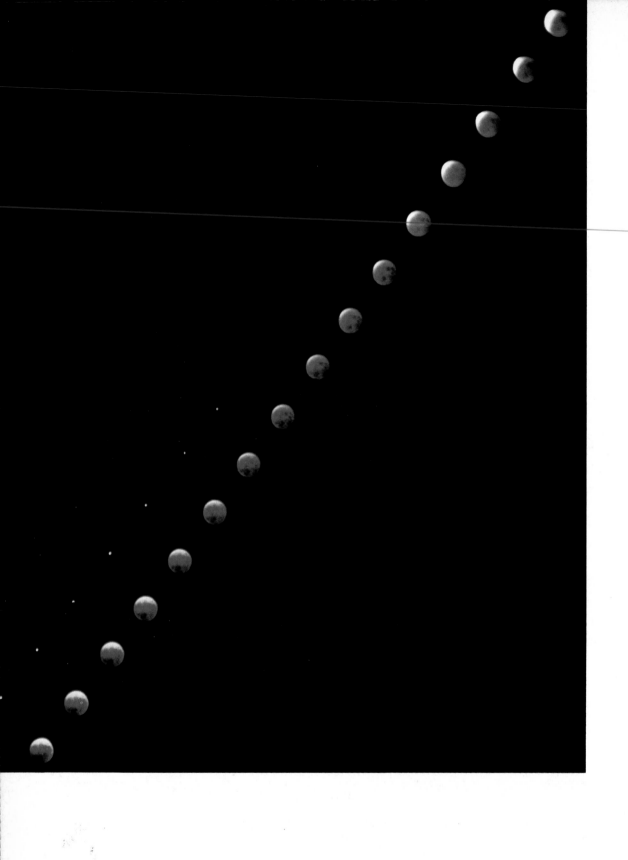

30. Total eclipse of the moon, October 6, 1968. The exposures were
made every five minutes. Saturn appears in some of the exposures, the
lowest image of the planet corresponding to the lowest image of the
moon (lower left). The copper hue of the moon at totality is characteristic of lunar eclipses. (L. Larmore, Advanced Research Laboratory,
McDonald-Douglas Aircraft Company)

31. Right: The planet Jupiter, showing the Great Red Spot. (Kitt Peak
National Observatory)

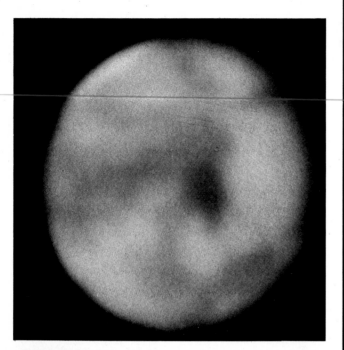

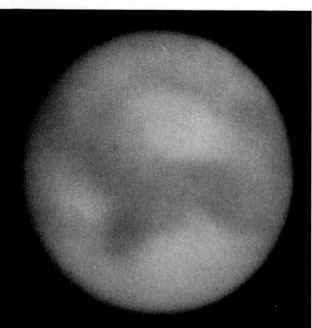

32, 33. Mars photographed on July 14, 1954 (top) and September 5, 1956 (bottom). The differences in apparent diameter of the planet result from differences in actual distances from the earth. (W. S. Finsen, Republic Observatory, South Africa)

34. Right: The planet Saturn. (Hale Observatories)

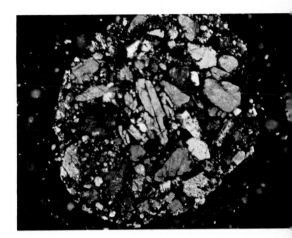

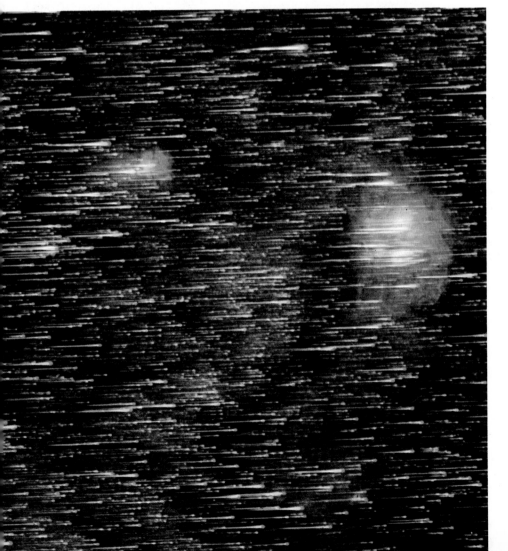

38, 39. Above: Crystals
in meteorite. The colors were
produced by using polarized light.
(John Wood, Smithsonian
Astrophysical Observatory)

35. Above left: Comet Humason.
(Hale Observatories)

36. Far left: Objective prism
spectrum, region of Eta Carinae.
(Boyden Observatory)

37. Left: Objective prism
spectrum, section of the Milky
Way. (Boyden Observatory)

40. Above: Veil Nebula in Cygnus. (Hale Observatories)

41. Left: The Pleiades. An open star cluster with the stars individually surrounded by wisps of luminous gas. (Hale Observatories)

42. Above right: Omega Nebula in Sagittarius. (Hale Observatories)

43. Right: Irregular Galaxy in Ursa Major. (Hale Observatories)

44. Overleaf: The Great Nebula in Orion. The gas is excited to luminosity by bright, very hot stars imbedded in the nebula. (Hale Observatories)

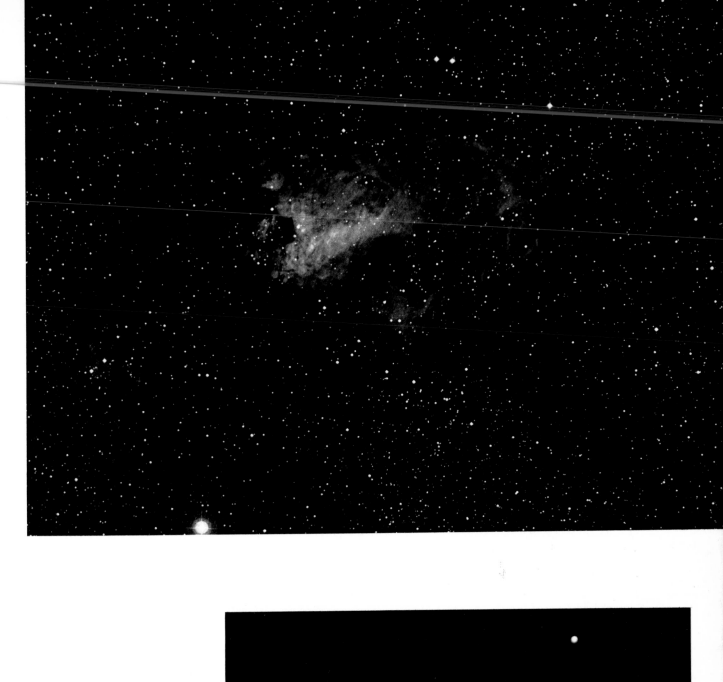

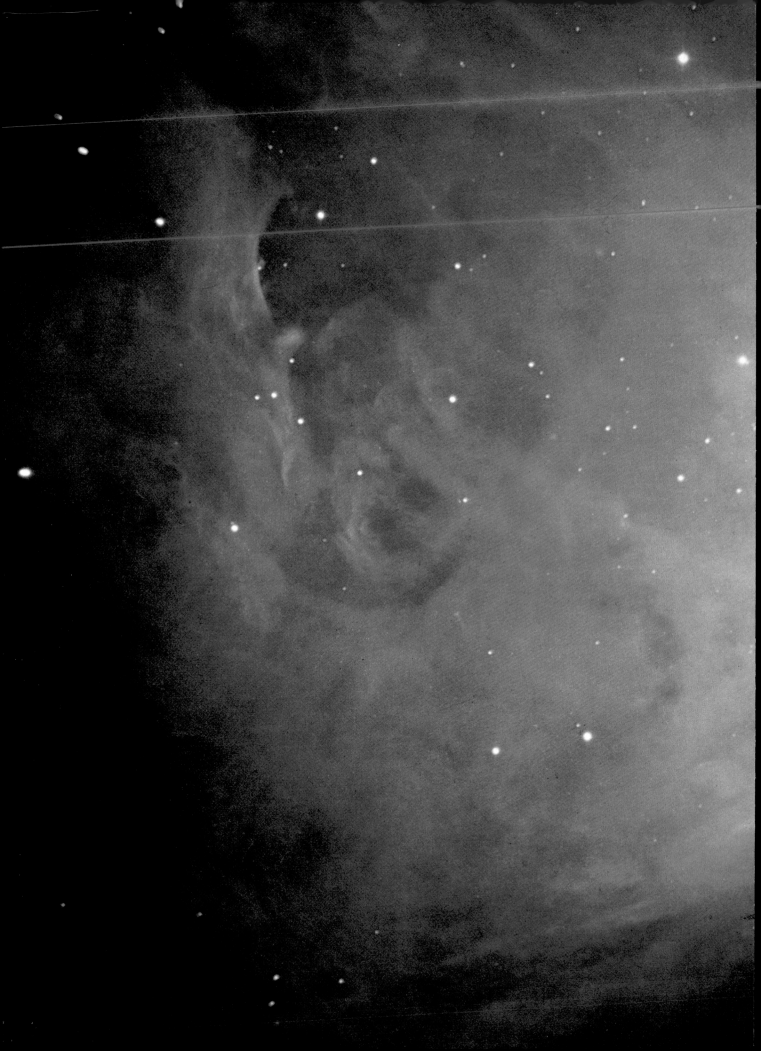

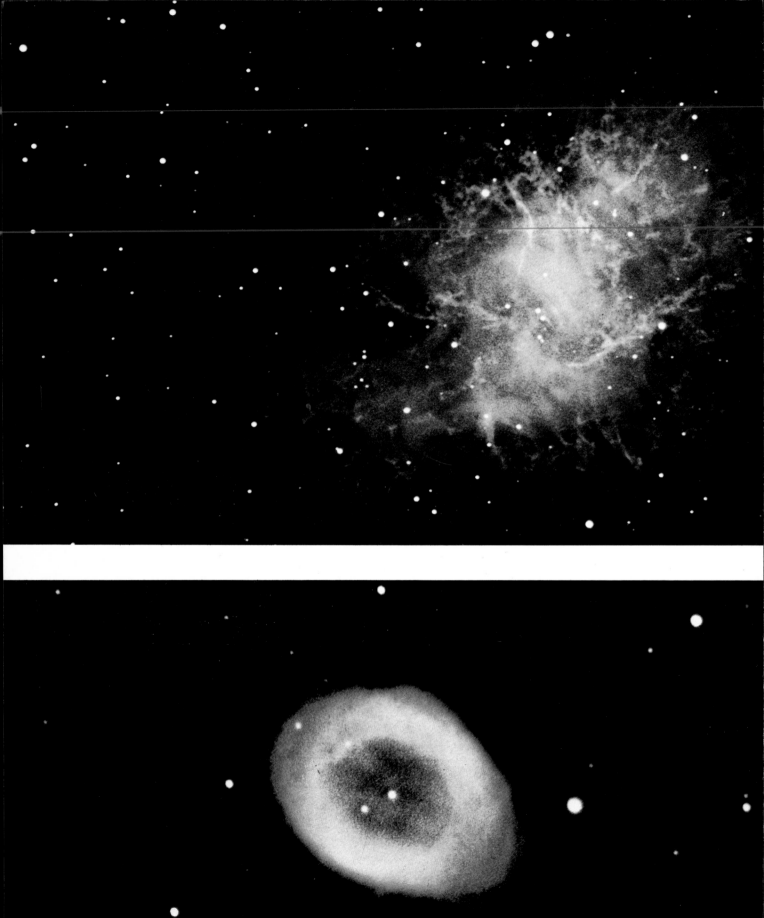

45. Above left: Crab Nebula in Taurus. This is the remnant of a supernova that flared in 1054 A.D. (Hale Observatories)

46. Far left: Ring Nebula in Lyra, a planetary. (Hale Observatories)

47. Above: Eta Carinae Nebula. (Harvard College Observatory, Boyden Station)

48. Left: Horsehead Nebula in Orion. Dark dust silhouetted against a bright background. (Hale Observatories)

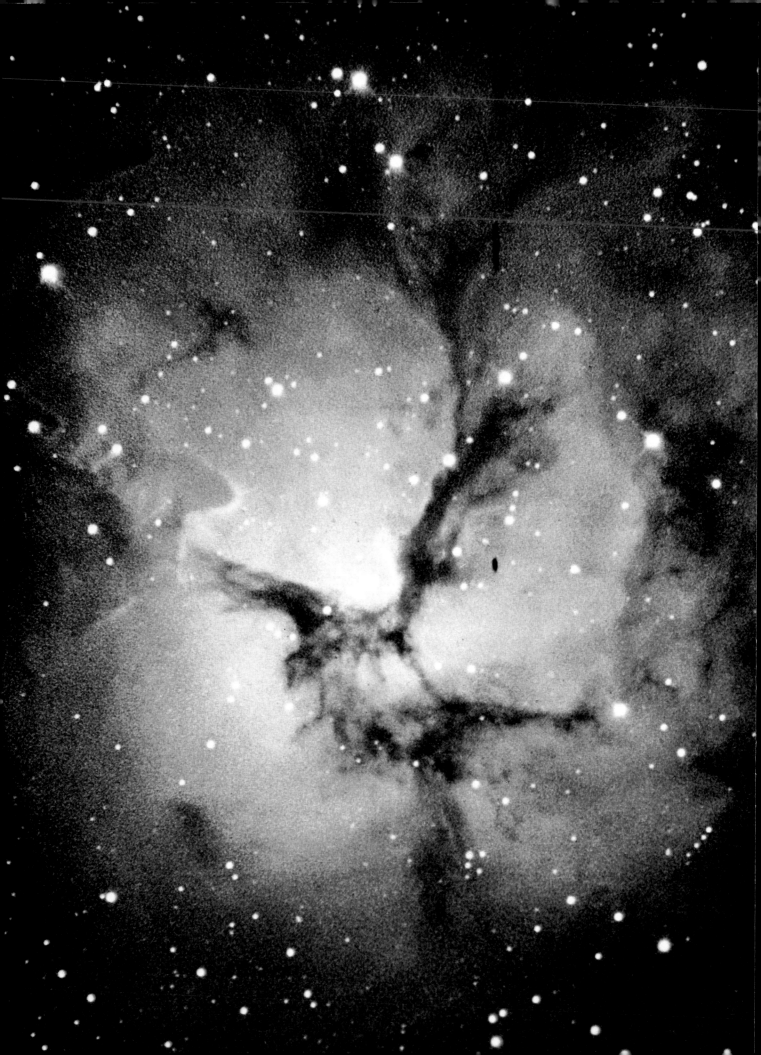

10

The Sun, Our Nearest Star

Our sun is a star, bright only because it is so close. If it were as far away as Alpha Centauri, the next nearest star (which is a quarter of a million times more distant) the sun would be indistinguishable from other bright stars. Aside from the fact that the sun is the center of our solar system, it has no special features that distinguish it from a billion or more similar stars in our Milky Way—at least as seen from the vast distances we must view them.

Of course, from the point of view of earth-dwellers, the sun plays a particularly important role: it is the source of the light and heat that permit life to exist on earth. But, vital as the sun may be to man's existence, that existence is of no importance in the cosmos as a whole.

The nearness of the sun does enable us to study features that would otherwise be invisible and that we simply could not have conceived of. We infer that other stars probably possess them too, because our sun can scarcely be unique. These special features include the sunspots, which appear as dark areas on the shining solar disk. Then there is the upper solar atmosphere, the chromosphere, above which we see flame-like clouds—solar prominences—sometimes raining hot gases back upon the solar surface or exploding fiery geysers into space. Finally there is the outermost layer of all, the delicate solar corona, so faint that until about 1930 astronomers had been completely unable to detect it except during total solar eclipses, when the moon obscures the bright solar disk. We further know that the outer parts of this corona are escaping into space in variable amounts and speeds, producing the phenomenon of the solar wind. In a sense, then, our earth is still "inside the sun," since these tenuous streamers extend well beyond the earth's orbit. The early theories of the nature of these outer layers would never have led us to suspect that the sun was emitting X-rays, radio waves, or showers of energetic atoms.

Structure of the Sun

The knowledge of atomic nuclear reactions, detailed in an earlier chapter, has enabled the astrophysicist to construct a satisfactory model of the main body of the sun, from its visible outer surface, often called the *photosphere*, or "sphere of light," down into its core. The layman usually thinks of the sun as a gaseous ball of fire; actually the weight of the outer layers compresses the inner layers until we find, at the center, matter some 350 times denser than water and even denser than lead.

If the sun were cool throughout, the outer layers would collapse upon the inner regions to form a body smaller than our earth, with a density millions of times greater than that of water. Under such enormous pressures, the negative electrons would combine with the positive protons to form neutrons. Astronomers term such an object a *neutron star*. Neutron stars do exist, but, judging from its huge size, our sun cannot be one of them. To prevent its collapse, however, the sun needs high temperatures—as much as 16,000,000° K—in its core. Despite its high densities, the sun is gaseous right down to its center. By "gaseous," we mean that it expands or contracts with changes in pressure, unlike a solid, which resists compression. The central pressure is more than 400 billion times greater than that of the atmosphere at the surface of the earth. These figures are not precise and vary somewhat as we change certain assumptions about the sun's interior, but they do indicate the extreme conditions that may be encountered near the center of the sun. Our calculations

49. M 20, the Trifid Nebula in Sagittarius, a cloud of glowing gas silhouetted by dark filaments of dust. (Lowell Observatory)

149

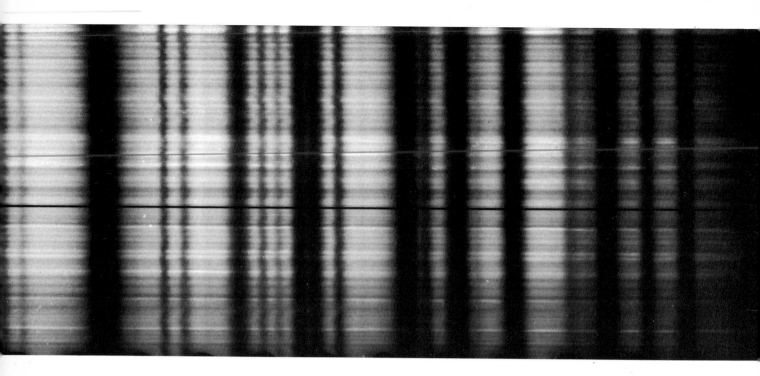

show that such densities and temperatures are high enough to support the successive captures of protons—the *proton-proton* reaction that builds hydrogen into helium in a series of steps and releases the energy necessary to sustain solar radiation for billions of years.

The inner core, some 10 per cent of the total volume of the sun, is *convective*; that is, bubbles of hot gas ascend in a sort of boiling action while other bubbles of cool gas descend. When somewhat similar convection occurs in the earth's atmosphere we get the "bumpy" effect that causes airplanes to be tossed violently about. The outer 10 per cent or so of the sun's radius is also convective and is known as the hydrogen convective zone since de-ionization of hydrogen in the upper levels causes the phenomenon.

Convection appears to account for the fact that the photosphere is by no means uniformly bright. The solar surface is mottled or granular in structure. An early astronomer once compared it to "rice grains floating in a bowl of

Above: A small part of the solar spectrum. The vertical lines appear wavy because of the small Doppler displacements resulting from the ascent or descent of gases in the convective solar atmosphere. (Sacramento Peak Observatory, Air Force Cambridge Research Laboratories)

Right: Figure 10–1. Darkening of the solar limb occurs because we can see to levels where the temperature is lower and where the emission of energy is correspondingly less.

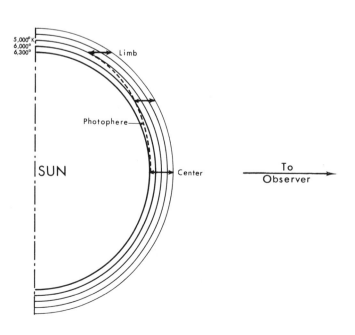

The solar telescope of Sacramento Peak Observatory, Arizona. The entire optics of the telescope operate in a vacuum to minimize the effect of air turbulence. A turret with mirrors that rotate and incline at a controlled rate directs a beam of sunlight 132 feet to the foot of the tower, and then down to other mirrors capable of spectroscopic analysis. Using an altazimuth mount instead of the more conventional equatorial mount, its turret mirrors keep the beam of sunlight oriented down the shaft. To compensate for the resulting rotation of the image, the entire telescope floats in a huge tank of mercury near the top of the shaft. (Sacramento Peak Observatory, Air Force Cambridge Research Laboratories)

soup." The metaphor is imperfect, perhaps, in that rice, unless stirred, tends to sink rather than float in a soup bowl. The transient character of the individual flakes, however, suggests that vigorous boiling causes the phenomenon. The individual grains are about 200 miles across on the average but they are visible only under the best conditions in the terrestrial atmosphere, whose turbulence tends to distort and obscure them.

The French astronomer Pierre J. C. Janssen (1824–1907) obtained many photographs of the granulations late in the nineteenth century. To study these formations under the most favorable conditions, a Princeton University astronomer, Martin Schwarzschild, arranged to send a telescope far above the lower, turbulent regions of the earth's atmosphere. And thus Project Stratoscope, combining the most advanced concepts of science and industry, came into being. The telescope, lifted to about 80,000 feet, took thousands of photographs under electronic and radio control. These pictures showed remarkably clear details of the granulations and other solar features. Projected as a motion picture, they revealed the granules forming, breaking up into smaller grains, and finally disappearing, with a life of from 5 to 10 minutes.

Through the central 80 per cent or so of the solar radius, the gas is nonconvective. The energy from the interior has to work its way through from atom to atom by continual absorption and reemission. So opaque to radiation is the body of the sun that energy requires about 50,000,000 years from its release in the core until it finally can escape from the surface.

Photographs of the sun show a disk that seems to have a sharp edge. The sharpness is illusory, however; if we were closer to the sun we would see that the edge dissolves into a hazy layer from 500 to 1000 miles thick. Like our terrestrial smog, the opacity increases with depth. The lowest layer that sends us light and heat is the one called the photosphere.

Our own atmosphere, apart from smog content, is reasonably transparent down to the earth's solid surface. If we were to heat our atmosphere to 6000° K, the temperature of the sun's visible outer layers, the air would become even more opaque than the traditional London fog. The atmosphere would be about as transparent as a brick wall, and visibility would be reduced

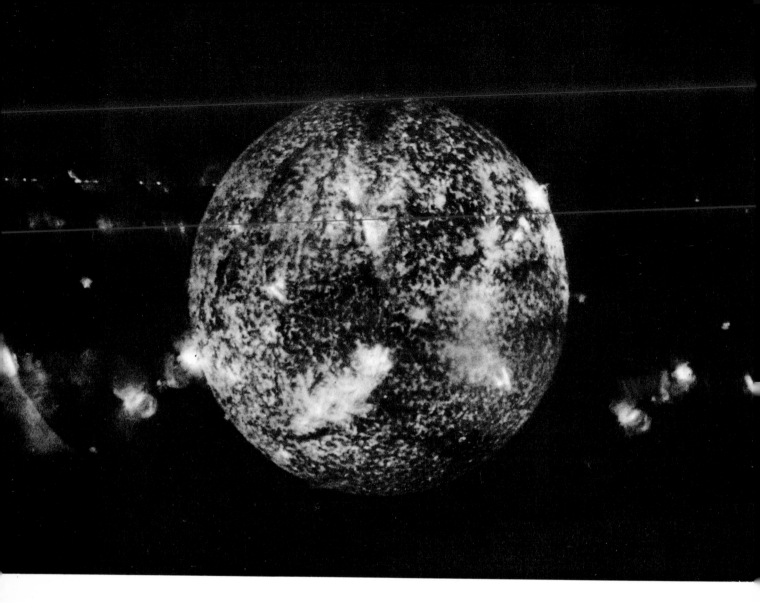

Extreme ultraviolet images of the sun, photographed from a rocket. The helium image at the center comes from the sun's chromosphere; the highly-ionized iron images at either side come from the corona. Note the dots that are the spectrum of the flare, and the cloud of intense solar activity in the corona. (U.S. Naval Research Laboratory)

to only a few feet. A similar phenomenon occurs in the sun's photosphere. The photosphere is a region a few hundred miles thick, with an average pressure about a thousandfold less than the atmospheric pressure near the earth's surface. Photographs of the sun show the center brighter than the edge. Near the edge of the disk we look diagonally into layers that are farther out and cooler than the inner levels (fig. 10–1). Being cooler, they send out less radiation; hence the sun appears darker toward the edge.

From the amount and quality of radiation reaching us, we infer that the photosphere has a temperature of about 6000° K, or about 10,000° F. The total solar energy falling on a single square centimeter outside the earth's atmosphere is two calories per minute. This amounts to about one horse-power per square yard, or one kilowatt per square meter. From this figure we can calculate the amount of energy escaping from each square centimeter of the sun every second. Since we know how the intensity of emission varies with the temperature, we can deduce the surface temperature of the sun.

The Solar Spectrum

A beam of sunlight, passed through a glass prism, spreads out into a band of rainbow colors known as the spectrum (color plate 29). The spectrum of the sun consists of two parts. First, the photosphere emits a continuous band of colors over the entire range of wavelengths from the ultraviolet through the visible on into the infrared. Second, the somewhat cooler and more tenuous atmospheric layers outside the photosphere absorb the various colors characteristic of the atomic constituents of that region. Thus, thousands of

152

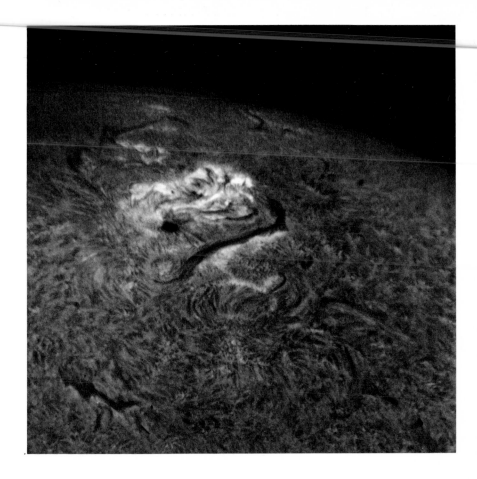

Filtergram in hydrogen light of an active sunspot. Near the edge are dark filaments and bright plages. (Lockheed Solar Observatory)

Overleaf left: Sunspot. The umbra and the filamentary penumbra grade into finely-structured solar granules. (Sacramento Peak Observatory, Air Force Cambridge Research Laboratories)

Right: Active sunspot area photographed in hydrogen light, showing the structure of the swirling hot gases. Some of the dark striations are probably associated with the magnetic fields of the sunspot. (Sacramento Peak Observatory, Air Force Cambridge Research Laboratories)

dark lines appear against the bright continuous background. The English chemist William H. Wollaston (1766–1828) noted a few of these dark lines as early as 1802. In 1814, the Bavarian physicist Joseph von Fraunhofer (1787–1826) was the first to record these dark lines, mapping some 600 of them in systematic fashion. He assigned capital letters from A to G to the strongest of these lines from red to violet. With some extensions, we still use this system of *Fraunhofer lines*, referring, for example, to the D lines of sodium.

The Chemicals in the Sun

By comparing the solar spectrum with the spectra of various chemical substances, astronomers have achieved a qualitative analysis of the solar atmosphere and its elements. The modern astrophysicist can do even better than that. Each atomic vibration capable of emitting or absorbing a given line can be assigned a specific index—an *oscillator strength*—which measures the potential capability of the atom for producing that spectral line. The index can be determined theoretically or measured in the laboratory.

It would not be altogether true that the strongest Fraunhofer lines come from the most abundant chemical substances. For example, the most intense lines in the entire solar spectrum are those we call H and K, which are found in the extreme violet. They come from atoms of calcium that have lost one outer electron in the hot solar atmosphere. We say that such an atom is "singly ionized." An atom that has lost no electrons is said to be "neutral" because it possesses no residual electric charge. In the red region we find a much weaker line, known as C or usually as Hα, which comes from neutral hydrogen. It turns out that almost every calcium atom in the sun's atmosphere is capable of absorbing the H and K lines, but not more than one hydrogen atom in a billion can absorb the C line. When we allow for this difference, we discover that hydrogen is actually about a million times more abundant than calcium.

153

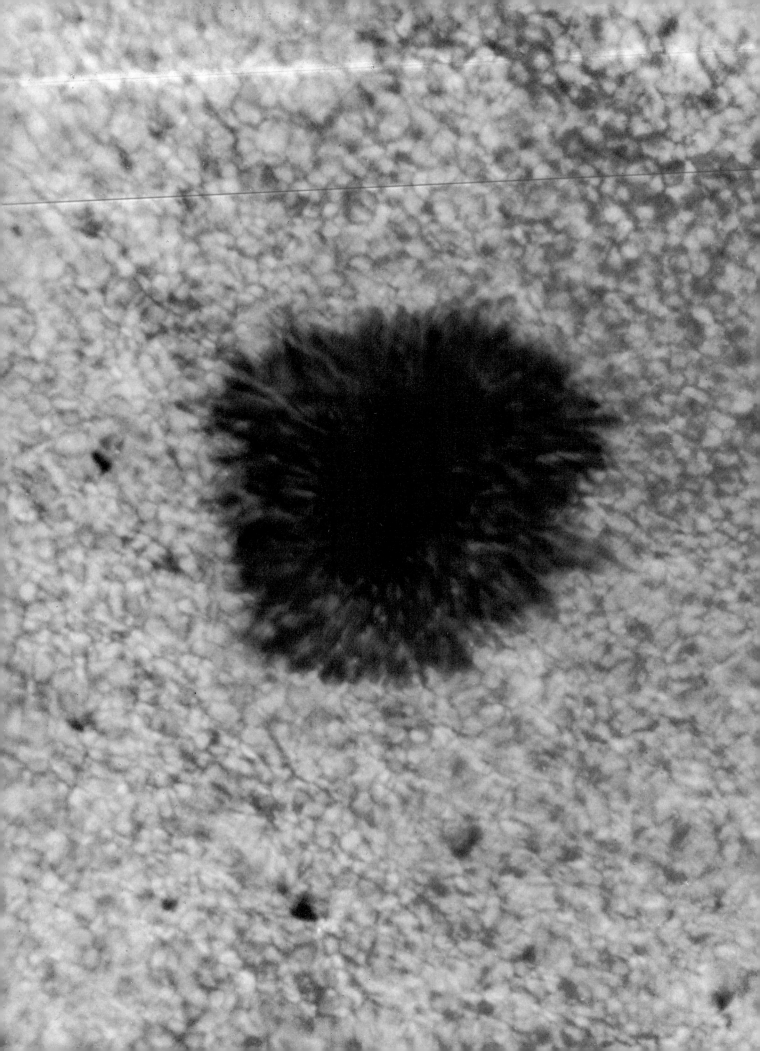

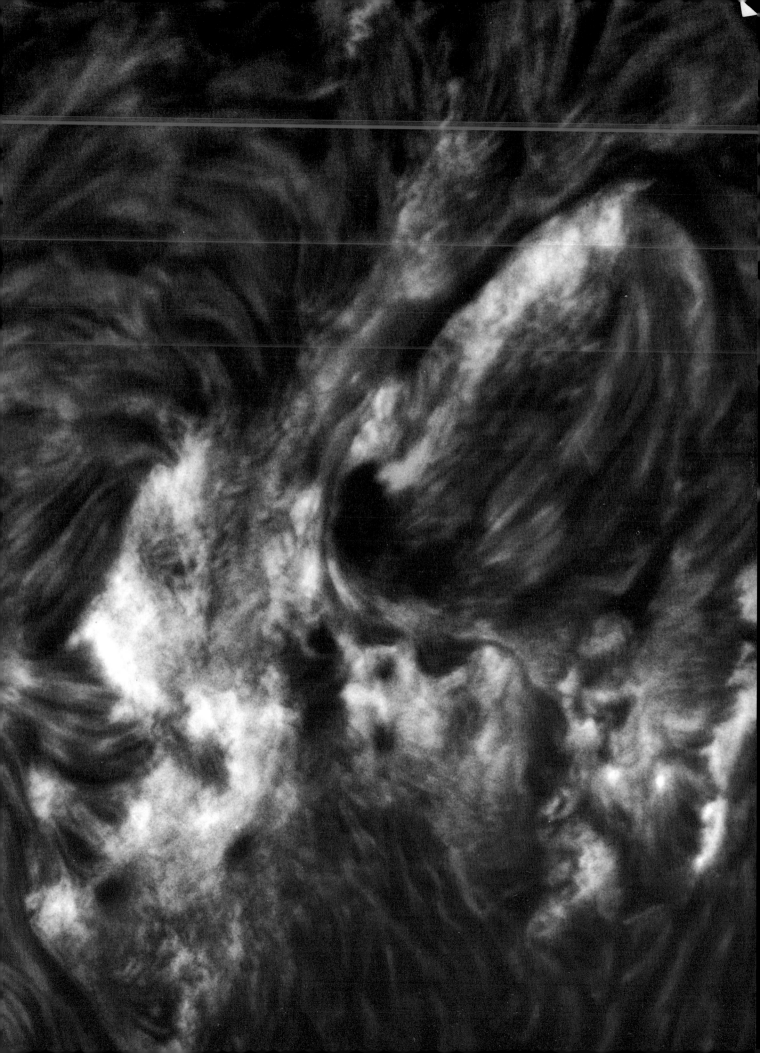

Indeed, making similar determinations of all the various chemical elements, astronomers have found that about 90 per cent of all the atoms of the sun are hydrogen and about 9 per cent helium. The remaining 1 per cent is made up of other constituents from lithium to lead. The chemical composition of that small residue appears to be very similar to that of the earth. Indeed, if the earth had originally been formed from solar material, from which the lightest gases, hydrogen and helium, leaked away into space, we would expect it to have about its present composition. As we shall see in a later chapter, we cannot infer with any certainty from this meager evidence that the earth was once part of the sun.

Sunspots

Sunspots are the most conspicuous feature of the sun. Long before the invention of the telescope, the Chinese Annals recorded many observations of such dark areas on the solar disk, seen presumably when the sun was dimmed by clouds or haze, especially near sunset. The Chinese often referred to them as "flying birds." Galileo and other astronomers of his time, using telescopes, independently discovered the spots. They thereby provoked the criticism of contemporary philosophers, for Aristotle himself had declared that the sun was pure fire; and since nothing that was pure could possibly possess blemishes, sunspots could not, according to medieval logic, exist. Many people refused to look through that wicked instrument, the telescope.

Sunspots are usually present and are plain to see. Occasionally they appear as a single spot; most frequently the spots occur in pairs or in groups. Groups of multiple spots can be large enough to be visible to the unaided eye (but no one should stare directly at the sun). Individual spots have a black center, usually somewhat irregular in shape, known as the *umbra*. The gray *penumbra* outlines this area, radiating from the center like the petals of an aster. The terms umbra and penumbra do not imply that the spot phenomenon has anything to do with shadows. In simplest terms, spots appear dark because they are cooler than their surroundings. Sunspots are not, however, completely black. If a magician could cause the sun to vanish, leaving just a single large sun spot, the earth would not immediately be plunged into darkness. That single spot would continue to radiate about as much light as we would receive from a hundred full moons. The darkness of a spot, therefore, is simply a matter of contrast.

Observations of a spot or group from day to day disclose that spots drift across the solar surface from east to west as we view the sun's near side. This means that the sun rotates like the earth and in the same direction—west to east. Technically we say that the rotation is direct rather than retrograde. The rotation enables us to determine the positions of the poles and equator. We find that the sun's axis is tilted 7° with respect to the plane of the earth's orbit. But the sun is not a solid body and does not rotate like one. A series of spots lined up on a given meridian of the sun would, after a single rotation, form a curve. Similarly, spots near the solar equator complete their revolution in a shorter time than those at higher latitudes. Thus we know that the rotation period of the sun varies from some 25 days at the equator to about 29 days near the poles.

As observations accumulated over the centuries, astronomers realized that sun spots did not occur at random but according to a well-defined cycle. It was found that if the number of spots visible at any one time were averaged over a week or month, the figures yielded a curve like that in Figure 10–2. A single cycle—that is, from one minimum to the next—takes slightly more than eleven years on the average, the exact duration varying from as few as nine years to as many as sixteen. And the average maximum spottedness also varies, seemingly in random fashion, though some astronomers have suggested that every other cycle is higher. Spots occur most frequently between the sun's equator and latitudes 35° and almost never at latitudes higher than 40°, north or south. The British astronomer E. W. Maunder (1851–1928)

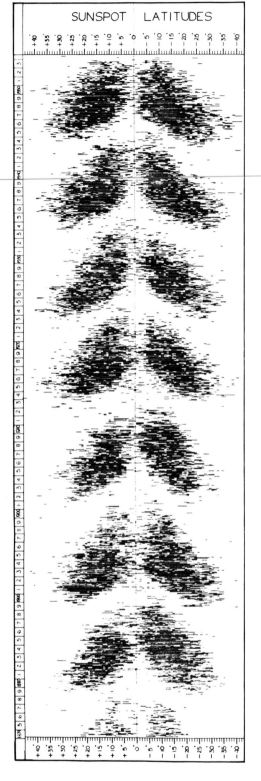

Figure 10–2. Left: Butterfly diagram of individual sunspots plotted according to latitude of occurrence. Right: The curve of a sunspot cycle.

156

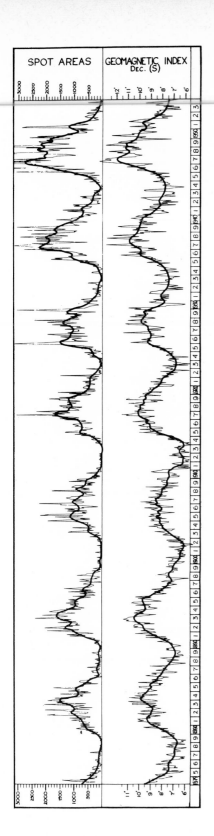

devised an interesting way of plotting the individual spots. A glance at his diagram (fig. 10–2) will confirm the fact that, early in the cycle, spots tend to form at higher latitudes. As the cycle progresses, the spotted areas tend to occur at lower latitudes, until the last spots of a cycle lie very near the equator. Since the plot of one complete cycle makes a pattern resembling the wings of a butterfly, one wing for the northern and one for the southern hemisphere, astronomers usually refer to Maunder's plot as the "butterfly diagram."

Sunspots as Magnets

Taking care to minimize scattered light from the photosphere, astronomers have photographed the spectra of sunspots. Since the spots are cooler than their surroundings, the electrons have largely recombined with the ions to form neutral atoms and some atoms have combined to form molecules. Hence, the spot spectra, as compared with the normal Fraunhofer spectrum, exhibit a decrease in the intensity of lines from ionized atoms and an increase in the intensity of lines from the neutral atoms and molecules. But the major difference, as the American astronomer George Ellery Hale (1868–1938) discovered in 1914, lay in the fact that many lines, single in the Fraunhofer spectrum, appeared to be triple or multiple in the sunspots. The light in the spectral lines was polarized. From the behavior in the laboratory of similar lines in gases excited in intense magnetic fields, Hale deduced that the spots were strong electromagnets.

The phenomenon, which had been discovered earlier by the Dutch physicist Pieter Zeeman (1865–1943), is called the "Zeeman effect." Further studies indicated that the magnetic fields resulted from the presence of strong electric currents within the solar atmosphere. One can calculate that the magnitude of the current necessary to account for the field of a single large spot is of the order of ten million million (10^{13}) amperes. The polarization of the spot spectrum enables astronomers to determine whether the spot field is a north pole or a south pole. And the magnitude of the separation of the components shows that the intensity of the magnetic field is on the order of thousands of *gauss*, the electromagnetic unit of measurement. By comparison, the magnetic field of the earth is less than one gauss.

Sunspots often occur in pairs and Hale found that the two components of the pair have opposite magnetic polarities, say a north pole on the right and a south pole on the left. If this holds for the northern hemisphere, spot pairs in the southern hemisphere of the sun will be opposite, with a south pole on the right and a north pole on the left. This pattern of magnetic polarities persists for a complete cycle, after which the fields suddenly reverse for the second cycle. Hence, a full cycle is twenty-two instead of eleven years.

Sunspots are transient phenomena, often changing their patterns within an interval of a few hours or days. Some large ones may, however, last for five or six weeks, long enough to reappear on the face of the sun after one or more complete rotations. Single, "unipolar" spots occasionally occur. When they do, the missing field of opposite polarity can be detected in the appropriate position, as if an invisible component lay beneath the photospheric surface. And it often appears a day or two later. When, as frequently happens, a spot group is complex, consisting of many instead of just two components, the average magnetic fields of the preceding and following components possess polarities in accord with the general rule for bipolar spots.

Sunspots present many unsolved problems. Astronomers do not know precisely what causes them or why they exhibit the 11- or 22-year cycle with the characteristic butterfly diagram. The answer to these questions lies in the circulation of the solar gases. As the American astronomer Horace Babcock discovered from extremely sensitive measures of the Zeeman effect, the sun as a whole is a great magnet, although the intensity of its field is far less than that of the spots. The field varies and appears to reverse every eleven years though not quite in phase with the sunspot cycle.

Astrophysicists have studied the way in which rotation and convection of the solar envelope may interact with the general solar field and, by a reaction similar to that of a dynamo, generate currents that could cause the magnetic fields of sunspots. This highly specialized subject, known as magnetohydrodynamics, embracing the flow of matter in the presence of magnetic fields, was first developed by Hannes Alfvén, a Swedish physicist.

One can understand a few of the features of sunspots in terms of the familiar properties of magnets, such as that "like" poles repel one another, whereas "unlike" poles attract. But in one major respect, a sunspot differs markedly from the familiar bar or horseshoe magnet: it is composed of gas and is thus mobile and flexible. To help understand a simple spot, we may imagine a bundle of fine iron wires imbedded in a flexible rubber matrix (fig. 10–3a). If these wires could all be magnetized, with north poles at one end and south poles at the other, the ends of the wires would repel one another, stretching the rubber and causing it to form a bell or funnel at each end (fig. 10–3b). In an actual sunspot, expansion of the gas—analogous to the stretching of the rubber—cools the vicinity, thus explaining the darkness of the spot. Finally, if we can imagine our wires bent into a loop so that the opposite poles are brought close to one another (fig. 10–3c), we have the remarkable situation of two unlike poles attracting each other. It is not difficult to visualize the result of this: the two opposite poles compress the rubber matrix between them and the compression produces a heated area between the two spot components. Here, major instabilities can occur, resulting in a solar flare, an explosive ejection of clouds of hot gases.

Both theory and observation indicate that the sunspot gases flow upward and outward along the lines of force of the spot field. This flow causes the gas to expand, maintaining the spot at a temperature some 2000° K cooler than the surrounding surface. The slight displacement of the spectral lines, attributed to the Doppler effect of the outward flow, is known as the "Evershed effect." Sunspots are, so to speak, nature's gigantic refrigerators. Without the flow, expansion, and resultant cooling of the gas, a dark spot would rapidly absorb heat from the neighboring photosphere and vanish within minutes or hours.

Monochromatic Pictures of the Sun

White-light photographs of the solar surface show edge or "limb" darkening, sunspots, and granulation but little else. Color filters are helpful in ordinary photography. A red filter, for example, removes the blue light of the sky and greatly increases the contrast between clouds and the sky background. Such common filters usually consist of colored glass, which pass relatively broad

Figure 10–3. The birth of bipolar sunspots and accompanying flare is here represented by a bundle of fine iron wires imbedded in an elastic matrix (a). If the wires are all magnetized parallel to one another, with north poles (+) at the top and south poles (−) at the bottom, the fact that like poles repel each other causes the matrix to expand as the flexible wires move away from each other, resulting in a funnel at both ends (b). If the wire bundle is bent into a U, with both ends lying on the same surface (c), the attraction of the unlike north and south poles tends to heat and compress the gas trapped between them. Such a formation may explain the behavior of the highly magnetized sunspots. The expansion near the top tends to cool the spot regions. The heated gas rises to the surface and breaks the magnetic barrier that tends to confine it, causing a solar flare. The gas sometimes explodes violently, forming a shock wave.

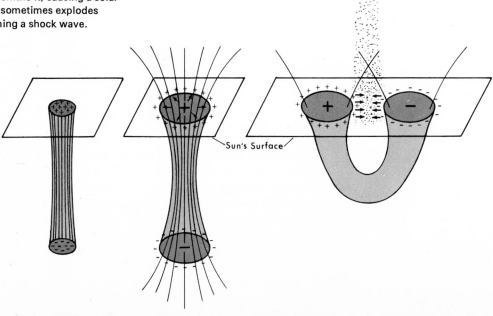

(a) (b) (c)

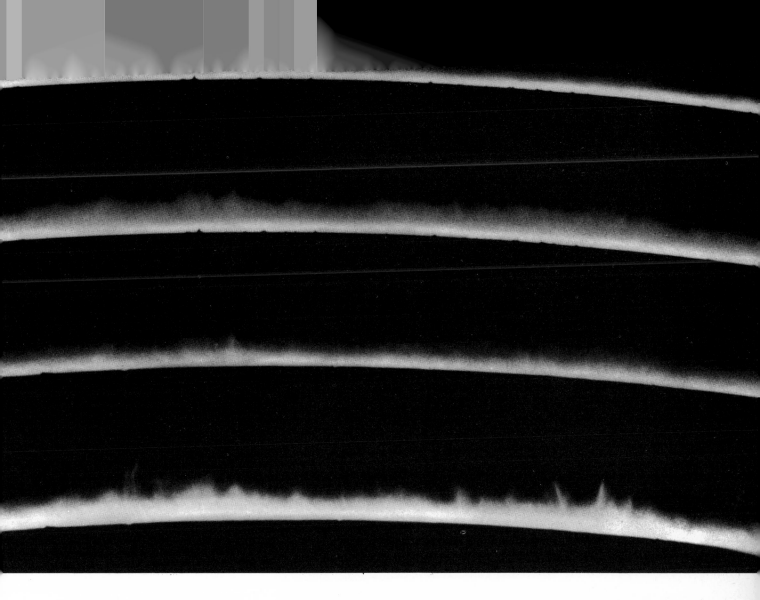

Structure of the sun's chromosphere in Hα light as recorded by a coronagraph. (Richard F. Dunn, Sacramento Peak Observatory, Air Force Cambridge Research Laboratories)

spectral regions while absorbing others. However, a monochromatic filter has been developed that transmits only a very narrow band of the spectrum. Perhaps the most familiar device of this kind is the spectroheliograph. As an image of the sun drifts over the entrance slit of a spectrograph, a photographic plate moves over a narrow aperture set to transmit light from some selected spectral line. Thus, one may photograph the sun in the red line of hydrogen (Hα), the violet line of ionized calcium (K), or any other line. Similar results can be achieved with filters of alternate plates of quartz or calcite, layers of polaroid, or layers of various substances deposited on a glass plate.

Filtergrams exhibit details of the sun and solar atmosphere, most of which are completely invisible on white-light photographs. Photographs taken in the Hα light show bright areas in the neighborhood of sunspots with a fine mottling apparently caused by the magnetic fields known to be present in those regions (color plate 18). Occasionally, and most frequently within a large complex spot group, a brilliant eruption, known as a solar flare, will appear and quickly increase in size and intensity. Photographs taken in the K line exhibit marked differences from those taken in Hα. In particular, they show huge patches of bright emission, known as calcium plages, around sunspot groups. These bright areas usually appear before and persist even after the spot has disappeared. Motion pictures taken at rates of several frames per minute and projected at the normal 24 frames per second reveal startling solar events that would be completely lost in ordinary photographs.

Under ordinary conditions, the limb of the sun, as we have noted, appears perfectly sharp. However, during a total solar eclipse, just as the moon hides,

or occults, the last trace of the sun's brilliant photosphere, a much fainter region, which clearly represents an extension of the sun's atmospheric envelope, flashes into view. Its faint pink hue led early astronomers to call this region the *chromosphere*, or sphere of color—an effect caused by intense emission of Hα. The chromosphere resembles the fine fringe of a circular doily. The individual filaments, which have been compared to blades of grass, are called *spicules*. We know something about their behavior from motion pictures in Hα light taken with a large coronagraph by Richard Dunn at the Sacramento Peak Observatory in Arizona. The individual spicules last for only a few minutes. The rough correspondence between this lifetime and that of the underlying granules has suggested that the two phenomena are physically associated. For example, the spicules could conceivably be the upper portions of the rising and descending jets associated with the convective granules. The fact that the number of spicules and jets are roughly equal also favors this concept. The earlier view that spicules represented the tips of only ascending jets is now rejected; many of the spicules are clearly descending, while others simply become visible and then fade without displaying any appreciable vertical motion.

The spectrum of the solar chromosphere has been of special astrophysical interest for many years. It is best photographed during the few seconds just after the beginning or before the ending of a total eclipse of the sun. Its evanescent character led astronomers to call it the flash spectrum. It consists of thousands of bright lines, characteristic of a gas under low pressure. At first glance, these lines seem to correspond in both position and intensity to the dark lines of the normal Fraunhofer spectrum. There are, however, many significant differences. First, the lines of the ionized metals appear much stronger in the flash than in the dark-line spectrum. This may be attributed in part to lower gas pressure in the chromosphere, a condition that tends, as we have noted, to favor increased ionization. But the surpassing brilliance of lines of neutral and ionized helium, which do not appear at all in the Fraun-

Rapid development of an active solar prominence, photographed in hydrogen light. (Sacramento Peak Observatory, Air Force Cambridge Research Laboratories)

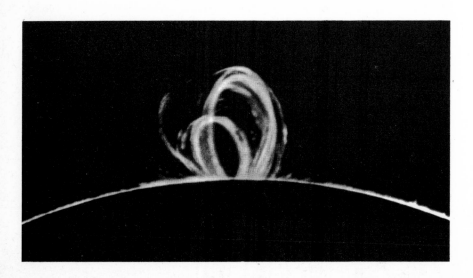

Loop prominences, photographed in hydrogen light. (Sacramento Peak Observatory, Air Force Cambridge Research Laboratories)

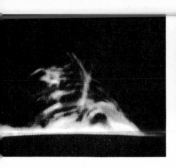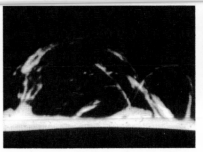

hofer spectrum, cannot be explained so simply. Astrophysicists have concluded that the chromosphere, with temperatures up to 25,000° K or higher, is much hotter than the lower atmospheric levels responsible for the Fraunhofer spectrum, where temperatures are about 4,500° K. Theoretical analysis indicates that shock waves rising from the noisy, chaotic convection of the lower levels provide the energy for this excess heating. If our sky were full of planes, all flying faster than sound, the total energy of their sonic booms could similarly raise the temperature of the earth's atmosphere. Such reasoning seems to account for the apparent anomaly of an upper level of the solar atmosphere that is significantly hotter than the levels below.

The Solar Corona

The spiculed chromosphere can be detected to heights of from 10,000 to 15,000 miles above the photospheric surface. Above the chromosphere, visible to altitudes of several solar diameters, extends a still fainter region of the solar atmosphere: the *solar corona* (color plate 20). Its total brightness, which approximates that of the full moon, is about 500,000 times fainter than the sun itself. The corona is ordinarily invisible except at a total solar eclipse. However, with a coronagraph operated at high-altitude stations, the inner corona can now be observed more or less continuously

It is the corona that lends to a total solar eclipse its strange and spectacular beauty. During totality, it forms an irregular halo of white light around the black circular disk of the moon. Near sunspot minimum, the corona generally displays long extensions from the sun's equator, with tufted bristles near the poles. Near maximum, the corona often shows fan-like structures in each hemisphere. The corona sometimes has long streamers, as in the total eclipse of 1970, where rays were detected as far out as five diameters from the sun.

Photographs show that the corona has a delicate, wispy structure, as if composed of long fibrous streamers gracefully blended and interwoven. The corona tends to form arches or caps, resembling the peaked helmets of ancient

A surge prominence from an active flare attains an altitude of 100,000 miles above the solar surface. (Sacramento Peak Observatory, Air Force Cambridge Research Laboratories)

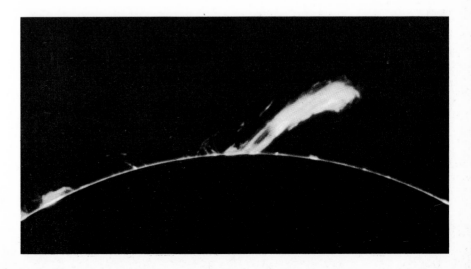

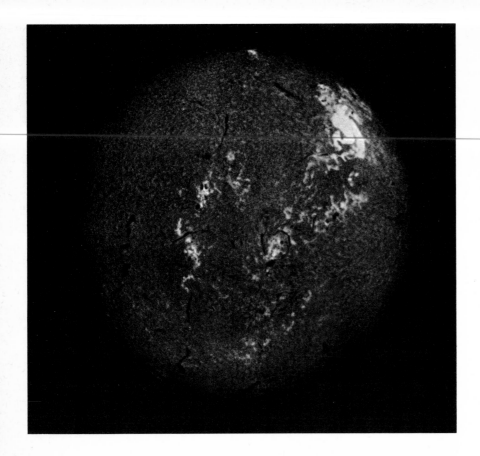

A hydrogen filtergram of the sun, including bright plages and dark filaments. (Sacramento Peak Observatory, Air Force Cambridge Research Laboratories)

warriors, over certain "active" regions of the sun's surface. The interiors of the helmets show bright and dark regions nested within one another. I have attributed these structures to magnetic fields within the corona, which impart to the ionized gas a certain elasticity. Motion pictures taken with the coronagraph occasionally show a coronal wisp moving back and forth like a whip, in reaction to nearby explosive forces.

For many years after it was first photographed, the spectrum of the solar corona resisted all attempts to identify the sources of its numerous bright lines. None appeared in the laboratory spectra of ordinary chemical elements. And so the legend continued that the corona consisted of some new chemical element, and this received the provisional name of "coronium." Bernard Lyot (1897–1952), of France, finally solved the problem. Coronium proved to be only iron, nickel, magnesium, and a few other elements in extraordinarily high states of ionization. The strongest of the coronal lines, the one in the green part of the spectrum, proved to come from iron atoms that had lost 13 electrons, exactly half of their normal complement. And the other lines also originated in atoms with large numbers of electrons missing.

Here was a new solar puzzle! For astrophysical calculations plainly showed that such wholesale stripping of electrons from atoms could occur only within gases having temperatures of at least 1,000,000° K! Other evidence finally confirmed this conclusion, and some regions proved to have temperatures twice as high. Since astronomers once raised their eyebrows at the idea of chromospheric temperatures of even 25,000° K, the vastly greater coronal temperatures really confounded them. Then they found that shock waves expanding upward from low-level explosions could produce heat in the more tenuous coronal gases in much the way the waves heat the chromosphere.

Prominences

At levels high above the solar surface but well within the corona, huge, pinkish clouds, called *solar prominences*, occasionally form (color plate 19).

Their spectra prove that they are more like the chromosphere than like the corona. In other words, prominences appear to be relatively cool condensations within the corona itself.

Like the earth's clouds, prominences vary greatly in size and constantly change their shape. Astronomers used to apply the term "quiescent prominences" to a form that extends upward from the surface like a hedgerow, sometimes winding over half the solar disk. Direct photographs of the sun in Hα show such prominences as long, narrow, dark filaments projected against the solar disk. Motion pictures reveal that the adjective "quiescent" does not accurately describe the behavior of these prominences. Their shape may remain roughly constant for days or even weeks. But matter constantly flows through the volume during all this time, condensing from the hotter corona near the top and raining into the chromosphere near the bottom. These formations are now more accurately called "hedgerow prominences."

After some time, the rate of flow often tends to increase. And then the upper boundary of the prominence will begin to ascend, matter streaming through it all the while. The prominence starts to fade and then disappears. Some of the matter may leave the sun completely or evaporate into the corona; the rest falls slowly and gracefully back into the sun in huge droplets of luminous rain, the individual drops often exceeding the earth in diameter. Here again we face a choice in nomenclature: the term "ascending prominence" seems to be more appropriate than the older "eruptive prominence."

Unlike a fog-bank, however, prominences are almost never structureless. They are more like a loosely-woven tapestry in which the individual vertical strands are well defined. Since blobs and condensations freely flow along the bent and twisted strands, the basic structure remains constant for long periods of time. Here, as in other solar features, the character of the strands is probably controlled by tangled magnetic lines of force rather than a solid substance. The downward-flowing prominences assume many forms in addition to that of hedgerows: one of the more common shapes resembles a funnel with matter flowing into the top and out of the stem at the bottom.

A second type of prominence involves matter whose predominant motion is upward. *Surges* comprise the more spectacular members of this class. Like giant geysers, they spout to heights sometimes as great as 1,000,000 miles, with velocities up to 1,000 miles a second. Some leave the sun entirely, fading as they travel outward. Others come to a complete stop, reverse their direction and reenter the sun along the same path. Occasionally the surges are oscillatory, repeating almost the same pattern several times.

Solar Flares

The surges usually occur in the vicinity of active spots. Indeed, the presence of surges and other explosive features tells whether a spot is active or not. But the most distinctive feature of active areas are the solar *flares*. These flares are best seen on direct-disk photographs taken with an Hα or a K filter. They are often true explosions. A bright patch of hydrogen emission builds up within a complex spot group. Within a minute or two it reaches maximum brilliance, after which a tremendous explosion occurs. Motion pictures clearly show the supersonic shock wave racing over the solar surface at speeds of 1,000 miles a second or more, disturbing prominences and other features in the process. The spot field appears to focus the explosion, so that it is all the more intense in certain directions (color plates 21, 22, 25.).

Such focusing is characteristic of most explosions, which tend to occur in the direction of the weakest part of the barrier enclosing the region. In flare phenomena, the "enclosure" is the invisible magnetic field which, stretched beyond its elastic limit, bursts like an overinflated balloon, allowing the enclosed gas to escape explosively. These and other shock waves raise the temperature of the corona to one or two million degrees. Escaping from the sun, the expanding shell of gases forms the variable solar wind, which we generally think of as an extension of the solar corona.

No elementary theory of the sun forecast the emission of X-rays from the active areas of the solar surface. Nor had anyone predicted that the sun would send out raucous blasts of short radio waves during periods of high activity. The solar static consists of several distinct types. There are, first, short random bursts. Second, we find long emissions, minutes in duration, whose frequencies drift from high to low. Third, there are short emissions whose frequencies shift rapidly from high to low.

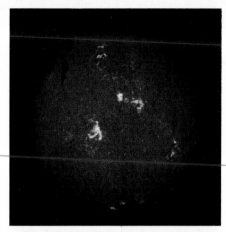

Apparently the higher frequencies reach us first because they escape more readily through the ionized coronal gas, whereas the lower frequencies are retarded in their journey. The frequency emitted may, in addition, depend on the density of the gas, the higher frequencies coming from the denser material. Hence, if the excitation depends on the interaction between the corona and an upward-moving surge, the higher frequencies will be emitted first since the surge moves through the corona from the denser low levels to the more tenuous upper regions. Radio telescopes, with their huge dish-shaped antennas, collect the radiation and feed it into sensitive receivers. Special techniques enable us to map the sun in radio frequencies. Such diagrams show that the corona responsible for the radio emissions is, unlike the visible sun, brighter toward the limb.

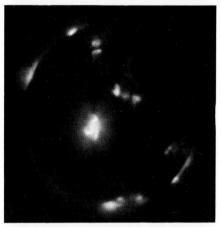

The fast-moving atoms and electrons escaping from the sun fill the entire solar system, dwindling as they reach the greater depths. Striking a wandering comet, they cause part of it to evaporate and stream outward to form a tail extending away from the sun. They blast the surface of the moon, causing profound changes in the lunar surface. Astronauts in orbit far from earth could conceivably be endangered by these particles from the solar flares, which comprise a sort of cosmic "fallout." During times of maximum sunspot activity, this solar wind increases in intensity and size. The earth's magnetic field, however, acts like an umbrella, shielding us from the main impact of the solar wind. The atoms and electrons become entrapped within this field to form the Van Allen belts. The electrons and ions, occasionally spilling out of the belt and falling into the earth's upper atmosphere, induce numerous secondary effects of solar activity. The most remarkable features are the Aurora Borealis and the Aurora Polaris (color plates 1, 23, 24, 27), the glowing upper atmosphere most conspicuous in the polar regions in a belt around the earth's magnetic pole. The fast-moving electrons collide with atoms in the tenuous regions of the earth's atmosphere, exciting them and causing them to emit radiation. These effects also include ionospheric layers of increased electron density, especially near the magnetic poles, which resist the passage of radio waves through the regions. This phenomenon is known as polar cap absorption, and the occurrence is termed a PCA event.

The ultraviolet and X-radiation from the sun directly enter the earth's upper atmosphere, tearing electrons from the atoms present and producing the ionosphere. A bright flare perturbs these upper layers, causing a "sudden ionospheric disturbance," whose characteristic feature is the absorption of radio waves on the sunlit hemisphere of the earth. Such an occurrence can completely block out long-distance, overseas reception of shortwave radio signals. During all such events, transient electric currents flow in the earth's upper atmosphere, producing changes in the intensity and direction of the earth's normal magnetic field. Such happenings, known as magnetic storms, have been charted for more than 150 years. The close correlation of magnetic and auroral phenomena with the sunspot cycle led scientists to recognize, long before the physical cause of the phenomenon was known, the existence of earth-sun relationships. A century ago, however, the English astronomer Richard Carrington (1826–1875), observing the sun in England, saw what was clearly an immense flare, intense enough to be visible in white light. For several days, brilliant auroras and magnetic disturbances were observed.

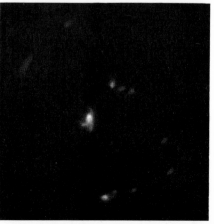

Various scientists have tried to establish the existence of other earth-sun relationships, such as the effect of sunspots on weather and especially rainfall, animal and plant life, and even on human affairs. So far, none of the the proposed correlations appears convincing. It would not be surprising if sun-weather relationships were eventually established. Perhaps one may eventually be able to forecast, if not the day-to-day weather, the character of the next growing season: hot or cold, wet or dry, late or early.

Meanwhile, astronomers have built a huge, international network of solar observatories. Most of them have telescopes fitted with monochromatic filters. In the United States, the National Aeronautics and Space Administration, the National Science Foundation and the Air Force have supported the construction of such a network for the primary purpose of keeping close watch on solar activity. The safety of astronauts from the dangerous solar fallout is the prime consideration here. Of great importance also is the fact that many space experiments depend directly or indirectly on solar activity. So scientists keep the sun under almost continual surveillance; when some stations are beclouded, others can take up the observation. The occurrence of major flares is reported to NASA through a worldwide network. The Environmental Sciences Service Administration (ESSA) also employs the solar data to issue regular forecasts of ionospheric conditions, especially those that could affect radio communication.

As we have already noted, the earth's atmosphere absorbs strongly, especially in the ultraviolet region of the spectrum. Hence observations of the sun and other celestial bodies from rockets and satellites are playing an important role in our understanding of the sun's outer corona. One special program of the series of the Orbiting Solar Observatories (OSO), under Leo Goldberg of Harvard, has sent back telecommunications records of the solar ultraviolet spectrum. It has also transmitted maps of the sun in selected atomic lines of the far-ultraviolet region. These records refer mainly to the solar corona, and enable astronomers to probe its radial structure. Herbert Friedman, of the United States Naval Research Laboratory, has obtained spectacular records of active solar regions, in the X-ray region of the spectrum, from rockets that go far above the earth's atmosphere.

The outer corona merges, at some distance from the sun, into that faint glow extending parallel to the ecliptic in regions near the sun. This phenomenon, called the zodiacal light, is ordinarily attributed to a zone of fine dust or other particles orbiting the sun inside the orbit of Mercury. But the outer corona and the zodiacal glow are so faint that ordinary methods of observing them near the sun have unfortunately failed. Richard S. Tousey and his colleagues of the Naval Research Laboratory succeeded in photographing these external regions from rockets. These records show outer corona streamers extending outward from the sun by 8 or 10 diameters as they merge into the structureless glow of the zodiacal light. To prove that the light so photographed comes from regions near the sun, Tousey took records at new moon, so that the dark lunar disk could clearly be seen eclipsing the background corona.

The sun is important to scientists because it is the only star whose surface and behavior they can study in detail. It is particularly interesting because of the great range of its temperatures and densities from its core to its outer corona. It provides, in fact, a huge laboratory where they can observe the effects of high temperatures on matter. And it challenges scientists with many mysteries such as the origin of magnetic fields and the sunspot cycle.

X-ray photographs of the sun taken by a rocket-borne X-ray telescope on June 8, 1968. A number of bright hydrogen plages on the Hα photograph in the top picture (taken by a ground-based coronagraph) show up with increased brilliance in the photographs taken with filters transmitting only X-rays. These photographs show enhanced excitation in the solar corona, the "normal" solar surface being almost black. The dark, stellated patterns around the bright central image are optical effects. (Solar Physics Group, American Science and Engineering, Inc.)

Eclipses

11

Solar and lunar eclipses are among the most spectacular natural events. Even today, many sects regard eclipses with superstitious awe. In India, for example, certain groups believe that when the moon enters into eclipse it is being swallowed by a dragon; fortunately, according to tradition, a hero chops off the dragon's head, so that the moon shortly reappears. Whether or not people still believe in these fantasies is not important; their mere existence reflects the fear with which eclipses have been universally regarded.

Total Eclipses of the Sun

Total solar eclipses are by no means rare events. One occurs somewhere in the world about once every year and a half. At such times the moon comes between the sun and the earth so that the moon's oval shadow falls on the earth (color plates 26, 28). Since both the moon and the earth are moving, the shadow races at high speed across the earth's surface, sweeping out a track known as the path of totality. Anyone standing in that track will be able to see the total eclipse, provided the weather is clear. The track is so narrow, however, that total solar eclipses at any given location on earth are extremely are, occurring only about once every 300 years or so.

The beginning of the eclipse is relatively uneventful. A shadow creates a small indentation on the western edge of the sun, indicating that the moon has started to cover up the disk. The bite grows in size until, about an hour later, the sun is almost completely covered and only a narrow crescent of light remains. These constitute the partial phases of eclipse. The last few minutes before totality can be very dramatic. The temperature in the region of the viewer drops sharply because of the decrease in solar radiation. The sky darkens and often deepens in blueness. A yellowish haze envelopes the distant landscape. Birds, confused by the unexpected twilight, fly about, looking for their nests. Suddenly everything seems hushed.

The narrowing crescent of the sun breaks into a series of beads where the sun shines through the valleys between peaks on the moon's rough edge. This phenomenon is known as "Baily's Beads," although the American astronomer Samuel Williams (1743–1817) observed and properly interpreted them in 1780, some fifty-six years before the English astronomer Francis Baily (1774–1844) made his studies. One or two of the bright beads may hang on for a second or two, providing what is sometimes called the "diamond ring" effect. At totality the faint outer atmosphere of the sun comes into view, surrounding the moon's black silhouette. This atmosphere, called the corona, is pearly-white in color and has a fibrous, feathery quality suggesting the wings of a bird. Indeed, the ancient Egyptians often represented the sun with wings and it is probable that this legendary representation resulted from the appearance of the sun at total eclipse.

If the observer uses a telescope or binocular at this point, it will provide an excellent view of the delicate structure of the sun's corona. Probably pinkish spots will appear within the corona close to the edge of the sun. These are the solar prominences already described, bright clouds of glowing hydrogen gas imbedded in the corona. Both the corona and prominences are manifestations of solar activity. A few bright-pink surges, prominences that shoot up like geysers from the borders of sunspots, may appear. These change so slowly that they do not seem to move during the few minutes of totality. As

Facing page: Total eclipse of the sun on March 7, 1970, (as observed from southern Mexico), showing extended rays and streamers. (Harvard College Observatory, Smithsonian Astrophysical Observatory, National Geographic Society)

we mentioned previously, some of these areas occasionally explode, expelling material with speeds as high as 1,000 miles per second.

The solar corona itself, forming an extended atmosphere around the sun, is one consequence of this tremendous solar activity. At totality, one can usually see the corona out to a distance of two or more diameters from the sun. The shape of the corona varies from one eclipse to the next, but it is known to have a sort of tufted structure probably caused by intense magnetic fields within the sun and the sunspots. Near sunspot minimum, it exhibits long, equatorial streamers and brush-like fibers near the pole. Near sunspot maximum, the corona is more nearly symmetrical, with a petaled structure somewhat like a dahlia.

Observing an Eclipse

It is dangerous to observe an eclipse with the unaided eye. Many persons—especially children—tend to stare directly into the sun during an eclipse and may sustain severe burns of the retina. In such a situation the lens of the eye acts like a magnifying glass, focusing the sun's light upon the retina and burning it, sometimes severely enough to cause blindness.

There are several safe ways of watching the partial phases of an eclipse. If a telescope is used, the viewer should not look directly at the sun but focus a bright image of it on a sheet of paper placed a foot or two behind the eye-piece. A practical substitute for a telescope is a $1/8$-inch hole carefully punched through a large piece of cardboard, which is then held several feet above the ground. Light coming through the hole will be focused.

The most common device for viewing a partial eclipse is a piece of ordinary glass that has both sides heavily smoked in candle flame so that only a dim image of the sun comes through. Photographic film developed until it is almost black may also be used. However, neither of these devices gives complete protection. The best screen is the goggles or safety glass used by welders. During totality, however, it is entirely safe to gaze directly at the eclipse since the brightness will then be reduced to about that of the full moon. At that point, the moon, a round, black disk, will be silhouetted against the sun, and all that will be visible of the sun will be its shining corona—one of the grandest spectacles in nature.

Total, Annular, and Partial Eclipses

Total solar eclipses occur only when the shadow of the moon falls somewhere on the surface of the earth. Since the lunar orbit is a distinct ellipse, such eclipses occur only when the moon lies in the half of its path nearest the earth, that is, near *perigee*. The maximum duration of a total eclipse for a ground-based observer is seven minutes. By observing from a modern supersonic jet that follows the spreading shadow, this figure can be lengthened to perhaps as much as a couple of hours. During the other half of its orbit, around the point farthest from the earth, or *apogee*, the tip of the moon's conical shadow does not reach the earth, and the moon appears to have a diameter somewhat smaller than that of the sun. When an eclipse occurs at

Figure 11-1. Diagram showing both solar and lunar eclipses. In a solar eclipse, the moon, which appears to cover the sun, throws a tapering shadow on the earth. The eclipse is total over the shadow track, or path of totality, and partial over the region of the penumbral shadow. If the eclipse occurs when the moon is farther from the earth than the average, at apogee, the tip of the shadow cone will not reach the earth. The moon then appears slightly smaller than the sun, and the eclipse is annular, or ring-form. The earth also has a shadow with a tapering umbra and diverging penumbra. A lunar eclipse occurs when the sun and moon are at opposite nodes, so that the shadow of the intervening earth falls on the moon.

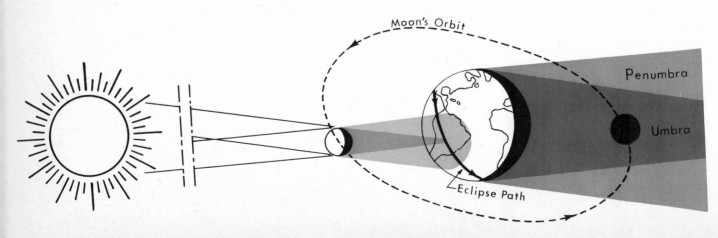

Eclipse of June 8, 1918. Visible here is the so-called "diamond ring" effect. (Lick Observatory)

Solar corona, June 19, 1936, of maximum type with many petals, but with some polar brushes at the upper left. The bright spots at points around the lunar disk are prominences. (Irvine C. Gardner, National Geographic Society)

such a time, a small ring of bright sunlight appears around the edge of the moon. Such an eclipse, called an annular, or ring-form, eclipse, is interesting but by no means as beautiful and spectacular as a total eclipse. On the average of about once in 18 years, the tip of the lunar shadow barely grazes the earth, and the eclipse will then be total over part of the path and annular over the rest. These are called central eclipses.

Observers located not too far outside the zone of total or annular eclipse will usually see a partial eclipse, with the sun's disk only partly covered by the moon. Partial eclipses are fairly frequent in the polar regions when the shadow of the moon comes near the earth but fails to touch it. Total and annular eclipses, almost as frequent, occur every 1.6 years on the average. The polar partials are more frequent, coming at average intervals of 1.33 years; they are relatively unimportant, however, as scientific events.

Only one more total solar eclipse will be visible from the continental United States in this century. It will be visible along the Canadian border, from Washington, Idaho, and Montana, on February 26, 1979. The most recent American eclipse took place on March 7, 1970, but it was clearly visible only over southern Mexico, where I was fortunate enough to observe it. Annular eclipses are scheduled to occur on May 30, 1984 and on May 10, 1994. The next total eclipse visible from the United States will not take place until August 21, 2017. Europe will also be singularly lacking in total solar eclipses, not having one until August 11, 1999.

Dates and Locations of Solar Eclipses, 1970–1988

1970	March 7	t	Mexico, USA, Canada
1970	August 31	a	South Pacific
1972	January 16	a	Antarctica
1972	July 10	t	Northern Canada
1973	January 4	a	Chile, Argentina

1973	June 30	t	Africa
1973	December 24	a	South America, Africa
1974	June 20	t	South Indian Ocean
1976	April 29	a	Africa, Asia
1976	October 23	t	South Australia
1977	April 18	a	Africa
1977	October 12	t	Pacific, South America
1979	February 26	t	USA, Pacific NW, Canada
1979	August 22	a	Antarctica
1980	February 16	t	Africa, India
1980	August 10	a	South Pacific, South America
1981	February 4	a	South Pacific
1981	July 31	t	USSR
1983	June 11	t	Indian Ocean, New Guinea
1983	December 4	a	Atlantic, Africa
1984	May 30	a	Mexico, USA
1984	November 22–23	t	New Guinea, South Pacific
1985	November 12	t	Antarctica, South Pacific
1986	October 3	c	North Atlantic
1987	March 29	c	Atlantic, Africa
1987	September 23	a	China, South Pacific
1988	March 18	t	Pacific, Sumatra, Borneo

a = annular; c = central; t = total.

Eclipses of the Moon

Solar eclipses occur at new moon. Conversely, lunar eclipses occur at full moon, when the shadow of the earth falls on the moon (color plate 30). The earth's shadow, where it crosses the lunar orbit, is always larger than the moon, so that annular lunar eclipses cannot occur. Total eclipses of the moon occur on the average of once every 13.5 months. Partial lunar eclipses are somewhat less frequent, coming about every 22 months.

Although total lunar eclipses are on the whole less frequent than total solar eclipses, they are much more frequent from a given location on the earth's surface. To see a total eclipse of the sun, you must stand somewhere in the narrow belt of totality, approximately 100 miles wide, that marks the path of the lunar shadow on the face of the earth. A total lunar eclipse, however, can be seen from any point on the hemisphere of the earth facing the moon. At that time the curved shadow of the earth creeps over the lunar surface, throwing it into darkness, but not complete blackness. At totality the moon shines with a dull, coppery hue as a result of illumination reaching it from the sunset glow around the edge of the earth. This reddish tinge frightened the ancients into thinking that the moon was covered with blood. It is a spectacular event, well worth viewing through even a small telescope. In any one calendar year we may have as few as two eclipses, both of the sun. The maximum number in a year is seven, five of the sun and two of the moon, or four of the sun and three of the moon.

Predicting Eclipses

Reflecting the earth's motion, the sun, as we have seen, traces out a great circle called the ecliptic. The apparent path of the moon around the sky also appears to be a circle, inclined at an angle of about five degrees to the ecliptic. However, this orbit is not fixed. Like a wheel on a bent shaft, it slowly changes its position, making a complete circuit of the sky in about 19 years. The moon's orbit intersects the ecliptic at two opposite points, the nodes. Eclipses of the sun occur only when the moon and the sun lie simultaneously close to one of these nodes. Eclipses of the moon occur when the moon and the sun occupy opposite nodes, so that the shadow of the intervening earth falls on the moon (fig. 11–1). Indeed, the term ecliptic derives

Inner corona prominences. (Lick Observatory)

170

Total eclipse, September 21, 1922 at Wallal, West Australia. A minimum type, showing pronounced polar brushes and double equatorial extension. (Lick Observatory)

from the fact that eclipses occur only when the moon is near that great circle. Thus eclipses occur in seasons when the sun is near one or the other of the nodes; there are at least two such seasons every year and sometimes three. The node is moving in a direction opposite to that of the apparent sun, so that the interval between the sun's crossing of the same node is 346.62 days rather than the conventional year of 365.242194 days. The interval of 346 days is sometimes called the eclipse year.

There are various kinds of months, related in one way or another to the occurrence of eclipses. The *synodic month*, which is the ordinary month, is the period between successive new (or full) moons—that is, the time required by the moon for a complete circuit of the sky relative to the sun. The *sidereal month* is the time required by the moon to make a complete circuit with respect to the stars; it is a little more than two days shorter than the synodic month. Because the nodes are moving, the interval between the moon's successive passage of the same node is slightly less than the sidereal month, a figure defining the *eclipse*, or *draconitic month*. A fourth kind of month, the *anomalistic month*, is defined with reference to the elliptic orbit of the moon. This interval is the time it takes for the moon to go from the point nearest the earth, the perigee, back to the same point. It is longer than the sidereal month because the moon's orbit is itself turning around in space.

From the standpoint of eclipses, we know that the synodic month of 29.530589 days is important because the moon must be either new or full to produce a solar or a lunar eclipse. The draconitic month of 27.212220 days

Total eclipse of the sun, September 22, 1968. (M. Laffineur, Institut d'Astrophysique, Paris)

is also important because the moon must be near one of the nodes. The anomalistic month of 27.554551 days is relevant because the position of the moon in its orbit determines whether the eclipse will be total or annular. If we analyze the following table,

223 synodic months = 6585.3213 days
242 draconitic months = 6585.3572 days
239 anomalistic months = 6585.5377 days

we find that 6585.32 days is equal to 18 years 11 1/3 days if only four leap days occur during that interval. However, if five leap days should occur, the figure is 18 years 10 1/3 days. The close coincidence of these two figures means that eclipses must recur at this interval. The agreement with the anomalistic month is purely a coincidence, but a significant one. For it means that when the eclipse recurs, the moon will occupy essentially the same position in its orbit that it did 18 years earlier. Its distance from the earth, therefore, will be approximately the same, so that the eclipse will be of the same type as the earlier eclipse.

We may test this out with the eclipse of March 7, 1970. Since the 18 years that will elapse after that date will contain five leap days, a total eclipse of the sun will occur 18 years 10 1/3 days later, that is, on March 17, 1988. During the last one-third of a day, the earth will have turned one-third of a revolution toward the east; hence the eclipse track will lie approximately 120° west of the previous track. The beginning of the eclipse will be visible from Sumatra and Borneo, but most of the path will lie in the Pacific. Since the eclipse will

172

have moved across the international date line, we must add one day, March 18, to the date of the beginning of the eclipse.

This interval of 18 years 11¹/₃ days, called the Saros, was known to the early Chaldean astronomers and they used it to predict solar and lunar eclipses. We still find it helpful in tracing eclipses back into early history. For example, the first eclipse of the series containing that of 1970 started on May 17, 1501 as a partial eclipse visible from the Arctic zone. In 1582, the Gregorian calendar supplanted the older Julian calendar, and ten days were dropped to bring the vernal equinox back to March 21, where it belongs. (This shift must be kept in mind when we compute the dates of eclipses.) After seven partial eclipses, the shadow track touched the vicinity of the North Pole on August 11, 1627 in a central eclipse. This was followed by eight more central eclipses as the tracks continued to move southward. The first total eclipse occurred on November 6, 1771, and the one on March 7, 1970 was the twelfth total eclipse in the series. We can expect about 36 more totals and half a dozen or so partials before this particular Saros vanishes over the South Pole. Eclipses occurring at one of the nodes all show this southward drift; those at the opposite node drift northward.

Several other numerical relations between the three kinds of months can be used in predicting eclipses other than the Saros cycle. For example:

$$135 \text{ synodic months} = 3986.6295 \text{ days} = 10.91503 \text{ years}$$
$$= 11 \text{ years less } 31 \text{ days}$$
$$146.5 \text{ draconitic months} = 3986.5902 \text{ days}$$
$$144.5 \text{ anomalistic months} = 3981.6326 \text{ days}.$$

The close agreement between the synodic and draconitic intervals indicates that eclipse will recur after 11 years less 31 days. Hence, again starting from the March 7, 1970 total eclipse, we calculate that eclipses will occur on February 4, 1981, January 4, 1992, and so on. Both of the later eclipses, however, will be annular rather than total, because the anomalistic period—which governs the position of the moon's elliptic orbit—does not agree with the other two periods. This relationship, sometimes called the Tritos, is not as accurate as the Saros and does not extend as far into the past or future.

More accurate for eclipse prediction is the relationship known as Inex

$$358 \text{ synodic months} = 388.5 \text{ draconitic months} = 10,571.95 \text{ days}$$
$$= 28.9450 \text{ years} = 29 \text{ years less } 20.1 \text{ days}.$$

Here again the anomalistic month is not commensurate, so that successive eclipses will generally differ considerably from one another. Eighteen of these Inex periods are equal to 521 years and 3.6 days in the Gregorian calendar and almost exactly 521 years in the old Julian calendar. One series of eclipses in Inex intervals is particularly interesting because it seems to go back to a reference in the Biblical quotation in Amos viii.9: "I will cause the sun to go down at noon, and I will darken the Earth in the clear day." This clearly refers to an eclipse of the sun and probably to a prediction that such an eclipse will occur. Historians generally agree that this eclipse occurred on June 15, 763 B.C. We can represent the year 763 B.C. by the symbol −762. Applying the 521-year cycle five times, we arrive at eclipses in 242 B.C., 280 A.D., 801 A.D., and 1322 A.D., all on June 15 on the Julian calendar. We then turn to the Gregorian calendar, dropping ten days, and using the interval of 521 years 3 days. This brings us to June 27, 1843. Four applications of the Inex cycle cause us to add 116 years and subtract 80 days, which brings us to the partial eclipse of April 8, 1959. But then an application of the Tritos, which requires us to add 11 years and subtract 31 days, brings us to March 7, 1970. In this way, combining the different relationships, we can predict eclipses accurately for hundreds of centuries into the past or future. Further calculations enable us to predict precisely the kind of eclipse that will occur and its visibility from various parts of the earth's surface.

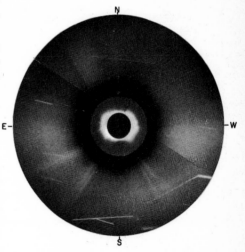

Composite photograph of the inner and outer corona of the eclipse of September 22, 1968. The inner record was taken from a ground-based site in the USSR; the outer corona came from a US-based rocket fired above the earth's atmosphere with a coronagraph that blotted out both the sun and the inner corona. The radial streamers in the picture tend to lie along extensions of the more brilliant regions of the inner corona. (Inner circle photo by D. H. Menzel and J. M. Pasachoff of Harvard-Smithsonian Observatories; photo of outer corona by Richard Tousey, Naval Research Laboratory)

12

The Terrestrial Planets

Within the family of planets are four—Mercury, Venus, Mars, and Pluto—that closely resemble the earth in size, mean density, and abundance of heavier elements. They are called the terrestrial planets. These planets are small compared with such giants as Jupiter and Saturn. They are fairly dense, rotate slowly, and have few if any satellites. With the exception of Pluto these planets lie nearest the sun.

Mercury: The Innermost Planet

Over the past decade new techniques have provided us with data about Mercury, drastically changing what we know about it. The accepted rotation period and temperature of the planet were found to be wrong, and even the basic assumption that the planet had no atmosphere was challenged.

The planet Mercury is relatively bright, varying in magnitude from +1.7 to —1.6, depending upon the phase. In fact, Mercury is exceeded in brightness only by Jupiter, Venus and, occasionally, Mars. Even so, Mercury is not easy to observe. Because of the proximity of its orbit to the sun, it never lies farther than 28° away from the sun, and it is visible without a telescope near the horizon only during evening and morning twilight. To complicate observations even further, the disk of Mercury is very small, even as seen through a telescope. Its apparent diameter is only 12.9 seconds of arc at inferior conjunction, when the planet lies between the earth and sun. At superior conjunction, on the far side of the sun, its diameter is about three times smaller.

For the past half century Mercury was thought to be in synchronous rotation, that is, moving in its orbit with one side always facing toward the sun. The length of Mercury's sidereal day thus coincided with its sidereal year of 88 days. The 88-day rotation rate was well established historically. The famous Italian astronomer Giovanni B. Schiaparelli (1835–1910), who first described the canals of Mars, observed Mercury over a long period of time from his observatory in Milan. He had to carry out his observations in broad daylight, when Mercury was in its full phase near the time of superior conjunction. These daylight observations were hindered by scattered light within the telescope and in the earth's atmosphere. Schiaparelli saw and sketched the features of the planet in a delicate brown tint barely distinguishable from the reddish tone of the background. He observed that the markings seemed to be the same from hour to hour and day to day, a fact that led him to conclude that the planet always kept the same face turned toward the sun. Observations in Europe and the United States appeared to confirm his interpretations. Thus the 88-day rotational period of Mercury seemed demonstrated.

This conclusion, however, was challenged when, in 1965, scientists from Cornell University used the 1,000-foot radio telescope at Arecibo, Puerto Rico, to record radio pulses bounced off the surface of Mercury. The changes in frequency and the time delay in the returning pulses of radio energy provided measurements of both the rotational rate of the planet and its diameter. The rotational period for Mercury turned out to be 59 days, with an uncertainty of plus or minus 5 days, or two-thirds of the 88-day Mercurian year. In other words, the planet made three rotations while executing two revolutions around the sun. It was this coincidence of apparent surface features every other revolution that had confused the observers. In support of this new

Daylight photographs of Venus in five different phases taken through a yellow filter. The photographs show faint, irregular markings on the disk. In the crescent phase, extensions of the crescent horns beyond the geometric semicircle are produced by the planet's impenetrable atmosphere. (Earl C. Slipher, Lowell Observatory)

value, the French astronomers Audoin Dollfus and H. Camichel carefully reexamined the many photographs and drawings made at the observatories of Meudon and Pic du Midi and announced at the International Astronomical Union meeting in Prague in 1967 that their analysis had yielded a rotational period for Mercury of 58.646 ± 0.010 days.

Theoretical studies showed that the strong tides in the body of the planet produced this peculiar pattern of rotation and revolution. This condition is somewhat similar to that of our moon, except that the extremely elliptical orbit of Mercury brought about the condition of three rotations for two

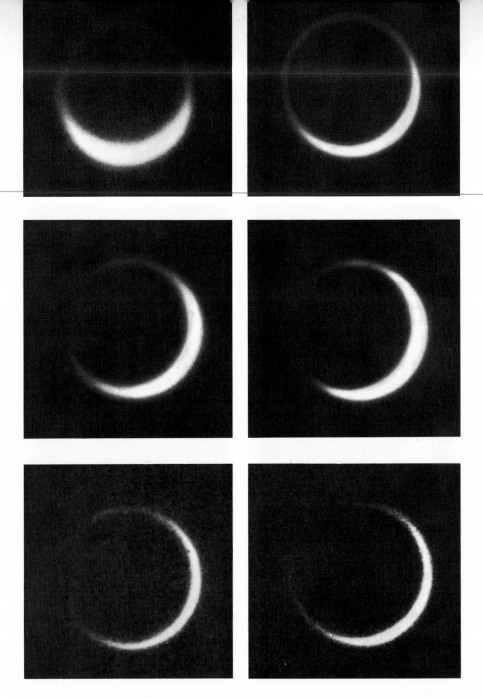

A series of photographs of Venus taken near inferior conjunction. The complete ring around the planet is caused by light scattered from the planet's atmosphere. (Earl C. Slipher, Lowell Observatory)

revolutions instead of the exact equality of periods shown by the moon. When nearest the sun, Mercury would have an orbital velocity that exceeded its rotational speed. Thus, an observer standing on Mercury would see a phenomenon unique in the solar system. For several days the sun would undergo a reversal of its motion across the sky and then double back, continuing its journey across the heavens. If the observer were located so that the sun were on the eastern horizon near perihelion, he could witness, in rapid succession, a sunrise followed by a sunset below the same horizon, and that followed by a second sunrise.

Early reliable temperature measurements of the surface of Mercury were carried out at Mt. Wilson by Edison Pettit (1890–1962). Using a thermocouple, he measured the amount of infrared energy radiated from the hot surface of the planet. When the planet was at perihelion, he found the temperature of the subsolar point was 610° K. This temperature is high enough to melt tin and lead. At aphelion, the point farthest from the sun, the planet is some 17,000,000 miles more distant from the sun and receives only half as much radiation. The temperature of the subsolar point at aphelion rises to only 558° K.

176

The amount of infrared radiation coming from the darkened side of the planet was too small to be measured. Hence one concludes that, during the long night, lasting 29 earth days, the surface rapidly cools to a very low temperature. Measurements with modern infrared detectors seemed to verify the low temperature of the night side of Mercury, establishing an upper limit of 150° K for this region. The surface of Mercury certainly embraces the greatest extremes in temperature of any planet in the solar system.

In the early 1960's, measurements made in the microwave region of the spectrum showed that the temperature of the daylight hemisphere was only some 300° K instead of 600° K. The two values are not inconsistent, however, since the radiant energy in this wavelength region originates in a layer of the planet slightly below the surface. The very hot layer, therefore, is only skin deep. Surprisingly, radiation in the 11 cm wavelength, which comes from a somewhat deeper layer, shows virtually no variation in intensity between the day and the night side of the planet. The estimates of 600° K surface temperatures are still correct, but it is now believed that just a few inches below the surface the temperature is a relatively constant, cool, and comfortable 300° K.

These observations should immediately have suggested that Mercury could not be in synchronous rotation. The only way for the dark side, forever screened from sunlight, to be heated would have been by thermal conduction from the hot, sunlit hemisphere. This method of heating is very inefficient and the temperature of the dark side, calculated theoretically, would be only 28° K.

Antoniadi and several other early observers claimed to have seen transient, low-contrast clouds, or haze, on the surface of Mercury, but modern observations have failed to verify such a condition. Probably Mercury does not have any appreciable atmosphere. Because the daylight portion of the planet is very hot, we would expect all but the heaviest gaseous constituents to have been driven off. In addition, Mercury has the lowest reflectivity of all planets, a characteristic of an opaque surface similar to that of the moon. Finally, a spectroscopic analysis of the sunlight scattered from the surface of Mercury gives no hint of an atmosphere.

Recently, Dollfus made a study of the polarization of the light from Mercury. The comparison of theory with these observations indicated that the surface pressures on Mercury are at most about 1 millibar, or $1/1000$ of the pressure at the earth's surface—very tenuous indeed. These studies also showed differences in the polarization of radiation coming from various parts of the surface of Mercury. These irregularities may arise from suspended clouds of dust or vapor released from the planetary interior and may explain the haze reported by early observers.

Although Mercury may appear to be an insignificant planet because of its small size and extremely thin atmosphere, it has made one outstanding contribution to the cause of science. The excess motion in the forward movement of the perihelion of Mercury, amounting to 43 arc seconds per century, had puzzled astronomers ever since the announcement of its discovery by Leverrier in 1859. In 1916 Albert Einstein (1879–1955) published his treatise on the General Theory of Relativity. One of the predictions in his theory was a precessional advance in the perihelion of 43.03 arc seconds per century, which turned out to be in precise agreement with observation.

Venus: The Veiled Planet

Since it is among the most luminous objects in the heavens, Venus is appropriately named for the goddess of beauty. It is the brightest of all the planets and only the sun and moon exceed it in brilliance. At maximum, Venus has a magnitude of —4.4, nearly 15 times brighter than Sirius, the brightest star in the sky. At night the light from Venus can cast a noticeable shadow. An observer who knows where to look can see the planet in broad daylight without the aid of a telescope.

Venus, like Mercury, is an inferior planet and seems to pass from one elongation to another in the course of its journey around the sun. It appears both as an evening and morning "star." Some ancient astronomers thought they were two different celestial bodies. They named the morning apparition after Phosphorus, bringer of light, and the evening apparition for Hesperus, son of Atlas. It was the Greek philosopher and mathematician Pythagoras who first realized that Phosphorus and Hesperus were the same astronomical body.

At elongation, the greatest angular distance of Venus from the sun can be as large as 48°. When observed through a telesope, the planet shows phases like those of our moon. Near inferior conjunction, we see only a thin crescent. The prolongations of the horns of the crescent that extend around the limb of the planet are the result of the scattering of sunlight by the atmosphere of Venus. When Venus lies very near the sun-earth line (corresponding to the phase of new moon) a delicate atmospheric halo encircles the entire planet. When the planet is farthest away, at superior conjunction, the entire disk, resembling a full moon, is visible.

As Venus moves from inferior to superior conjunction its distance from the earth increases by a factor of more than six. Venus reaches maximum brilliance about 36 days before and after inferior conjunction. The sidereal period of revolution of Venus is 224.7 days. The orbit is the most nearly circular of all the planets, the distance of the planet from the sun not varying by more than 1,000,000 miles from its mean distance of 68,270,000 miles. At inferior conjunction, it approaches to within 26,000,000 miles of the earth, closer than any other planet.

Since Venus has no satellite revolving around it, we must compute its mass from its gravitational pull on other bodies. The body that came nearest Venus and hence experienced the greatest deflection was the Mariner IV space probe in 1967. The mass was determined to be 0.815 that of our earth. Venus has a diameter of 7,600 miles and hence a mean density of 5.1. Because the size, mass, and density of Venus are much like those of the earth, it is sometimes referred to as earth's "sister planet." A dense layer of clouds continuously envelops the planet. In contrast to the low reflectivity of dark, solid surfaces like those of the moon and Mercury, Venus reflects almost three-fourths of the light falling upon it.

At times, shadowy markings on its surface have been observed, but they were so vague and transient that astronomers could not map them. Attempts to penetrate the cloud layer by means of infrared techniques have proved unsuccessful. Photographs taken in ultraviolet light reveal indistinct bands that probably are related to upper layers of the cloud structure. Because the surface of the planet is buried in what seem to be dense layers of clouds, determining the period of rotation appeared impossible. Efforts to measure Doppler shifts in the spectrum of Venus also failed. The period of rotation was finally determined, as for Mercury, by the analysis of radar pulses reflected from the surface of the planet. The returned signals revealed the presence of mountains and valleys on the surface. The sidereal period of rotation derived from these data is 243.1 ± 0.2 days. What is most surprising is that the rotation is not direct, as with the other planets, but retrograde.

Radio studies of Venus made from the earth's surface as well as from two Mariner fly-by probes have shown that, beyond all question, the surface of the planet is extremely hot, with a temperature perhaps as high as 600° K, which is nearly 600° F! This high temperature apparently results from the trapping of radiation by the lower atmosphere of the planet, called the "greenhouse effect." This temperature exceeds that of the hottest bake oven, though it still falls short of being red hot.

The atmosphere of Venus is very thick and far greater in density than that of the earth. In fact the pressure at the planet's surface exceeds that of the earth at sea level by a factor of at least 20. Most of the atmosphere is carbon dioxide, but some water vapor appears to be present. And traces of the noxious chemical hydrogen chloride (hydrochloric acid) as well as hydrogen fluoride

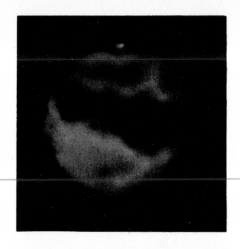

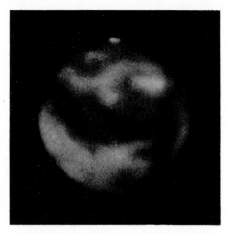

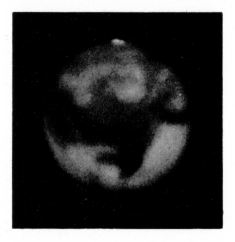

Photographs of Mars showing the planet's principal regions between approximately 0° and 180° west longitude and 70° north and south latitude. (Earl C. Slipher, Lowell Observatory)

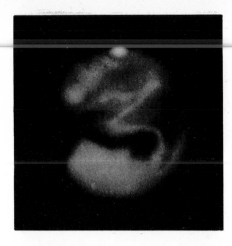

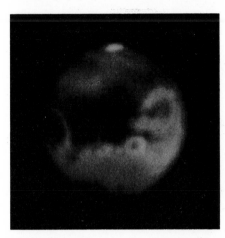

Photographs of Mars showing the planet's principal regions between approximately 0° and 180° east longitude and 70° north and south latitude. (Earl C. Slipher, Lowell Observatory)

(hydrofluoric acid) also occur. According to Gerard P. Kuiper, the Dutch-born American astronomer, the thick, opaque clouds of Venus contain a substance known as ferrous chloride dihydrate. Where this material comes from no one knows, but strong vertical convection may lift it all the way from the hot, dusty surface of the planet.

With reference to the tremendous amount of free carbon dioxide in the atmosphere of Venus, note that the earth's atmosphere may once have contained an equal amount of this chemical but that most of it is now locked up in the limestone of sedimentary rocks. Water, serving as a sort of catalyst, was very necessary to this process. If Venus had ever had great oceans, perhaps its atmosphere, too, would now be similar to the earth's.

Mars: The Red Planet

Ever since 1877, when Schiaparelli announced his discovery that a network of straight lines covered its surface, Mars (color plates 32, 33) has been the subject of much controversy. The American astronomer Percival Lowell (1855–1916) thought that the lines represented the work of intelligent beings, interpreting them as an elaborate system of canals that brought water from polar icecaps to arid equatorial regions. And many science fiction writers have since expanded on that theme, endowing Mars with highly varied forms of life, animal and vegetable.

The three successful fly-by probes of Mars, Mariners IV in 1964–5, and VI and VII in 1969, completely changed these traditional concepts of the planet. The earlier probe obtained 22 photographs, which were automatically scanned, encoded print by print, and then transmitted back to earth by radio in the form of separate picture elements, called "pixels." The pictures, reassembled by high-speed electronic computers, showed the Martian surface as heavily pockmarked with craters but with no trace of the "canals." The more recent pair of probes came to within 2,000 miles of the planet and obtained 200 pictures, 74 through Mariner VI and 126 through Mariner VII. These photographs showed an immense amount of detail, including thousands of craters, large and small. The similarity between Mars and the moon was clearly evident.

Astronomers quickly recognized that these craters, ranging from about 1,000 feet to several hundred miles in diameter, probably came from impacts by asteroids, a result of the proximity of Mars to the asteroid belt. Most of the alleged canals, patiently drawn by observers using terrestrial telescopes, proved to consist of irregularly-spaced, unrelated spots and dark patches, which the eye aligned and viewed as continuous. A few dark linear streaks remained, but these too may well disappear under closer scrutiny.

Of particular interest was the edge of the polar cap, with hundreds of craters partially or completely filled with white, frozen material. This material was once thought to be ice or hoar frost, but is now regarded as probably dry ice or a mixture of dry ice and snow. The surface of Mars seems rugged, forbidding, and even hostile. Many scientists who once believed that life could have developed on the planet are having second thoughts, but a final answer will have to wait for some years, that is until one of the probes can soft-land the proper equipment on Mars.

Various other facts have emerged from analysis of the basic data. Mars does have an atmosphere, consisting mainly of carbon dioxide. Traces of hydrogen and the lethal gas carbon monoxide were found but, strangely enough, no trace of nitrogen. The total amount of the Martian atmosphere above a given area is only about one per cent that of the earth. But, with the lower surface gravity of Mars, the atmosphere is not pulled down so firmly and thus the actual surface pressure is about $1/3$ of one per cent that at the earth's surface. Even so, the planet does have several distinct types of clouds. Like our earth, Mars also has an ionosphere, a layer of ionized gas whose maximum lies about 130 kilometers, or 80 miles, above the surface.

From measures made by Mariners VI and VII of the amount of heat received

Mars as photographed by Mariner VII from a distance of 293,000 miles. The white, circular patch is known as Nix Olympica. The dark patch toward the left edge is Lacus Solis, Lake of the Sun, often called the "eye of Mars" because of its resemblance to an eye with a dark pupil. The south polar cap is at the top. The features interpreted as "canals" by early observers have vanished, disolving into a multitude of fine detail. (NASA)

from the planet's surface, Gerry Neugebauer of the California Institute of Technology determined that the equatorial surface temperature reaches 60° F during the daytime, but falls to —100° F at night. As expected, the darker areas, which absorb more solar radiation, are warmer than the brighter ones.

The interaction of the Mariners with the gravitational pull of Mars gave a more accurate determination of the mass of the planet—0.107447—slightly more than 10 per cent that of the earth. However, magnetometers recorded no evidence whatever of any planetary magnetic field.

Since the orbit of Mars lies beyond that of the earth (fig. 12–1), the planet is best observed at opposition, when it is nearest the earth. Because its orbit is highly eccentric, Mars will be almost twice as close to the earth when it is in opposition near perihelion than when it is at aphelion. The synodic period of Mars is 780 earth days. Thus, the favorable oppositions with Mars near perihelion recur at intervals of seven or eight synodic periods, or every fifteen or seventeen years (fig. 12–2). These favorable oppositions always occur in late August. The last favorable opposition occurred in 1956; the next two will take place in 1971 and 1988.

Because Mars is a superior planet it does not, like the planet Venus, display the complete sequence of phases from crescent to full. When Mars is 90° away from the sun, it appears distinctly gibbous. Much of its surface has a distinct orange or reddish color, broken only by white patches in the polar regions and large dark areas. The red regions probably consist of sand or rock. The dark areas were once thought to be bodies of water and were called "maria," as were the darker areas of the moon.

At closest approach to the earth, Mars subtends an angle of about 25 seconds of arc. Knowing its distance we can compute its diameter—about 4,200 miles. The planet is actually slightly ellipsoidal, having an equatorial diameter of 4,220 miles and a polar diameter of 4,180 miles. The smallest features of Mars that can be discerned on photographs taken from the earth's surface are about 150 miles in extent. In those rare moments when atmospheric viewing conditions are at their best, experienced observers claim to have detected some features as small as 30 miles across. There is no evidence of mountain ranges such as we might recognize from shadows cast on the planetary surface or from irregularities at the shadowy boundary when Mars is in a gibbous phase. All experienced observers agree that the grosser surface features, such as the dark markings and the polar caps, are real and, except for seasonal variations, permanent; however, under close study with sensitive instruments they may appear very different from the features delineated by visual observers.

Like the earth, Mars rotates on its axis. The rotation period is quite accurately determinable from a study of permanent surface markings: the length of the sideral day is 24 hours 37 minutes 22.7 seconds, not greatly different from that of the earth. Since the diameter is 4,200 miles, the mean density turns out to be about four times that of water, or somewhat less than that of the earth. The force of Martian gravity is only 0.38 that of the earth; so that a man weighing 150 pounds on the earth would weigh only 57 pounds on Mars.

Like that of the earth, the equator of Mars is inclined about 24° to the plane of its orbit about the sun. The southern polar cap is pointed toward us at the most favorable oppositions. To study northern polar regions we must observe them at less favorable oppositions, when Mars is much farther away. Because of this inclination, Mars experiences seasons much like those of the earth. Since the Martian year is twice as long as the terrestrial year, the seasons are also twice as long.

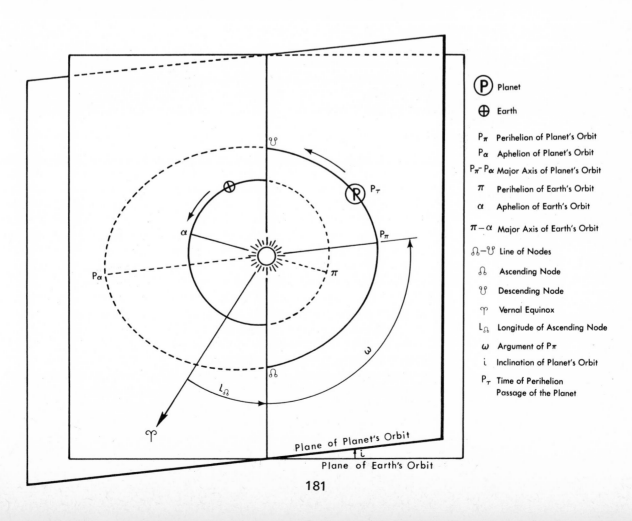

P	Planet
⊕	Earth
P_π	Perihelion of Planet's Orbit
P_α	Aphelion of Planet's Orbit
P_π-P_α	Major Axis of Planet's Orbit
π	Perihelion of Earth's Orbit
α	Aphelion of Earth's Orbit
$\pi - \alpha$	Major Axis of Earth's Orbit
☊–℧	Line of Nodes
☊	Ascending Node
℧	Descending Node
♈	Vernal Equinox
L_Ω	Longitude of Ascending Node
ω	Argument of $P\pi$
i	Inclination of Planet's Orbit
P_τ	Time of Perihelion Passage of the Planet

Plane of Planet's Orbit

Plane of Earth's Orbit

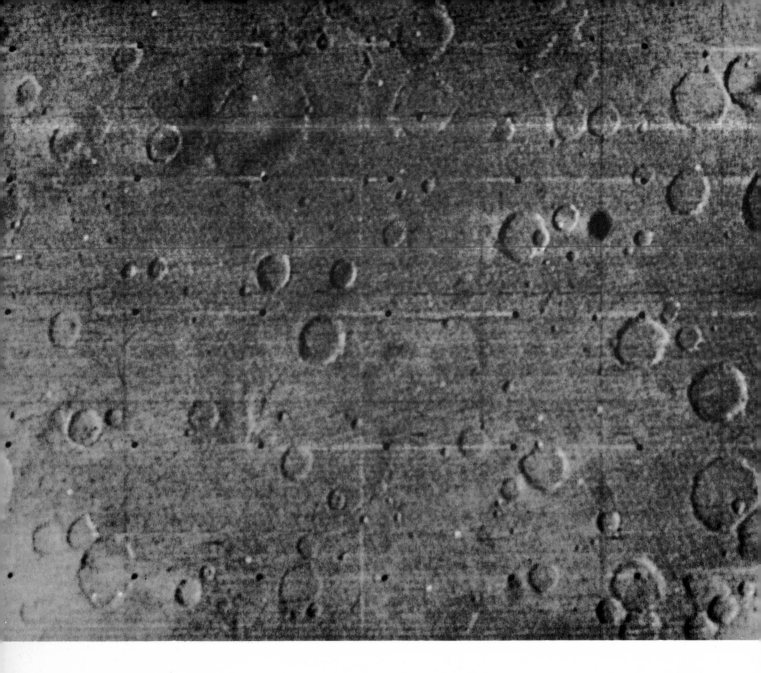

Mars in a photograph taken by Mariner VI from a distance of 2245 miles. The area photographed is about 450 by 620 miles. The abundance of craters is evident; those shown here range in diameter from about 3 to 80 miles. (NASA)

Definite seasonal changes in Martian features have been observed. The most conspicuous are the variations in size of the polar caps. As winter progresses in the southern hemisphere of Mars, the polar cap increases until nearly half of the hemisphere is covered. In the spring the polar cap diminishes, and it frequently disappears altogether with the coming of summer. The sequence in the northern hemisphere is similar except that the polar cap does not vanish completely during the summer and does not extend as far toward the equator during the winter. These differences result from the extremes in intensity of solar radiation received by the southern hemisphere. The orbital eccentricity causes hotter summers and colder winters in the southern hemisphere as compared with the northern hemisphere.

Intensifications of contrast and color changes in the dark areas also vary seasonally. These dark markings, the maria, are more prominent in whichever hemisphere the polar cap is receding. During the spring and summer, many dark areas appear to have a strong blue-green color, which fades with autumn and becomes brownish with the onset of winter. It is these seasonal variations that gave rise to the theory that the maria are areas of vegetation. Considerable haze and variable cloud formations, some of which move rapidly over the surface of the planet, are observed from time to time. The haze becomes evident when we compare photographs of Mars taken in red light

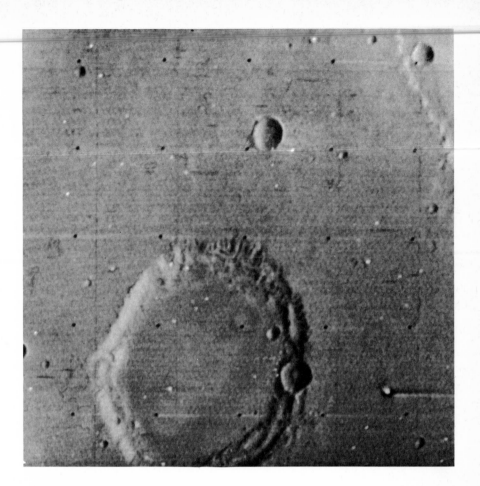

Mars as seen from Mariner VI at a distance of 2300 miles. This high-magnification photograph covers an area 63 by 48 miles. The large crater, about 24 miles across, shows many features similar to those of lunar craters. (NASA)

with those taken in blue light. At times, the blue haze clears briefly, affording an unhindered view of the surface. The reason for this "blue clearing" is unknown, but it is generally thought to be a property of the Martian surface rather than of the atmosphere.

Whitish clouds appear from time to time on Mars. Their movements resemble those of the more extensive systems of terrestrial clouds. Often they overlie the polar caps like a hood or canopy, covering them persistently throughout much of the late autumn and winter in each hemisphere. We can distinguish the clouds from the polar caps because they show up clearly in the blue photographs, although they are nearly invisible in the red; whereas the underlying polar caps show clearly in both blue and red light. Other white clouds occur at lower latitudes, forming in the late afternoon and persisting until well after local sunset. On occasion, they have risen high enough in the atmosphere to appear as projections beyond the terminator, that is, the night edge of the planet, and estimates of their height run up to 4.5 miles. Single clouds have been known to cover as much as 400,000 square miles of the surface of Mars. Apparently they dissipate during the night, since they are gone at sunrise and reappear only after midday. Studies of the polarization of sunlight scattered from these white clouds suggest they are composed of thin strata of frozen carbon dioxide.

Another type of cloud is a short-lived, bluish formation observed in the equatorial regions. These clouds persist for only a few hours near Martian sunrise and sunset. From his polarization studies, Dollfus concluded that these clouds were more likely to be liquid droplets than crystalline, solid particles.

Large, yellow clouds can also be observed in the Martian atmosphere probably no more than two to three miles above the surface of the planet. Although they can be seen on photographs taken in blue light, they are most

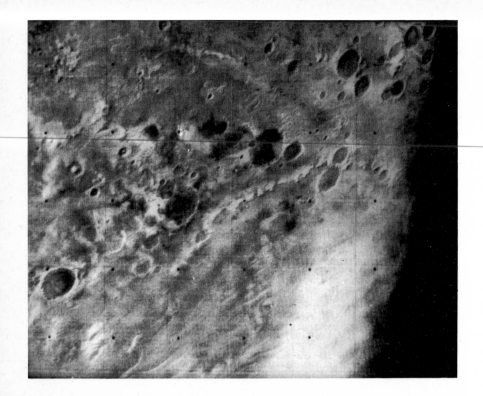

This photograph of Mars, by Mariner VII, shows the region of the south polar cap, and clearly illustrates the thinness of the Martian polar cap cover. A peculiar form called the "giant's footprint" (toward the right and slightly above center) is reproduced in higher magnification in the following photograph. (NASA)

clearly visible in red light. Antoniadi interpreted these clouds as dust storms generated by strong winds in the Martian deserts. These storms have been measured at velocities as high as 60 miles per hour and in some instances they have risen to a height of nearly twenty miles, well above the layers of white clouds. The clouds are most common during periods of warm weather, when Mars is near perihelion. During the favorable opposition of 1956, a dust storm that lasted several weeks obscured large areas of the planet.

Mars has two satellites, both discovered by Asaph Hall (1829–1907) of the United States Naval Observatory during the opposition of 1877. He aptly named them Phobos (fear) and Deimos (panic) after the two horses that drew the chariot of Mars, the god of war. It is interesting that almost three centuries earlier, Kepler had thought it possible that Mars possessed two moons. Even more remarkable was the fanciful description by Jonathan Swift in his *Gulliver's Travels* (1726) of astronomers in the land of Laputa who discover "two lesser stars, or satellites which revolve about Mars; whereof the innermost is distant from the center of the primary planet exactly three of his diameters, and the outermost, five; the former revolves in a space of ten hours, and the latter in twenty-one and a half . . ."

Phobos, the largest of the two satellites, revolves in an orbit only 5,850 miles from the center of Mars once every 7 hours 37 minutes. Phobos has the distinction of being the only natural satellite in the solar system revolving about its primary in a time shorter than the planetary "day," so that an observer on Mars would see Phobos rise in the west rather than in the east, and could witness two moonrises in a single night. Phobos is so close to the planet that, when the satellite is over the equator, observers at latitudes higher than 71° would be unable to see it. The smaller satellite, Deimos, is 14,400 miles from the center of the planet and revolves once every 30 hours 18 minutes, only a few hours longer than the Martian day. An observer on Mars would see Deimos rise very slowly in the eastern sky and take more than two days to pass to the western horizon. During this time Deimos would have completed two sets of lunar-like phases.

The satellites are so small that even in a large telescope they appear as points of light. If their surfaces have reflecting powers similar to that of

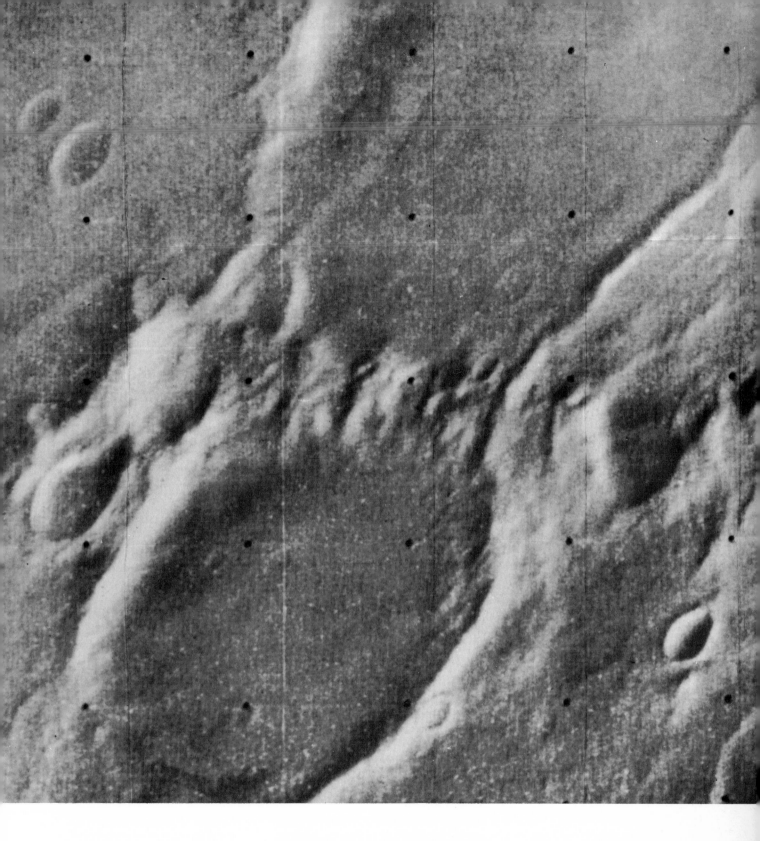

"Giant's footprint," two overlapping
Martian craters in an area of about 85
by 200 miles. (From Mariner VII,
NASA)

Mercury or the moon, their diameters, calculated from their apparent magnitudes, are 9.6 miles for Phobos and about 4.8 miles for Deimos—mere flyspecks compared with other satellites in the solar system.

Pluto: The Frontier Planet

Far out on the edge of the solar system lies the planet Pluto. It is the most remote and the faintest member of the family of known planets and it takes 248.4 years to go around the sun. Its orbit has an eccentricity of 0.249, greater than that of any other planet (fig. 12–3). At aphelion Pluto is 4.566

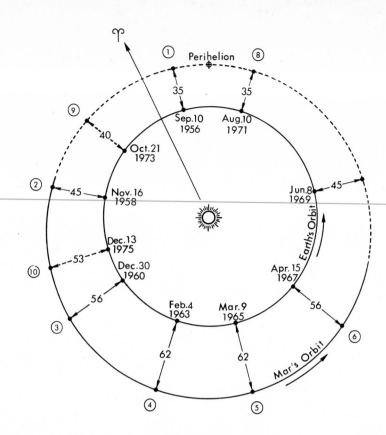

Figure 12–2. Oppositions of Mars. The figures, expressed in millions of miles, indicate the distance of Mars from the earth.

billion miles (49.12 A. U.) distant from the sun and, with an apparent magnitude at opposition of +15.9, is about 10,000 times too faint to be seen with the naked eye. At perihelion the planet approaches to within 2.766 billion miles (29.76 A. U.) of the sun and has an opposition magnitude of +13.6. The orbit is inclined 17° 08′ to the ecliptic, more than that of any other planet.

In 1914, the famous planetary observer Percival Lowell published the results of his analysis of the minute variations in the observed motion of Uranus. Lowell concluded that residual deviations in this motion could be explained only in terms of an unknown planet beyond Neptune. Lowell searched unsuccessfully for this unknown planet from 1905 until his death in 1916. The actual discovery of Pluto was made by Clyde W. Tombaugh, a research assistant at the Lowell Observatory in Flagstaff, Arizona, who was engaged in a systematic photographic search for the trans-Neptunian planet X. Using a blink comparator—described in an earlier chapter—Mr. Tombaugh scanned two plates that had been taken with a 13-inch refractor. He found an object that was within 6° of one of two alternate positions predicted years earlier by Lowell. The discovery of the planet was announced on March 12, 1930. The planet was named for Pluto, god of the underworld— quite appropriate for a planet moving in the dark outer regions of the solar system. Astronomers now agree quite generally that the discovery of Pluto so close to the place predicted by Lowell was just a happy accident. For it seems inconceivable that so small a planet could possess enough mass to have appreciably deflected the planets Uranus and Neptune.

When Pluto is near perihelion, as it will be in 1989, the planet will be actually closer to the sun than Neptune. Because of differences in the space orientation of their orbits there is no danger of collision between the two planets. The closest Pluto will approach Neptune is 240,000,000 miles. This proximity of the orbits of Pluto and Neptune has led to the suggestion that Pluto may at one time have been a satellite of Neptune. But recent studies indicate that gravitational interactions make it unlikely that there ever was a sustained planet-satellite relationship. The final answer to this question will

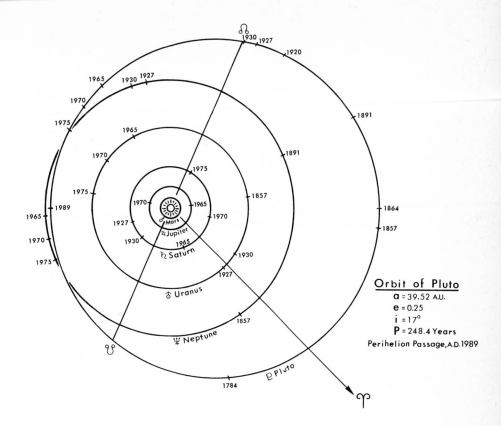

Orbit of Pluto
a = 39.52 A.U.
e = 0.25
i = 17°
P = 248.4 Years
Perihelion Passage, A.D. 1989

Figure 12–3. Orbit of Pluto in relation to orbits of the other outer planets of the solar system.

depend on a better understanding of the formation of planet-satellite systems.

The mass of Pluto, calculated from long-term observations of its perturbative effects on Neptune and Uranus, is about nine-tenths that of the earth. Interestingly enough, Lowell's calculation required this hypothetical planet to have a mass more than six times that of the earth. If Pluto had a density comparable to that of the earth and a reflecting power similar to that of Uranus and Neptune, the planet should have presented a disk 1 arc second in diameter and have an apparent magnitude of +12. In actual fact, the newly discovered planet showed no discernible disk, even when observed with the 24-inch refractor of the Lowell Observatory; and it was only about the 15th magnitude.

In 1950 G. P. Kuiper and M. L. Humason measured the diameter of Pluto with the 200-inch Hale telescope atop Mt. Palomar in California. They detected a disk 0.23 arc seconds in diameter, corresponding to a planetary diameter of 3,700 miles. In 1965 attempts were made to observe an occultation by Pluto of a star in the constellation Leo. Measurement of the duration of the occultation from several observatories enabled astronomers to determine the true diameter of Pluto. Although the occultation did not occur, the observations served to place an upper limit of 4,225 miles to the diameter of Pluto.

Recent observations of Pluto have revealed distinct fluctuations in brightness with an apparent period, as seen from the earth, of 6 days 9 hours 16 minutes 54 ± 26 seconds. This variation is interpreted as a rotation of the planet about an axis, where parts of the planetary surface, having different reflectivity, reappear periodically. The orientation of the rotational axis in space and the direction of rotation are as yet unknown.

From a human point of view, Pluto is not a particularly inviting planet. In all likelihood it possesses little or no atmosphere. Spectroscopically, no gases have been detected on it. The computed equilibrium temperature of Pluto is 63° K (—346° F). At such low temperatures the heavier gases would

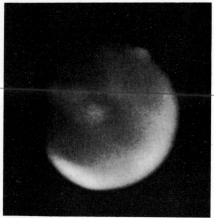
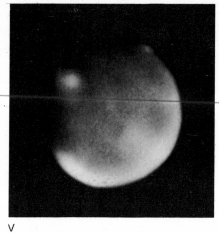
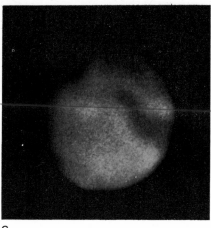

U-V   V   G

Six photographs of Mars taken in colors ranging from ultraviolet (U-V) through violet (V), green (G), yellow (Y), red (R), and infrared (I-R). The surface markings appear most clearly in the longer waves. Visible are the violet clouds near the terminator and also near the south polar cap at the top. (W. H. Wright, Lick Observatory)

be frozen out; the lighter ones, such as hydrogen and helium, would long since have escaped because of the low planetary mass.

Whether other planets are present in the solar system beyond Pluto, we cannot say. If there are any, they must either have a small mass or be very far away. Otherwise they would produce significant perturbations in the orbits of the outermost planets. Under such circumstances they would be quite faint and difficult to observe with any but the world's largest telescopes.

Elements of Orbits of Terrestrial Planets

	Mean Distance from Sun (A. U.)	(1,000,000 miles)	Sidereal Period (days)	Synodic Period (days)	Inclination to Ecliptic	Eccentricity
Mercury	0.39	36.0	87.97	115.88	7° 00'	0.206
Venus	0.72	67.2	224.70	583.92	3° 24'	0.007
Earth	1.00	92.96	365.26	—	—	0.017
Mars	1.52	141.6	686.98	779.94	1° 51'	0.093
Pluto	39.7	3,690.0	248.4*	366.74	17° 08'	0.253

* years   A. U. = Astronomical Units

Satellites of Mars

	Distance from Planet (10^3 miles)	Sidereal Period (days)	Orbit Inclination *	Orbit Eccentricity	Radius (miles)	m_v +	Discovery
Phobos	5.8	0.32	1°.8	0.019	5.0	11.5	Hall 1877
Deimos	14.6	1.26	1°.4	0.003	2.5	12.5	Hall 1877

* from planet's equator
+ mean mag. at opposition

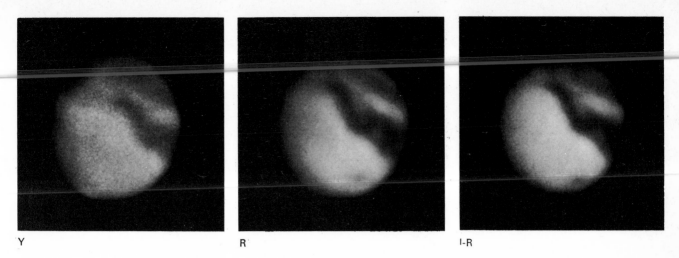

Y   R   I-R

Data for Terrestrial Planets

	Equatorial Radius (miles)	Equatorial Radius (earth = 1)	Volume (earth = 1)	Mass (earth = 1)	Density (g/cm^{-3})	Surface Gravity (m/sec^{-2})	Escape Velocity (m/sec^{-1})	Rotation Period	Inclination of Equator to Orbit
Mercury	1,504	0.38	0.05	0.0b	5.2	3.80	2.6	59 ± 3 days	28°
Venus	3,797	0.96	0.88	0.82	5.1	8.7	6.4	243.16 days	88°
Earth	3,963	1.00	1.00	1.00	5.52	9.78	7.0	23^{h}56^m 4.1^s	23° 27′
Mars	2,113	0.53	0.15	0.11	3.97	3.72	3.2	24^{h}37^{m}22.7^s	25° 12′
Pluto	1,860 ?	.47 ?	0.1 ?	0.8 ?	—	—	—	6.39 days	—

13

The Giant Planets

The four giant planets—Jupiter, Saturn, Uranus, and Neptune—are the largest in the solar system and have the lowest mean densities. One of them, Saturn, has a density so low that it would float on water if one could find a lake big enough to hold it. Except for Pluto, they lie farthest from the sun and receive only small amounts of solar radiation. Their chemical makeup is more like that of the sun than that of the earth. Hydrogen and helium must be their principal constituents.

Jupiter: The Giant Planet

Aptly named after the supreme Roman deity, Jupiter (color plate 31) is the largest and most massive planet in the solar system. Its mass is twice that of all the other planets combined. Among the family of planets, only Venus and occasionally Mars surpass Jupiter in brilliance. Because it rotates rapidly, the planet is very oblate, the polar diameter being about 6 per cent less than the equatorial.

As seen through a telescope, the most distinguishing characteristic of Jupiter is the system of dark and light belts that cross its yellowish face. These belts can easily be seen even with a small telescope or a pair of binoculars.

A bright band marks Jupiter's equatorial zone. On either side of this band lie the North and South Equatorial Belts, normally the most conspicuous features of the belt system. Adjacent to the Equatorial Belts are the North and South Tropical Zones. Next come the alternating Temperate Belts and Zones and, finally, the polar regions. At times the belts are divided into two or three parts. Variations of color, ranging from pink to blue, appear within the belts, principally in those at lower latitudes. The zones between the belts are generally white or pale yellow, with the polar caps usually gray but occasionally greenish.

Many kinds of irregularities appear in the belt system, some showing up as dark and others as light. They range from circular and elongated shapes to wisps and streaks, and often several of these link together to give a mottled or braided appearance that continually fluctuates in appearance.

An observer of Jupiter gets the distinct impression that he is viewing turbulent cloud formations that undergo changes in structure in a matter of hours, probably as a result of systems of currents that are an integral part of Jupiter's atmosphere. We do not know what processes give rise to these movements, but clearly the planet does not have a visible solid surface like that of the moon or Mars.

The most striking feature in Jupiter's cloud layer is the "Great Red Spot." It was first observed in 1665 by Jean D. Cassini (1625–1712), a French astronomer. The Spot, oval in shape, is approximately 30,000 miles in length by 7,000 miles in breadth, with its longer dimension parallel to the equator. Over the years it has undergone changes in size, shape, and coloration. In 1878 it became an intense brick-red, but has since then faded considerably and fluctuated in visibility.

A remarkable aspect of the Great Red Spot is its tendency to drift in longitude, as if it were a ship or floating island. Records over a span of three centuries indicate that the Spot has wandered as much as three complete rotations. From about 1830 to 1890 it lagged behind the rest of the planet

Saturn and its ring system. (Hale Observatories)

by as much as 1 1/2 rotations. Then it began to reverse its direction, and since then has moved irregularly, sometimes more rapidly and sometimes more slowly than its surroundings. An interesting interaction took place in 1902 between the Great Red Spot and a broad darkened area that became known as the Southern Tropical Disturbance. The disturbance first appeared in 1901 and was located about 90° ahead of the Spot. Because its rotation period was 21 seconds shorter than that of the Spot, the latter caught up to it in June 1902. The edge of the disturbance accelerated as it passed through the Spot and for a time actually appeared to drag the Spot along. This interaction repeated itself many times over the next forty years until the disturbance finally faded away in 1940.

No satisfactory explanation has been given for either the Spot or its peculiar behavior. Theorists have variously described it as a cyclone, a floating "island" of particles, and an atmospheric effect caused by volcanic activity far below the cloud layers. One recent theory suggests that it is a manifestation at cloud level of an irregularity on the solid surface of Jupiter. The airflow over this topographical feature would be relatively stagnant compared with the surrounding atmosphere. The drift in longitude can be explained on the assumption that slippage takes place between a fluid core and a thin outer mantle. We still do not know whether the Spot is an aggregate of particles

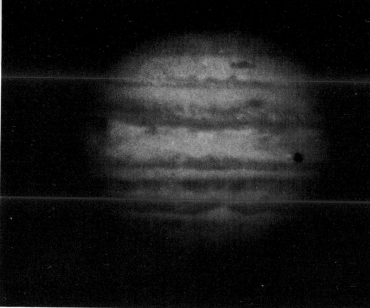

Left: The planet Jupiter photographed in yellow light. (L'Observatoire du Pic du Midi)

Right: Jupiter with the shadow of one of its satellites. (L'Observatoire du Pic du Midi)

or an atmospheric circulation. Nor do we know what substances cause its red color.

Jupiter rotates on its axis more rapidly than any other planet. Near the equator the rotational period is 9 hours 50.5 minutes, more rapid that at intermediate latitudes; in the polar regions the period is about five minutes longer. The periods were determined visually from the intervals between successive passages of well-defined features across the central meridian. The disadvantage of this method of analysis is that the irregularities in Jupiter's cloud layers are undergoing continuous changes in form and position. Thousands of observations over several decades, however, have established the reliability of the accepted figure.

The atmospheres of all four of the giant planets show absorption bands from the molecules of methane (CH_4) and molecular hydrogen (H_2). Jupiter also shows bands of ammonia (NH_3). Evidently the intensity of the ammonia bands decreases with distance from the sun whereas those of methane increase. This effect must be the result of surface temperature, which diminishes with increasing distance. Other gaseous constituents such as helium, neon, argon, and complex organic molecules are probably present. Confirmation of the existence of these gases will require more elaborate spectrographs and more sophisticated detectors, including observations from orbiting telescopes outside the earth's atmosphere.

In 1952 the American astronomers William A. Baum and Arthur D. Code observed the occultation of a faint star by Jupiter and watched it fade through the atmosphere of the planet. Using this observation they found a low value for the mean molecular weight of the gases above the cloud tops, indicating that they consist primarily of hydrogen and helium. The temperature of Jupiter at cloud-top levels is about 150° K, and the atmospheric pressure is similar to that on earth at sea level. Although methane would be gaseous under these conditions, most of the ammonia present would be frozen. Thus the gaseous ammonia we detect above the cloud tops must have evaporated from the solid particles of frozen gas crystals suspended in the atmosphere much like ice crystals in the atmosphere of the earth.

The central core of Jupiter is thought to be composed of a mass of solid rock surrounded by an extensive shell of metallic hydrogen, with pressures more than a million times greater than that at the surface of the earth. Oceans of liquid hydrogen float on top of the solid layer. We regard the liquid "sea" as the "surface" of the planet. Above this surface lie various cloud layers of ammonia and water in both crystalline and vapor forms. The surface temperature is estimated to be 2,000° K and the pressure 200,000 times that at the earth's surface. Hydrogen constitutes more than 76 per cent of the mass of the planet and helium about 22 per cent.

From time to time and for reasons still unknown, Jupiter sends out powerful blasts of radio static over several ranges of wavelengths. Some of these resemble the crackling noises heard in radio receivers during a heavy thunderstorm. Others may arise from free electrons whirling in the magnetic field of the planet. These sudden blasts appear to be triggered by the action of Io, one of Jupiter's main satellites. The emission also appears to be concentrated in fairly sharp beams rather than dispersed at random, for we get repetitions of the bursts once every revolution of the planet. This phenomenon has, in fact, enabled astronomers to check the visual determinations of the rotation period of Jupiter.

Jupiter has twelve known satellites. The four largest—Io, Europa, Ganymede, and Callisto—called the Galilean satellites, were discovered by Galileo in 1610 shortly after he constructed his first telescope. A fifth satellite was not detected until 1892, when Edward E. Barnard (1857–1923) found the tiny moon revolving about Jupiter only 68,000 miles from its surface. The other seven satellites are very small and so faint that a telescope would be necessary to observe them even from Jupiter. The Galilean satellites are bright enough to be seen by the unaided eye. Only the overwhelming brilliance of the planet itself prevented their discovery even earlier. They are large, and a good-sized telescope can pick up faint surface markings. The smallest, Europa, has a diameter of 2,000 miles, about that of our moon; the largest, Ganymede, is 3,200 miles across, or as large as Mercury. All four have nearly circular orbits close to the plane of Jupiter's equator. Although the Galilean satellites are massive enough to have an atmosphere, spectrographic studies have failed to reveal any gases. Observations of Io after an eclipse by Jupiter show a slight temporary brightening as the satellite emerges from the shadow cone; this has been attributed to ice crystals that froze out of the atmosphere as Io cooled during the eclipse.

The Galilean moons frequently undergo transits, occultations, and eclipses as they revolve about Jupiter—phenomena that can be studied with even a small telescope. (An occultation occurs whenever a satellite passes behind the disk of Jupiter.) The Galilean satellites proved outstandingly useful to science when observations of their eclipses led to an estimate of the finite velocity of light. Ole Roemer (1644–1710), a Danish astronomer, noticed that eclipses occurred about 16 minutes (1,000 seconds) earlier when Jupiter was at opposition than when it was near conjunction on the opposite side of the sun. He attributed the difference to the time necessary for light to cross the diameter of the earth's orbit, 186,000,000 miles. This gave a figure of 186,000 miles per second for the speed of light (fig. 13–1).

The outer seven satellites fall into two groups. The inner group, VI, VII,

Figure 13–1. Roemer's method of determining the velocity of light from observations of eclipses of Jupiter's satellites (J_1 and J_2) from the earth at positions E_1 and E_2. Since the path J_2E_2 is longer than J_1E_1 by about the diameter of the earth's orbit, Roemer attributed the late occurrence of eclipses observed from E_2 to the time required for light to traverse the earth's orbit.

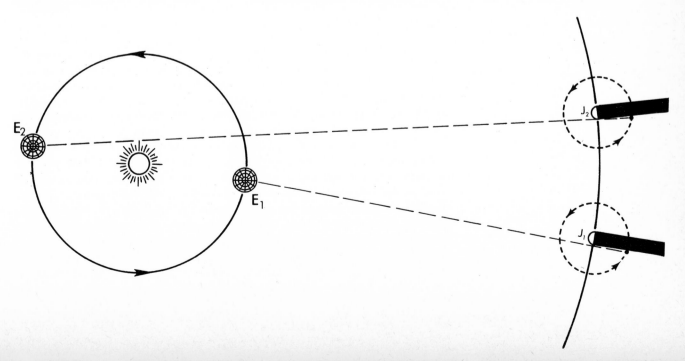

and X, is situated about 7,000,000 miles from Jupiter. The outer group, XII, XI, VIII, and IX, is located more than twice as far from the planet.

Saturn: The Ringed Planet

Saturn (color plate 34) is the most distant of the planets known to the astronomers of antiquity. As seen in a telescope, it is a magnificent object. Like Jupiter, it has a series of dark and light bands that parallel its equator. The bands are more regular than those on Jupiter, but they are less distinct and less brilliant in color. Mottling and occasional light spots are also much less evident on Saturn.

The disk of the planet is a distinctive yellowish color, the equatorial regions are a faint reddish hue, the belts have a brownish cast, and the polar regions are blue-green. These colors occasionally vary, but they are particularly evident when we compare photographs taken in red, yellow and blue light.

Saturn's mean distance from the sun is 887,100,000 miles (9.54 A. U.), and one complete revolution about the sun requires 29.46 years. It is the second largest planet in the solar system. Like Jupiter, it is quite oblate, the equatorial diameter of 75,200 miles being 10 per cent more than the polar diameter. As we have noted, the planet has a mean density of 0.68, smaller than that of any other planet in the solar system, and even less than that of water.

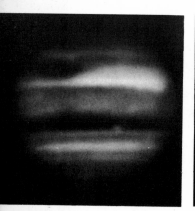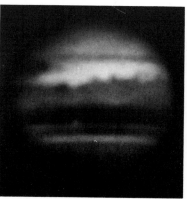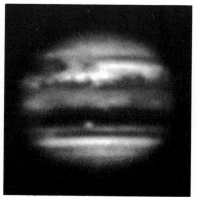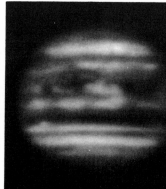

Four photographs of the same face of Jupiter taken in blue light and showing rapid changes. (Earl C. Slipher, Lowell Observatory)

The rings of Saturn lie in the plane of its equator. During the course of one Saturnian year we are able to see the ring system from above as well as below. When Saturn is near one of its solstices, that is, when the axis of rotation is pointed either toward or away from us, the planet appears almost circular. The ring system, on the other hand, opens up and presents the maximum area to the observer. As the planet approaches the equinoctial positions, when we see the rings edge on, the ellipsoidal shape of the planet is clearly evident. The angular tilt of the rings diminishes until at the equinoctial positions the rings appear as a very thin line or may even vanish for a few hours as the earth goes through the exact plane of the rings. The apparent tilt of the rings significantly affects the brightness of Saturn.

The rings were first observed by Galileo in 1610. However, he could not identify their true nature with his rudimentary telescope. He actually thought the planet was a triple one, and when some years later the earth went through the plane of the rings and he could no longer see its two companions, he invoked an ancient myth when he querulously commented, "Can Saturn have swallowed his children?" More than forty years passed before the Dutch astronomer Huygens gave the first accurate description of the rings.

Three concentric rings encircle Saturn. The broadest and most brilliant is the main ring, designated B. Outside the main ring lies a moderately bright ring, A, with an overall diameter of 171,000 miles. Just inside the main ring, a very faint ring, C, also known as the "Crepe" ring, girds the planet. The inside edge of ring C comes to within 7,000 miles of the sphere of the planet. Between the main ring and the outside ring there is a dark gap of about 2,500 miles, called "Cassini's division" after its French discoverer. The thickness probably does not exceed about 10 miles and may be considerably smaller.

In October 1969, French astronomer P. Guerin of the Institut d'Astrophysique discovered still another ring. It occurs inside ring C and extends into the planet itself but is separated from C by a division as distinct as Cassini's. The newly-discovered ring is very faint, having a brightness less than 5 per cent that of ring B, and it grows even fainter as it approaches the surface of the planet.

The rings are believed to be composed of swarms of minute particles, intermediate in size between fine dust and gravel. The particles move independently, as if each were a satellite in its own right. Analysis of the light reflected by the rings suggests that a layer of frost or ice covers the particles in them. The rings are definitely not solid or liquid layers. Stars can be seen through them and satellites located in their shadow remain faintly visible. This conclusion is borne out by studies of the motion of the rings. If the rings rotated as a solid body, the outside edge, like the rim of a phonograph record, would have a greater linear velocity than a point nearer the planet. On the other hand, if the rings had a discontinuous structure, with each mass or

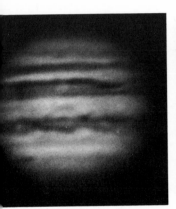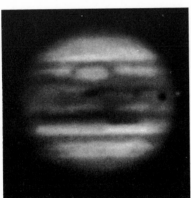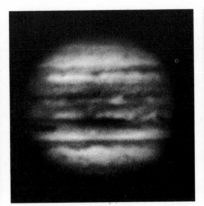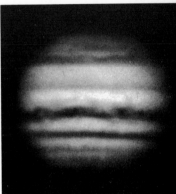

The belts of Jupiter in disturbed and quiescent states. (Earl C. Slipher, Lowell Observatory)

particle obeying Kepler's laws of motion, the particles farthest out would move more slowly. In 1895, James E. Keeler (1857–1900) of the Allegheny Observatory used a spectrograph and the Doppler effect to demonstrate that the outermost edges of the rings do indeed move more slowly than the inside sections (fig. 13–2). The spectral lines from the inner and outer edges had different displacements because of this differential in the speed of rotation.

In 1850, E. Roche (1820–1883) showed that gravitational forces would disrupt a satellite approaching a planet too closely because the part nearest the planet would tend to revolve in an orbit more rapidly than the outer portion, thus tearing the object to pieces. For a satellite and planet of the same density, this breakup occurs 2.44 planetary radii away from the center of the primary body. Mimas, the nearest known satellite of Saturn, lies outside this critical distance, but the rings lie entirely within it. The rings may have been either a satellite that fragmented, or material that was never able to coalesce in the early formative stages of the satellite system.

The gravitational pull of a satellite on the ring structure moves the particles around and produces Cassini's division. A particle located in the gap would revolve twice during a single revolution of Mimas, the innermost satellite. Thus, every second revolution the particle would come back to the same point and be subject to a second pull from Mimas. In this way a region

195

Various aspects of Saturn, 1933-1940.
(Earl C. Slipher, Lowell Observatory)

relatively free of particles eventually develops. Similar cumulative effects have created other gaps and contributed to the diffuseness of the Crepe ring.

A family of nine satellites accompanies Saturn in its journey about the sun. Audoin Dollfus tentatively identified a tenth satellite in 1966 when the ring system appeared edge-on. The satellite, named Janus, was photographed as a faint 14th-magnitude object located just 13,000 miles off the edge of the outermost ring. This moon was estimated to move in a nearly circular orbit with a rotation period of 17 hours 58 minutes. To confirm its presence, scientists must wait until 1981, when the ring system will again be observed edge-on.

In 1655 Huygens discovered the brightest of the Saturnian moons, Titan. With a diameter of 3,000 miles, Titan is far larger than any of the other eight satellites and has the distinction of being the only satellite in the solar system known to have an atmosphere. In 1944 G. P. Kuiper detected bands of the gas methane in the spectrum of Titan. This satellite retains its atmosphere whereas the more massive Ganymede, satellite of Jupiter, has failed to do so. This may have occurred because Titan is farther from the sun than Ganymede and therefore colder and less likely to lose its atmosphere by evaporation into space.

The slow variations in brightness that the satellites exhibit while orbiting the planet indicate that all nine of them keep the same face turned toward Saturn. The changes are apparently caused by surfaces that are not uniformly bright all over. These fluctuations are fairly small for all except the eighth satellite, Iapetus. Its brightness varies by more than two magnitudes during one revolution, resulting from the fact that one side has a reflectivity about six times higher than the other side.

The first seven satellites orbit the planet in the plane of the rings. The two outermost satellites, Iapetus and Phoebe, have orbits considerably inclined to the plane of the rings. Phoebe, the most distant moon, was found by William H. Pickering in 1898 and was the first satellite discovered by photographic methods. It is located 8,000,000 miles away from Saturn and orbits the planet in 550 days 11 hours. The satellite moves in a retrograde fashion, from east to west, whereas the others revolve in a direct manner.

Uranus: Herschel's Planet

Uranus was discovered on March 13, 1781 by one of the greatest observers in the history of astronomy—Sir William Herschel. Using a small seven-inch telescope that he had constructed himself, Herschel came upon Uranus unexpectedly while examining the sky in the vicinity of H Geminorum. Coming on an object that looked like an extended disk, quite different from the point-like stellar images nearby, Herschel thought he had discovered a comet. After many months of observation and calculation, he found that the orbit of the "comet" was fairly circular and lay well beyond the orbit of Saturn. The object was clearly a planet. Several names, including "Herschel," were proposed for the new planet, but it was finally named Uranus, after the mythological god of the skies.

Unlike Mercury, Venus, Mars, Jupiter, and Saturn, which were all naked-eye objects and were known to the earliest astronomers, Uranus was unknown to the ancients. Because of its distance from the sun, Uranus receives less than $1/360$ the amount of light falling upon the earth. At opposition, the planet has a magnitude of $+5.51$, just above the threshold of visibility for the unaided eye. At its strongest, Uranus has the appearance of only a faint star.

Because the planet presents a disk less than 4 arc seconds in diameter, useful observations of Uranus require a large telescope. Under good observing conditions, one can detect the slightly greenish color of the planet. Markings in the form of faint gray belts appear at a point parallel to the equator, but they are too indistinct to help determine the rotation period of the planet. As with Jupiter and Saturn, the brightness of the planetary disk decreases towards the limb.

Remarkably, the axis of rotation of Uranus lies nearly in the plane of its

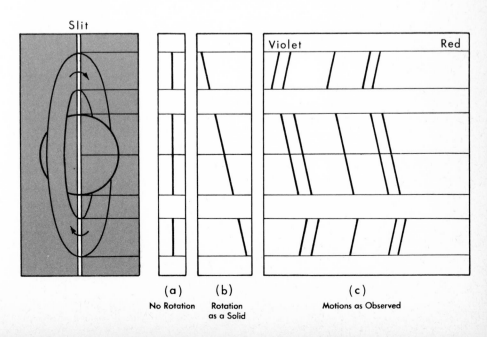

Figure 13–2. The spectra of Saturn and its rings, showing the displacement of the lines caused by rotation: (a) the spectral line that would come from a non-rotating planet and ring; (b) the spectral line as it would appear from connected body and ring; (c) actual situation of Saturn, showing the uniform rotation of the planet and the non-uniform rotation of the rings. The outer elements move more slowly than the inner elements.

Slit

Violet   Red

(a)   (b)   (c)
No Rotation   Rotation   Motions as Observed
               as a Solid

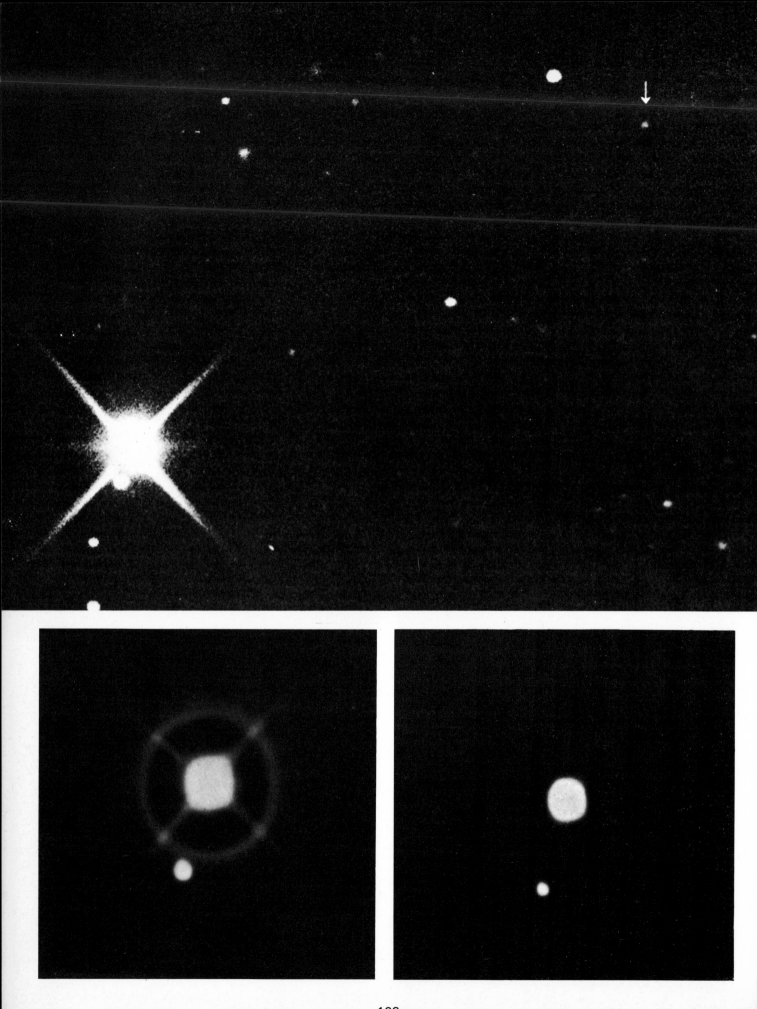

orbit. The plane of the equator intersects the plane of the orbit at an angle of almost 98°, more than a right angle. At certain positions in Uranus' orbit, one of the poles will point towards the earth. At such times, the belt-like markings are on the periphery of the disk and not readily visible. An observer standing on a pole of Uranus pointing toward the earth would have the sun near the zenith. The length of a day for that observer would equal the length of a Uranus year, 84 earth-years. The sun would remain above his horizon continuously for almost half that time. This phenomenon is an exaggerated version of the "midnight" sun as seen from the earth's north pole.

Uranus has five satellites: Miranda, Ariel, Umbriel, Titania, and Oberon. Miranda, the most recently discovered moon, was found by Kuiper in 1948. All five revolve in the same direction that the planet rotates. With diameters of only a few hundred miles, they are very faint. Their orbits, all nearly circular, lie in the equatorial plane of Uranus. From the satellite periods, we can determine the mass of Uranus as 14.5 times that of the earth.

Because of the indistinctness of the markings on Uranus, astronomers have had to employ the more difficult spectrographic techniques and the Doppler displacements of spectral lines at the limbs of the plane to determine its rotational period. The period of 10 hours 45 minutes thus obtained agrees well with the figure of 10 hours 49 minutes derived from the brightness changes caused by rotation of the planet. The temperature of Uranus is never more than 103° K (—274° F!) even on the sunlit side of the planet. One result of this is that the spectrum fails to reveal any ammonia, which is undoubtedly completely frozen out. The temperature range between Jupiter and Uranus clearly brackets the freezing point of ammonia: Jupiter at 135° K has the gas in abundance, Saturn at 125° K shows it faintly if at all, and Uranus has none.

Neptune: The Blue Planet

The discovery of Neptune in 1846 represented a monumental triumph for mathematical astronomy. Several decades of observations of the newly-found planet Uranus had shown that no simple computed orbit matched all the observed positions even when the perturbative effects of Jupiter and Saturn were taken into consideration. The discrepancies between the observations and the theoretical path far exceeded the possible errors. Some astronomers speculated that the force of gravitation began to fail at such great distances from the sun. Others argued that an unknown planet was affecting the motion of Uranus, pulling it out of its calculated orbit. Then in 1846, the French astronomer Urbain J. J. Leverrier (1811–1877), after a complex analysis of the problem, predicted the position of the perturbing planet. He sent his results to a German observer in Berlin, Johann Galle (1812–1910); the following day Galle found the planet within a degree of its predicted location.

Unknown to Leverrier, a young English mathematician, John C. Adams (1819–1892), had made similar calculations and arrived at a set of predicted positions a few years earlier. In the fall of 1843, Adams sent his results to the Astronomer Royal, Sir George B. Airy (1801–1892), requesting that a search be made for the planet. Airy, however, had no confidence in either the ability of the youthful Adams or his theoretical methods and failed to take advantage of his opportunity. The contribution of Adams has since been recognized and both Leverrier and Adams share the honor of discovering Neptune.

The planet, of magnitude +7.85 at opposition, is invisible to the unaided eye. Since its discovery 123 years ago, it has completed less than three-fourths of a single orbit around the sun.

Neptune has two known satellites. The larger of the two, Triton, named after Neptune's son, was discovered in 1846 by the English astronomer William Lassell (1799–1880) within weeks after the discovery of the planet itself. With an estimated diameter of 2,500 miles and a distance from the primary of 220,000 miles, Triton bears a striking resemblance to our moon. Its mass is 1.9 times that of the moon. In 1930 Joseph H. Moore and Donald

Neptune and its two satellites. Top: An exposure showing Triton and Nereid (arrow). Fuzzy spots in the background are distant galaxies. Bottom: Two photographs showing Neptune and Triton below the planet. (G. P. Kuiper, McDonald Observatory)

H. Menzel determined the character of the planet's rotation by spectrographic methods at Lick Observatory. The plane of the virtually circular orbit of Triton intersects the plane of Neptune's rotation at an angle of 20.1°. It is noteworthy that while the planet rotates in a direct manner, Triton moves in a retrograde orbit. This behavior contrasts with the direct motion of the more distant satellite, Nereid. Only the outermost satellites of Jupiter and Saturn move in retrograde orbits.

The second satellite, Nereid, discovered by Kuiper in 1949, can be observed only photographically. It is a very small body, less than 130 miles in diameter, and has an apparent magnitude of +19.5, well beyond the limit of smaller telescopes. Nereid's orbit has an eccentricity of 0.76, higher than any other satellite in the solar system. It can approach to within 900,000 miles of Neptune or range as far away as 6,000,000 miles. Nereid takes 360 days to revolve about Neptune.

Like Uranus, Neptune has a greenish-blue color attributable to the presence of methane in the atmosphere. Small amounts of hydrogen have also been detected there. At Neptune's cloud-top temperatures of 108° K (—265° F), any ammonia present would be solid and not visible in the upper atmosphere. No prominent markings appear on the planet, except for hints of a belt system parallel to the equator.

No one can say whether or not other planets exist beyond Pluto, although the immense surveys of the sky made with the great 40-inch Schmidt telescope at Mount Palomar showed no objects that might be planets. Still farther out, perhaps halfway to the nearer stars, lies the comet shell.

Elements of Orbits of Giant Planets

	Mean Distance from Sun (A. U.)	Mean Distance from Sun (1,000,000 miles)	Sidereal Period (years)	Synodic Period (days)	Inclination to Ecliptic	Eccentricity
Jupiter	5.20	484	11.86	398.9	1° 18'	0.048
Saturn	9.52	885	29.46	378.1	2° 29'	0.053
Uranus	19.27	1,791	84.02	396.7	0° 46'	0.051
Neptune	30.21	2,808	164.79	367.5	1° 46'	0.004

A. U. = Astronomical Units

Data for Giant Planets

	Equatorial Radius (1,000 miles)	Equatorial Radius (earth=1)	Volume (earth=1)	Mass (earth=1)	Density (g/cm^{-3})	Surface Gravity (m/sec^{-2})	Escape Velocity (m/sec^{-1})	Rotation Period	Inclination of Equator to Orbit
Jupiter	44.6	11.04	1,347	317.8	1.30	23.01	35.7	9^{h}50^m	3° 4'
Saturn	37.5	9.17	771	95.1	0.68	9.06	20.6	10^{h}14^m	26° 44'
Uranus	14.6	3.70	51	14.5	1.58	9.72	13.4	10^{h}49^m	98°
Neptune	13.9	3.50	43	17.2	2.22	13.47	15.3	15^h+	29°

Name	Mean Distance (10³ miles)	Sidereal Period	Visual Magnitude	Motion	Radius (miles)	Discovery	
Jupiter							
1 Io	262	$1^d18^h28^m$	4.8 variable	D	1,103	Galileo	1610
2 Europa	417	3 13 14	5.2 variable	D	963	Galileo	1610
3 Ganymede	665	7 03 43	4.5 variable	D	1,740	Galileo	1610
4 Callisto	1,168	16 16 32	5.5 variable	D	1,570	Galileo	1610
5	113	0 11 57	13.	D	34 ?	Barnard	1892
6	1,127	250 14	13.7	D	25 ?	Perrine	1904
7	7,295	259 16	16.	D	20 ?	Perrine	1905
8	14,500	738 22	18.8	R	<10	Melotte	1908
9	14,700	758	18.3	R	<10	Nicholson	1914
10	7,276	263 13	18.6	D	<10	Nicholson	1938
11	13,900	692 12	18.1	R	<10	Nicholson	1938
12	12,900	631 02	18.8	R	<10	Nicholson	1951
Saturn							
1 Mimas	116	$0^d22^h37^m$	12.1	D	150:	Herschel	1789
2 Enceladus	148	1 08 53	11.8	D	200:	Herschel	1789
3 Tethys	183	1 21 18	10.3	D	310	Cassini	1684
4 Dione	234	2 17 41	10.4	D	275:	Cassini	1684
5 Rhea	327	4 12 25	9.8 variable	D	470	Cassini	1672
6 Titan	760	15 22 41	8.4	D	1,500	Huygens	1655
7 Hyperion	920	21 06 38	14.2	D	50 ?	W. Bond	1848
8 Iapetus	2,210	79 07 56	11.0 variable	D	250 ?	Cassini	1671
9 Phoebe	8,030	550 11	14.7	R	50 ?	Pickering	1898
10 Janus	100	0 17 59	14.	D	?	Dollfus	1966
Uranus							
1 Ariel	120	$2^d12^h29^m$	14.4	R	250 ?	Lassell	1851
2 Umbriel	166	4 03 38	15.3	R	175 ?	Lassell	1851
3 Titania	272	8 16 56	14.0	R	300 ?	Herschel	1787
4 Oberon	364	13 11 07	14.2	R	250 ?	Herschel	1787
5 Miranda	81	1 09 56	16.5	R	93 ?	Kuiper	1948
Neptune							
1 Triton	220	$5^d21^h03^m$	13.6 variable	R	1,150	Lassell	1846
2 Nereid	3,460	359 10	18.7:	D	100 ?	Kuiper	1949

d = days	D = direct	< = less than
h = hours	R = retrograde	: = approximately
m = minutes		

14

Asteroids, Comets, and Meteors

We are so accustomed to the dominating influence of the sun and the march of the moon and brighter planets across the sky that we tend to ignore the myriads of less conspicuous members of our solar family. Some of them may be classed as minor planets; others are little more than interplanetary debris that reveal themselves in a glowing fireball flashing through the atmosphere, possibly leaving meteoritic remnants on the ground, or in a comet that draws its diaphanous tail across the heavens, or in the *zodiacal light*, a faintly luminous band that stretches upward from the horizon in the dawn or evening twilight. Through a study of such objects we get not only insights into their relationships but also into the history of the solar system.

The Asteroids

Tens of thousands of small planetary bodies revolve around the sun, moving mainly between the orbits of Mars and Jupiter. Because when viewed through a modest-sized telescope they appear more like stars than planets, Sir William Herschel gave them the name *asteroid*, meaning star-like. Even though they number in the tens of thousands, they attract little attention because they are very faint. Only one, called Vesta, occasionally becomes bright enough to be seen with the unaided eye.

An Italian astronomer, Giuseppe Piazzi (1746–1826), discovered the first asteroid on January 1, 1801 while charting a region of the sky in the constellation Taurus. Noting a seventh-magnitude star that moved across the stellar background from one night to the next, Piazzi thought he had discovered a new comet. But he was puzzled by its shape because it had the pointed image of a star instead of the diffuseness of a comet. Piazzi observed the "comet" for more than six weeks, during which it reversed its direction, very much like a superior planet during retrograde motion. Illness interrupted his observations and when he returned to study the object, it was lost in the glare of the sun. The object was seen again a year later, thanks to the calculations of a young German mathematician Karl F. Gauss (1777–1855), who had developed a method for computing orbits that utilized only a few observations. He found that Piazzi's "comet" had a planet-like orbit located between the orbits of Mars and Jupiter. The lost body was rediscovered on December 31, 1801 by Franz X. von Zach (1754–1832), half a degree from the predicted spot.

Because Ceres—as Piazzi named it—revolved about the sun at a distance of 2.8 astronomical units (A. U.), several astronomers thought it was the "missing planet" which, according to Bode's law, should occur in that location. Ever since 1781, when Uranus had been discovered and found to fit into the Bode's law sequence, astronomers had been searching for a planet to fill the gap between Mars and Jupiter. Thus, there was considerable surprise in 1802 when the German astronomer Heinrich Olbers (1758–1840) announced that he had discovered, in the constellation Virgo, another rapidly-moving seventh-magnitude object. Calculations indicated that this new body, which was named Pallas, moved about the sun in an orbit similar to that of Ceres. In September 1804 another asteroid, Juno, and in 1807 a fourth, Vesta, were found.

For the next forty years great efforts were made to find more of these minor planets, or asteroids, as they were called. But not until 1845 was a fifth

Comet Arend-Roland, 1957. This comet was bright enough to be seen with the naked eye. (Lick Observatory)

asteroid, Astrea, of the tenth magnitude, found by an amateur astronomer in Berlin. In 1891, Max Wolf of Heidelberg applied photographic techniques to the search for asteroids, using a clock-driven telescope equipped with a camera. Photographed in a long exposure, a star appeared on a plate as a point of light, while an asteroid showed up as a streak because of its orbital motion. With this method, Wolf made over 500 "finds." As of 1962, 1,647 asteroids had been assigned numbers and had well-determined orbits. More than 50,000 such minor planets are estimated to be within reach of the 100-inch Mt. Wilson telescope. The number of an asteroid indicates its order of discovery: thus the first asteroid to be identified is named (1) Ceres, the second is (2) Pallas, and so on.

Asteroid Orbits

The great majority of asteroids orbit the sun between Mars and Jupiter, the period of revolution averaging 4.6 years. Although they move in the same direction as the major planets, their orbits on the average have larger inclinations to the ecliptic (8°.6) and greater ellipticity (0.14).

The motions of certain minor planets tend toward extremes. For example, the elliptical orbit of (944) Hidalgo is the largest, with a semi-major axis of 5.79 A. U., and the longest period, 13.7 years. Because of its highly eccentric orbit, Hidalgo passes well beyond the orbit of Jupiter at perihelion. On the

Trail of the asteroid Eros. Its orbit brings it within the orbit of Mars and very close to earth. (Harvard College Observatory)

other hand, (1566) Icarus, discovered in 1949, has a semi-major axis of 1.077 A. U. and a period of just 408 days. Because it has the largest known orbital eccentricity, 0.827, Icarus can come within 17,000,000 miles of the sun. In June 1968 this planetoid approached within 4,000,000 miles of the earth and frightened a number of impressionable souls. Among the other asteroids that have made close approaches to the earth are (1932) Apollo, (1936) Adonis, and (1937) Hermes, the last being at one point only 600,000 miles away. When Hermes raced across the heavens on October 30, 1937, it covered nearly 5° per hour and thus passed from view within a short time. Even though it was of the eighth magnitude, it was too faint and moving too fast to be photographed. Although the probability of an asteroid colliding with the earth is small, the possibility always remains. We know that smaller but sizeable fragments frequently encounter the earth and that minute particles enter the earth's atmosphere continuously, with a mass accumulation of 10,000 tons per day.

Almost two hundred years ago, the French mathematician Joseph L. Lagrange (1736–1813), studying gravitationally attracting masses, showed that a small body located at one vertex of an equilateral triangle, and under the influence of two larger masses at the other two vertices, would remain permanently in its place. Years later, in 1906, Max Wolf discovered the asteroid (588) Achilles in just such a position with respect to the sun and Jupiter. Since then, at least seventeen such bodies have been discovered. Since the objects near these equilibrium points (one preceding and one following Jupiter) were named after Homeric heroes from *The Iliad*, they are known as the Trojan asteroids.

In 1898 astronomers first sighted an asteroid that had passed inside the orbit of Mars and was approaching the earth. During its favorable opposition in 1931, this body, named Eros, swept to within 16,000,000 miles of the earth. By direct triangulation from two observing stations on earth, the distance to Eros was determined with great precision. Since distances between various bodies in the solar system are well known in terms of astronomical units, the direct measurement of the distance to Eros provided a new measure of the dimensions of our solar system and the distance to the sun.

The Properties of Asteroids

Asteroids are considerably smaller than any of the planets. In 1894, E. E. Barnard, using the 36-inch refractor at Lick Observatory, found that the four largest asteroids, Ceres, Pallas, Vesta, and Juno, showed measurable disks. The sizes of the remaining asteroids can be estimated from their brightness if we assume that their reflectivities are similar to those of the larger ones. Studies of their sizes indicate that only about a dozen have diameters greater than 150 miles, and probably no more than about 500 have diameters greater than 25 miles. Most minor planets, and in fact all those discovered since 1930, have diameters of less than 25 miles. These smaller bodies are literally little more than "flying mountains." Although the smaller asteroids are much more numerous than the larger ones, most of the aggregate mass lies in the larger bodies. Thus Ceres, Pallas, and Vesta contain more than half the total mass in the asteroid belt, and yet they amount to much less than $1/1000$ the mass of the earth.

Several asteroids exhibit fluctuations in brightness with periods ranging from 5 to 17 hours. These variations result from the irregular shape and slow rotation of the asteroidal bodies. Eros fluctuates in brightness by as much as a factor of four in a period of 5 hours 16 minutes. When this asteroid made its close approach to earth in 1931, the brick-shaped form of the mass fragment, 15 miles long and 5 miles thick, was actually visible. The fluctuations in brightness correlated closely with the angle of rotation of the asteroid.

We still do not know how asteroids originate. An early hypothesis attributed them to the catastrophic breaking up of a larger planetary body. Since they have an aggregate mass of less than $1/1000$ that of the earth, the original planet could not have been very large unless most of the debris has somehow disappeared. If all the asteroids originated in the same event, their orbits would originally have had a common point of intersection; however, perturbations by Jupiter and other planets would by now have obliterated the original distribution of orbits. Even so, there are apparently several "families" of asteroid orbits, each with a common point of intersection. This raises the possibility that the members of each "family" are fragments resulting from collisions among larger bodies. Since perturbations have not destroyed the relationship, the collisions must have been relatively recent—probably not more than a few hundred million years ago.

Comets

Comets are unquestionably the most spectacular celestial objects visible to the unaided eye. Their awesome appearance, irregular occurrence, and peculiar orbits make them unique in the solar system. When first discovered, a comet is usually a faint patch of light, considerably smaller than the full moon. As larger comets approach the sun, they begin to develop a luminous tail stretching great distances from the diffuse central body (color plate 35). The Greek cognate for "comet" means, aptly enough, "the hairy one."

Man has observed comets since earliest times. The annals of Babylonian and Chinese astronomers record such observations more than 4,000 years ago. Numerous accounts of them occur in the works of Greek and Roman authors. Elaborate descriptions of brilliant comets, mixed with mystical interpretations, appear in Western writings well into the sixteenth century. Comets were long regarded by many as omens of disaster, war, and death.

Early astronomers generally regarded comets as an atmospheric phenomenon, a kind of exhalation of the earth. The notion that comets lie beyond the moon was not developed until Tycho Brahe studied the Comet of 1577. Tycho noted that the comet's position against the stellar background was the same regardless of the point of observation in Europe. Since he could not discern a measurable parallax, he concluded that the comet could not be located near the earth. Further study led him to believe that the comet moved in a circular path outside the orbit of Venus. His student Kepler studied the motion of several comets, and theorized that they moved in straight lines.

The problem was finally resolved by the English astronomer Edmund Halley (1656–1742), who treated comets as physical bodies moving about the sun in orbits consistent with Newton's newly-propounded law of gravi-

Halley's comet. Last seen in 1910, it will return again in 1986. (Lick Observatory)

tation. He calculated orbits for 24 of the brighter comets and noted, in particular, the striking similarity between the orbits of the comets of 1531, 1607, and 1682. Halley believed that these three comets, which had appeared every 75 or 76 years, might well be the same object, moving about the sun in a path that carried it beyond the orbit of Neptune. Halley went on to predict that this comet would reappear in 1758, but he died before the prophecy was fulfilled. Alexis C. Clairaut (1713–1765), a French astronomer, calculated the effect of planetary perturbations upon the comet and concluded that its reappearance would be delayed. He estimated that its perihelion passage would occur on April 13, 1759. An amateur astronomer first sighted the comet on Christmas night, 1758, and perihelion passage took place on March 12 of the following year. Halley's comet, as it is called, has been observed at every appearance since 1759, the most recent being in 1910. The records of antiquity show that it has been detected at each approach, at an average of about every 77 years, with one exception, as far back as the fifth century B.C. It will reappear again in February 1986 (color plate 2).

About a dozen new comets are discovered each year, often by amateurs systematically scanning the sky with homemade instruments. Images of comets often turn up on astronomical photographs taken for other purposes. About once a year a comet becomes bright enough to be seen with the naked eye: for example, Comets Mrkos and Arend-Roland, named for their discoverers in 1957. Every few decades a particularly bright comet, one that can be seen in the daytime, will appear. The only "daylight" comet since Halley's in 1910 was Comet Ikeya-Seki, which appeared in 1965.

When first detected, a comet is provisionally designated by the year of its discovery followed by a small letter indicating the order of its discovery; for example, Comet 1970a would be the first comet discovered in 1970 whereas 1970b would be the second, and so forth. After its orbit is determined, the

Head of Halley's comet, photographed May 8, 1910. (Hale Observatories)

206

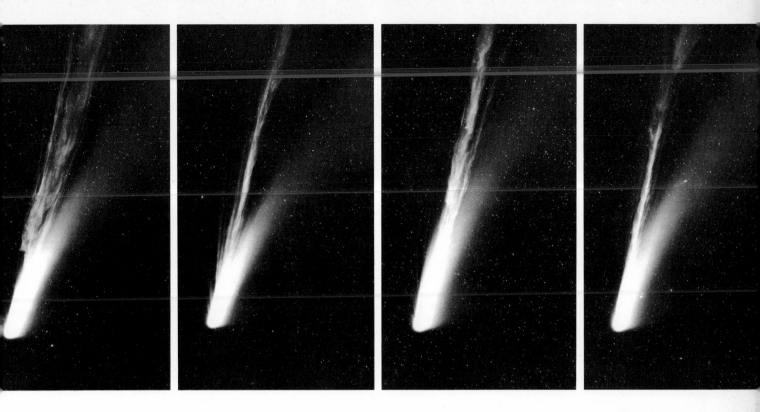

Four views of Mrkos comet, which appeared visible to the unaided eye in 1957. These records were made on August 22, 24, 26, and 27, and show the changes that occurred in the comet's tail. (Hale Observatories)

comet is relabeled with Roman numerals in its order of perihelion passage. Thus Comet 1970 I is the first comet to pass perihelion in 1970; 1970 II is the second, and so on.

Most comets have parabolic or near-parabolic orbits, that is, they move in an open-ended curve. A comet traveling in a truly parabolic path would be a visitor from interstellar space rather than a permanent member of our solar system moving in a closed elliptical orbit. We cannot, however, distinguish between an open-ended parabola and a long, closed ellipse because we see a comet only when it is near the sun. Astronomers have concluded that most comets have periods of millions of years and travel initially in extremely elongated orbits that carry them far beyond the orbit of Pluto. In contrast to these, we know of one group of comets whose orbits lie entirely within the orbit of Neptune. Unlike the near-parabolic comets that come near the earth only once in several thousand years, the short-period comets have undergone many perihelion passages in the course of modern times. The aphelion distances of those with periods of 5–12 years approach Jupiter's orbit, while those with periods of 80–100 years get as far out as Neptune.

Frequently, a near-parabolic or short-period comet passing close to Jupiter will be decelerated slightly and move into an orbit with a shorter period. A decrease in the orbital velocity of only a few feet per second can reduce the period of a comet by a thousand years. At least fifty comets have been affected in this way, resulting in orbits with aphelia near the orbit of Jupiter; they have become known as Jupiter's "family of comets." Other giant planets have similar but less distinct families of comets.

Heads and Tails of Comets

Seen through a telescope, the head of a comet exhibits a bright central "condensation" surrounded by a large, diffuse, nearly spherical cloud called the "coma," which looks like a streetlamp enveloped in fog. Some comae are no larger than the earth, but a few bright comets have had comae more voluminous than the sun. On the average, they approximate the size of Jupiter. Coma dimensions vary with their distance from the sun. Quite small when approaching from outside the earth's orbit, the coma increases in size

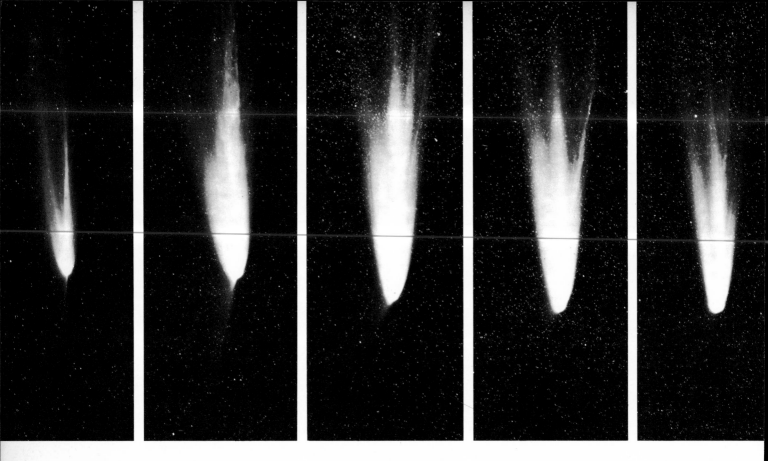

Five views of the Comet Arend-Roland, photographed from April 26 to May 1, 1957. (Hale Observatories)

until it is 1 A. U. away from the sun and then begins to shrink as it nears perihelion. The bright central condensations average slightly more than a thousand miles in diameter and tend to maintain their size throughout the comet's orbit. Within the condensation there is often a brighter "nucleus" with a diameter of only a few miles.

The majority of comets, including all of the faint ones and a few of the brighter ones, have no tails. But when a comet has a tail, it can be very long and the most impressive part of a cometary display. The longest one on record, that of the Great Comet of 1843, was more than 2 A. U. in length. The tail of Halley's comet in 1910 grew at a rate of 500,000 miles per day until it reached a length of some 90,000,000 miles.

In spite of their great size, comets have an insignificant mass. When Comet Brooks made a close approach to Jupiter, it passed among Jupiter's satellites without appreciably perturbing any of them. When Halley's comet passed in front of the solar disk in 1910, it proved to be completely transparent and had no sign of a nucleus. Stars can always be seen shining through the tail of a comet; and in Halley's comet they were visible in the outer parts of the coma. A typical comet will have a mass somewhat less than one billionth that of the earth.

The spectra of comets located more than 3 A. U. from the sun closely resemble that of the sun. This suggests that comets contain small, solid particles that can reflect sunlight. By the time comets have arrived at a distance comparable to the radius of the orbit of Mars, the spectra have changed, with bright lines and bands superimposed on the solar spectrum. These emission features arise from such molecules as C_2, CN, CH, OH, and NH_2, formed as a result of the action of solar ultraviolet radiation upon more stable molecules such as CH_4, CO_2, NH_3, and H_2O. Closer to the sun, the heads of comets begin to emit lines of various metals such as sodium, iron, chromium, and nickel.

A remarkable aspect of the "tail" of a comet is that it always points away from the sun, either following the comet during the approach or preceding it during the recession (fig. 14–1). Material seems to stream continually from the coma into the tail. Knots or clumps of material are often seen moving away from the head from one night to the next. Occasionally, what appear to be streams or jets of material are emitted by the head, creating ribbon-like striations in the tail.

The molecules and particles comprising the tails of comets are acted upon by a number of forces. One of these is the gravitational attraction of the sun, which causes each element of matter to behave as if it were a planetary body orbiting the sun. Another is the pressure of solar radiation falling upon a particle and causing it to accelerate radially outward from the sun. Such radiation pressure is, however, less important than a third force, that is, interaction with the solar wind, an outward flow of particles from the sun. At times concentrations of particles, moving at velocities of hundreds of miles per second, bombard the comet. Other forces include a coupling between charged particles in the comet and the interplanetary magnetic field as well as accelerations that cause particles to be ejected from the coma. The problem of the dynamics and interplay of these forces has not been solved, but the general picture seems clear. Matter from the head of the comet, encountering the solar wind, is literally blown from the coma into the tail. The matter that escapes from the comet in this way will generally be lost to our solar system.

Fred L. Whipple of the Harvard and Smithsonian Observatories, suggested that the nucleus of a comet is a kind of "dirty snowball." He hypothesizes a nucleus composed of a porous aggregate of "ices," or frozen gases, made of CH_4, NH_3, and H_2O. Scattered throughout this mass are metallic and silicate fragments. As the comet gets close to the sun, the increased warmth vaporizes the gases in the surface layers and breaks up the molecules into the less complex molecules seen in the spectrum. These molecules and other particles constitute the coma. Radiation pressure and corpuscular bombardment drive the coma material away from the head. Frequently, exposed bits of solid particles in the nucleus absorb considerable amounts of radiation, creating hot gas bubbles just under the surface layers. The bubbles can "explode" and send out bursts of gas at high velocities, possibly explaining the rapidly moving knots and filamentary jets often seen in comet tails.

In January of 1970, Dr. Arthur D. Code of the University of Wisconsin made a spectacular discovery concerning the structure of a relatively insignificant comet. Through space-borne instruments he observed its spectrum in the far-ultraviolet and found that a huge, glowing ball of hydrogen gas almost as large as the sun completely enveloped the comet. Since such radiation does not pass through the earth's atmosphere, astronomers have been completely unaware of this phenomenon. This discovery should throw new light on the relative importance of comets in our solar system. The main question is how such a tremendous and tenuous head could be stable in the weak gravitational field of the comet itself. The hydrogen may well be escaping gases drifting out to form the tail.

The Origin of Comets

We know that a comet loses some of its mass each time it approaches the sun. The amount of frozen gases vaporized at each perihelion passage may be small, but ultimately the material forming the coma and tail will be exhausted and only the metallic and silicate material will remain. Almost all short-period comets that have undergone scores of perihelion passages have the point-like appearance of a star and fail to develop a tail as they approach the sun. These observations support the theory that many comets have lost their contents of frozen gases and have been reduced to orbiting gravel banks, mere swarms of stony and metallic fragments.

If comets endure for a few hundred orbits at most, how can we account for the comets we are now observing? Those formed during the earliest stages of the solar system, more than 4.5 billion years ago, have long since been dissipated. The most convincing current theory is that proposed by

Jan Oort of Leiden, Holland. He suggests that a vast cloud of at least 100 billion comets, extending more than 100,000 A. U. into interstellar space —nearly halfway to the nearest stars—completely surrounds the solar system. The deflections caused by the gravitational pull of passing stars can send individual comets plummeting toward the sun. We see these comets when their new perihelia lie within about 3 A. U. of the sun. This theory can account for most of the characteristics of the near-parabolic comets such as the random orientation of their orbits, directions of approach and location of perihelia. The short-period comets are simply the ones the major planets have diverted from those coming in from the gigantic cometary reservoir.

Meteors

Anyone who has scanned the heavens on a clear dark night is familiar with the meteors or "shooting stars" that streak across the sky. These luminous trails of light appear when pieces of metal and stone collide with the earth. Heated by friction with atmospheric molecules, they quickly become incandescent. Within seconds, the meteoritic material burns up and vaporizes. From six to ten of these objects, called *sporadic meteors*, are visible every hour on the average. At certain times, often for several days in a row, the meteor rate will increase to as many as a hundred or more per hour. This enhanced meteor activity is known as a meteor shower and occurs whenever the earth encounters the remains of a debilitated comet.

Now and then the brightness of a meteor may exceed that of Jupiter or Venus. Such meteors, known as *fireballs* or *bolides*, often leave trains of luminous gas that persist for several minutes or longer. Solid bodies of larger size sometimes reach the ground without being consumed. These bodies, called *meteorites*, are too large for the earth's atmosphere to slow them up appreciably. Their impact may produce a large crater, with sizable portions of themselves fragmenting and vaporizing in the process. Whether the incoming particles strike the earth or are dissipated in the atmosphere, they are referred to as *meteoroids* while moving through space.

Historical records contain many accounts of meteorite falls, when flaming segments of fireballs are actually seen crashing to earth. One of the earliest accounts, in the Bible (Joshua X:11), tells of fleeing Amorite tribesmen who were killed by "great stones from heaven." Early Chinese astronomers described in great detail various meteor showers, fireballs, and meteorite falls. Several Greek and Roman authors such as Plutarch, Pliny, Livy, and Anaxagoras reported meteors and meteorite falls. Often the meteorites were regarded as messages from the gods and became objects of worship. Swords, knives, and other weapons manufactured from meteoritic material were supposed to give their owners invulnerability.

In order to ascertain the nature and origin of these visitations from outer space, we must determine their orbits before they entered the atmosphere. Observations, such as simultaneous photographs from two stations separated by ten or more miles, enable the astronomer to determine the orbit within the atmosphere and then extrapolate that back into space. This program employs special, high-speed cameras, with propeller-like shutters rotating at a known rate. These "chop" the meteor trail so that it appears on the film as a series of dashes. These dashes enable astronomers to locate, by triangulation, the point in space represented by each dash and then to calculate the velocity of the meteor all along its path. A second method utilizes simultaneous measurements from two radar sites. The radar pulses are reflected from the moving meteor and permit its position to be determined. This method is particularly valuable because it can be used during the daytime or in inclement weather, when optical observations are impossible. In addition, radar can detect particles far too small or faint to be seen visually or photographed with meteor cameras.

The results show that incoming meteoroids begin to produce visible trails at heights of between 80 and 50 miles. The faster meteors become incan-

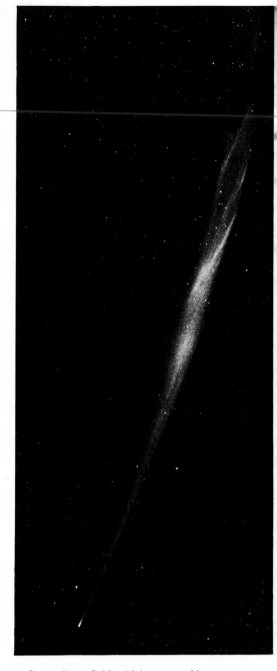

Comet Ikeya Seki, which appeared in 1965, was the only comet since Halley's (1910) to be visible in the daytime. (Lick Observatory)

descent at the greater heights, the slower ones at lower altitudes. The faster meteors are usually consumed when they reach within 60 miles of the earth's surface but the slower ones often persist to within 25 miles.

The Orbits of Meteoroids

The speeds of meteoroids range from 7 to 45 miles per second—what one expects of particles in our solar system. The maximum velocity of a body moving in a near-parabolic orbit in the vicinity of the earth is equal to its velocity of escape from the solar system—26 miles per second. Now, the earth moves in its orbit around the sun at a speed of $18\frac{1}{2}$ miles per second. Therefore, when a near-parabolic meteoroid strikes the earth head-on, its velocity relative to the earth is equal to the sum of $18\frac{1}{2}$ and 26 miles per second, that is, $44\frac{1}{2}$ miles per second. If the meteoroid came from outside the solar system and thus had a hyperbolic orbit, the relative velocity during such a collision would exceed $44\frac{1}{2}$ miles per second. But less than one per cent have nearly hyperbolic orbits. Probably the orbits are elliptic and the meteors all belong to the solar system. The speeds discussed above represent velocities relative to the earth. The actual velocities measured by an earth-bound observer may be somewhat larger if we take into account the influence of the earth's gravitational attraction, which can increase the speed of a meteor by as much as 7 miles per second.

More meteors are seen in the hours before dawn than just after sunset because in the post-midnight hours the observer is located on the forward part of the earth with respect to the motion of the earth and sees more high-speed, head-on encounters (fig. 14–2). After sunset, he is on the far side of the earth and sees only those meteoroids able to overtake the earth from behind. Meteors seen in the predawn hours also tend on the average to be brighter than those observed before midnight. The luminosity of a meteor is proportional not only to the mass of the body but to the square of its velocity relative to the earth. Hence, predawn meteors, with their larger average velocities, tend to be brighter than those seen in the early evening.

The majority of sporadic meteors move in orbits similar to those of short-period comets. Their orbits exhibit short periods, low inclinations and moderately high eccentricities. Over 95 per cent move in the direct sense—that is, from west to east. Those meteors that move in retrograde paths have longer periods and higher eccentricities as well as the more random distribution of inclinations typical of long-period, near-parabolic comets. At least 85 per

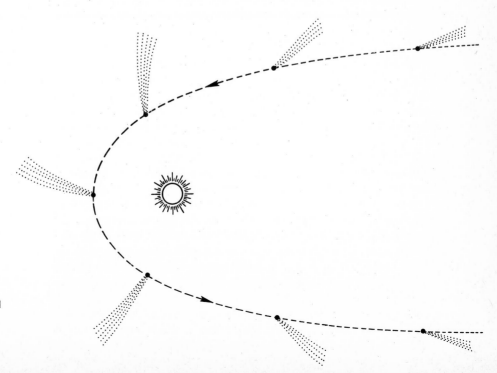

Figure 14–1. The orbit of a comet around the sun is either a highly elongated ellipse or an open-ended parabola. The comet's tail always points away from the sun.

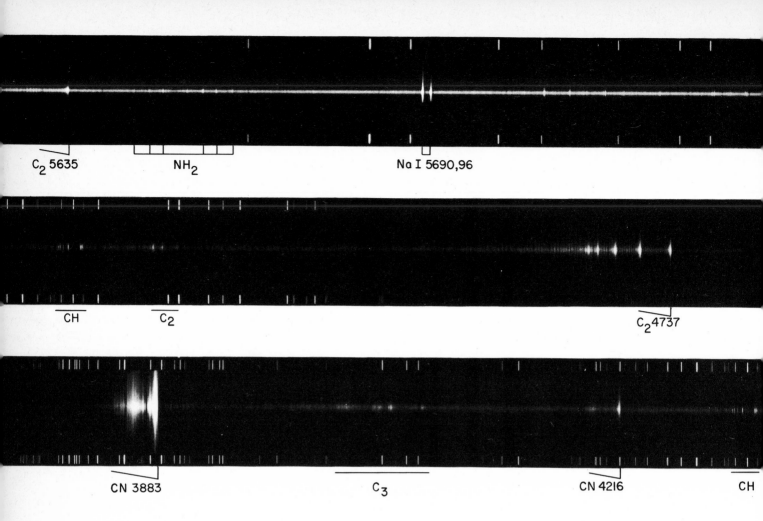

C₂ 5635   NH₂   Na I 5690,96

CH   C₂   C₂ 4737

CN 3883   C₃   CN 4216   CH

Sections of a high-dispersion spectrogram of the comet Seki-Lines (1962C). (Lick Observatory)

cent of sporadic meteors are probably remnants of defunct short-period comets. Most of the remainder represent fragments of longer-period comets or asteroidal matter. Very few have wandered in from interstellar space.

Meteor Showers

Meteor showers, when dozens of meteors flash across the sky every hour or even every minute, are among the most dramatic of astronomical events. A shower results when the earth encounters a swarm of meteoroids moving along an orbit in space. Although many showers recur from year to year, the earth occasionally and unexpectedly meets a cloud of particles that produces a single spectacular display and never returns.

The meteors within a shower have nearly identical velocities and appear to come from a common point in the sky known as the radiant. Usually showers bear the name either of the constellation in which the radiant is located or that of a nearby star. The radiant is not a point, but has a distinct breadth, varying from less than three minutes of arc to more than twice the diameter of the moon. Its size is important because it indicates the compactness of the swarm. Surprisingly enough, a typical swarm has a density of only one particle for every million cubic miles! The diameter of a swarm can be deduced from the time required for the earth to pass through it. For a good-sized shower such as the Perseids the diameter exceeds 50,000,000 miles.

In the mid-nineteenth century, it was discovered that the orbits of meteoroids producing the Perseid shower were virtually identical with that of Comet 1862 III. Although the comet itself has a period of 110 years, the earth encounters the Perseid swarm regularly each year about August 12. Similarly the Leonids were found to occupy the orbit of Comet 1866 I. Since then, more than a dozen showers have been associated with short-period comets, and astronomers now know that these showers are composed of cometary residue that has spread out along and filled the orbital regions. Several showers occur that cannot be associated with specific comets but in all likelihood even these originated in comets. Hundreds of comets have no shower associations whatever, apparently because a shower can occur only when the orbit of the meteoroid swarm intersects or closely approaches that of the earth.

Many showers have been observed annually for centuries, some of them far more spectacular than others. For example, the November Leonids appear every year but they seem to be particularly impressive at intervals of 33 years. Records as far back as the ninth century B.C. substantiate this periodicity. Perhaps the most remarkable display occurred in November 1833, when more than 200,000 meteors were visible during one hour, convincing many that the end of the earth was imminent. Another astonishing shower occurred in 1866, but those of 1899 and 1932 were disappointing; however, in November 1966 the meteor rate climbed as high as 100 per second for short periods.

Meteors as bright as a first-magnitude star seldom weigh more than $1/100$ of an ounce. For a meteoroid of modest density, one measuring only an inch or so across will produce a fireball as brilliant as a full moon. The densities of meteors, particularly those arriving at lower altitudes, can be calculated from the way the earth's atmosphere slows them down. A few appear to have densities less than that of water, lending credence to the theory that some meteoroids consist of the fragile, porous remains of comets.

Meteorites

Meteoroidal fragments beat down continually on the earth. The larger pieces that survive the trip through the atmosphere have usually slowed down enough so that they can be found on or just below the surface of the earth. These bodies, known as meteorites (color plates 38, 39) are found in two ways. Often a large bolide meteor is observed to break up and shower the earth with chunks of metal and stone. More than 2,000 falls of meteorites occur every year over the entire earth. Those that fall over the open sea or in remote areas usually go undetected, and in only about half a dozen instances each year are falls actually tracked down and meteorite samples recovered.

Figure 14–2. Frequency of meteors before and after midnight. As the earth moves in its orbit, rotating counter-clockwise, meteoroids hurtle about it from random directions, some faster than the earth and some slower. On the morning side (6 A.M.), when the earth is approaching the meteors, they crash head-on with the earth, and are more frequent and more brilliant than in the evening (6 P.M.). At that time only those meteors moving swiftly enough to overtake the earth flash in the earth's atmosphere.

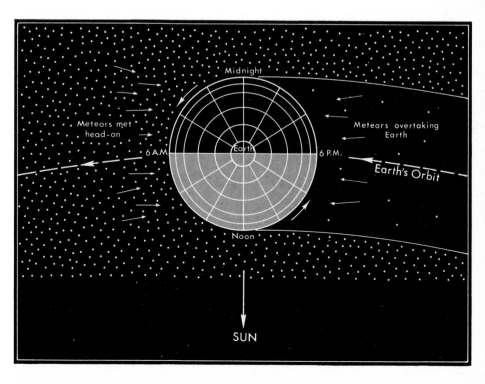

213

The other means by which meteorites come to light are "finds," as when a rock is picked up in the field and is later confirmed as a meteorite; only about twenty-five such finds are made each year. Altogether, meteorites from more than 1,800 falls have been identified. About 60 per cent of these are finds; the remainder come from observed falls. Although the typical find weighs only a few kilograms, estimates of the total meteoritic material in museums run to more than 500 tons.

The great majority of meteorites fall into three classes: stones, stony-irons, and irons. The stones, the most abundant group, consist primarily of silicate material. Although their composition resembles that of rocks in the earth's crust, they are relatively deficient in silicon and oxygen. Most of these meteorites have minute inclusions, called chondrules, made of metal, carbon, and various terrestrial minerals. The stony-irons, the rarest type of meteorite, which make up about 8 per cent of meteorite finds, contain about equal amounts of stony and metallic material, with the stony constituent distributed quite evenly throughout the metallic matrix. The irons, the third group, contain large quantities of iron and nickel. The nickel provides a good test for meteoritic character since the abundance of this substance ranges between 5 and 20 per cent, far above the amount in most terrestrial alloys. Moreover, when an iron meteorite containing between 6 and 12 per cent nickel is sliced, polished and etched with a dilute acid, a distinct crystallization network appears, called Widmanstatten after the director of a porcelain works in Vienna. Outside the 5–12 per cent range, the pattern usually does not appear.

There is a fourth category called tektites, whose extraterrestrial nature remains to be confirmed. These glassy objects in the shape of buttons, cones, and teardrops average about a gram in weight and from a few millimeters to three or four inches in size. Their colors range from a medium green to blackish. Essentially, they consist of glass with a silica abundance of at least 70 per cent. Their composition does not differ greatly from igneous rocks and they are chemically distinct from other meteorites. They are also different from other meteorites in that they are confined to certain localities. In one area in Australia more than 50,000 tektites have turned up, whereas in a nearby region they are virtually unknown. This irregular distribution has led scientists to speculate that they fell to earth as a shower of lunar ejecta resulting from the impact of a meteoroid upon the moon. Another theory is that they are impact residue created when a meteoroid struck the earth, but this hypothesis runs into a problem since most tektites differ markedly in chemical composition from the underlying rock.

We determine the age of meteorites much as we date terrestrial rocks, that is, by the natural radioactive decay of various elements. Unfortunately, the decay method that measures the lead and helium in uranium has not proved as applicable to meteorites, particularly iron meteorites, as to rocks in the earth's crust. The reason for this is that meteoritic helium is mainly the result not of radioactive decay but of the bombardment of the meteorite's iron atoms by cosmic rays while it was still orbiting in space. Thus, the amount of uranium, lead, helium, and intermediate radionuclides in the meteorite reveals only the length of time the original meteoroid was exposed to the space environment. Since cosmic rays penetrate only a few yards into meteoritic material, the "cosmic ray exposure ages" tell us only how long the body existed as a small fragment. The age determined in this way ranges from a few million years in some meteors to a billion years in others.

The uranium-into-helium test gives more reliable results when applied to stony meteorites where the uranium content is higher and the iron content lower. We can deduce not only cosmic-ray exposure ages but their "cooling ages" as well, that is, the time since the meteorites cooled sufficiently to retain substantial amounts of helium. These cooling ages are of the order of several billion years, much longer than the corresponding exposure ages. Apparently, fragmentation of all meteoroidal material took place, in astronomical terms, recently.

Bright meteor that fell in Oklahoma on January 3, 1970 and was recorded simultaneously by three camera stations. It lasted for nine seconds, as seen on the photograph. The parallel streaks are moving stars approaching the tilted horizon. Two freshly-fallen meteorites, weighing 22 pounds and 10 ounces respectively, were quickly recovered near Lost City, Oklahoma. (Prairie Meteorite Photography and Recovery Network, Smithsonian Astrophysical Observatory)

Meteor Craters

The average fragment that produces a meteorite probably weighs no more than a few hundred pounds before it enters the atmosphere. But about once in a decade a very large body will strike the earth and blast out a crater at least several yards across. The most spectacular such event in recent times occurred near the Tunguska River in Siberia on June 30, 1908. A bright fireball, easily visible in the daytime, flashed across the sky accompanied by tremendous explosions and fell to earth with a great crash. A cloud of dust and smoke rose many miles into the sky and the atmospheric blast wave knocked down men and animals more than one hundred miles away. Many windows were broken, walls and buildings collapsed, and the seismic disturbance was detected throughout Europe. For many days the twilight skies were brighter than normal because of sunlight scattered from smoke and dust particles in the upper atmosphere.

A field expedition was not dispatched to the remote site until nineteen years later, but the widespread destruction caused by the fall was still fully evident. Trees in a thick forest had been flattened and scorched as far as 30 miles from the impact zone and dozens of craters had been formed, some with diameters up to 150 feet. Although no meteoritic fragments were found, small quantities of fused silica with metallic inclusions were recovered in one of the craters. Investigators estimated that the original meteoroid weighed more

215

than 50,000 tons. The impact region lies at the same latitude as Leningrad: had the meteor arrived 4 hours 47 minutes later, it would have fallen upon the city and resulted in a catastrophe.

In February 1947, another large meteor as brilliant as the sun crashed to earth, again in the Soviet Union, just north of Vladivostok. This time a scientific team rushed to the scene and explored a fall area 8 miles long and 3 miles wide, containing more than 100 craters. A few craters had diameters of more than 80 feet and depths as great as 30 feet. More than five tons of iron were recovered from this site.

The outstanding crater in the United States is the Barringer Meteorite Crater in Arizona. Nearly circular, it is 4,200 feet across and, like lunar craters, has a sloping upturned rim. The rim rises 100 feet above a limestone plain and the crater floor lies some 600 feet below the top of the rim. Both metallic and stone fragments have been discovered there, often at sites located miles from the crater. No large fragments have turned up inside the crater, but a few heavily oxidized metal pieces, blended with particles of stone, have been found. Drillings show that the underlying rock strata have been crushed and pulverized, and many sandstone rocks bear evidence of having been fused under high pressures. Apparently the impacting body approached at a low-elevation angle and from a northerly direction. A sizable fragment is still believed buried 1,500 feet under the south rim. A rough estimate derived from assumed oxidation rates for the metal-stone aggregates indicates that the impact took place at least several thousand years ago, and some estimates place the crater's age as high as 75,000 years.

From time to time other prehistoric craters are identified. One of these, the New Quebec Crater, in northern Quebec, discovered in 1950, has a diameter of more than two miles and a rim towering 300 feet above the countryside. The crater is embedded in granite and forms a small lake. Even though no meteoritic material has been found around it, the crater is regarded as meteoric in origin because of its similarity to the Barringer Crater and the absence of other crater-producing forces, such as volcanic activity, in the area.

The peculiar geological structure of the Vredevoort Dam in South Africa, which is about 50 miles in diameter and has a crushed and fused core, strongly suggests meteoric origin. Undoubtedly many unrecognized "fossil" craters exist on the earth. Exposure to only a few tens of thousands of years of erosion would erase or drastically alter many prominent crater features: the sloping uplifted rim, pulverized rock layers, and even the circular shape.

Aerial view of the Barringer meteor crater in Arizona. The crater has a diameter of 4000 feet and its ridges rise 130 feet above the surrounding plane. (Donald Menzel)

Other Interplanetary Material

Interplanetary space contains a vast number of minute bodies, ranging from atoms and molecules to dust and small solid particles. Perhaps the best-known component of this interplanetary matter is the fine dust that manifests itself as "micrometeorites" and as the zodiacal light. Minute particles of dust frequently fall into the earth's atmosphere, but never produce a visible meteor. Because of their large radiating surfaces (as compared with their volume) they slow down to terminal velocities before heating up. Their diameters seldom exceed a few microns (about 4×10^{-5} inches). The presence of these particles is particularly evident from the erosive effect they produce on the surfaces of space vehicles. They are also readily detected by means of microphones and other sensors mounted on rocket and satellite packages. The micrometeorite particles themselves are directly recoverable in a number of ways: from rain water, from aircraft samplings of the upper atmosphere, and from borings taken in glaciers and the ocean floor, and from moon rocks.

The zodiacal light refers to a soft glow of white light sometimes seen extending upward from the horizon along the ecliptic. Particularly conspicuous in the tropics, the faint glow can be best seen just at the close of twilight, or in the morning immediately preceding dawn twilight. It is most apparent when the ecliptic makes a large angle with respect to the horizon. For an observer in the northern hemisphere, the favorable apparitions occur in the evening during the spring and in the morning during the fall. At its best, the display approaches the Milky Way in brightness, but it is so faint that even a small amount of atmospheric haze obscures it.

The spectrum consists only of sunlight scattered by small particles of matter. The flattened form of the region of radiation shows that the dust concentrates toward the plane of the ecliptic. The zodiacal light has been detected with sensitive instruments well away from the sun, even in the antisolar direction. An observer standing on the moon would see a moderately bright zodiacal light as an obvious continuation of the solar corona.

Another manifestation of dust particles in space is the *gegenschein* or "counter-glow" observed in the antisolar direction. This emission forms an oval patch of light $8°$ to $10°$ long and $5°$ to $7°$ wide. The patch seems to be superimposed upon the fainter background of the zodiacal light. The glow is very faint and often can be detected only with very sensitive photoelectric instruments. Like the zodiacal light, its spectrum resembles that of the sun and is believed to result from scattered sunlight.

The theory of planetary motions supports the possibility that a group of particles might be trapped in space on the side of the earth opposite the sun, about 700,000 miles beyond the orbit of the moon. Another hypothesis regards the particles as a kind of terrestrial dust tail created by the solar wind. If the particles making up the gegenschein, zodiacal light, and micrometeorites were more than a few microns in size, those striking the earth would produce visible meteors. If they were much less than a micron they would be blown out of the solar system by the solar wind or by radiation pressure. The particles simply tend to remain in orbits about the sun like a cloud of infinitesimal planets.

In addition to the dust, the solar wind itself—composed of charged particles, atoms, and electrons flowing outward from the sun—fills the interplanetary environment. Near the sun the velocity exceeds a thousand miles per second. Away from the sun both the velocity and particle density decrease. At the distance of the earth's orbit the gas density is only 10–20 atoms per cubic centimeter and the velocity a few hundred miles per second.

We still have much to learn about interplanetary material and, in particular, its relation to the more massive members of the solar family. Whatever the nature of that relation, we know it is important and has existed since the solar system was formed. From the study of this matter, we may even learn something of the early history of our solar system.

Iron-nickel meteorite from Edmonton, Kentucky, showing the characteristic crystalline structure known as the Widmanstatten figures. (John Wood, Smithsonian Astrophysical Observatory)

The Origin of the Solar System

15

The solar neighborhood is a hodge-podge of all kinds of bodies. The nine major planets show certain regularities and, with the exception of Pluto, the orbits of the planets occupy a volume as flat as a phonograph record. Some planets have satellite systems and some do not. The planets all revolve and most of them rotate in the same sense, that is, from west to east. Next are the minor planets, or asteroids, which occur mainly in the gap between Mars and Jupiter, though exceptional bodies occasionally come well inside the earth's orbit. An immense belt, or perhaps even shell, of comets envelops the solar system at distances comparable to those of the nearest stars. From time to time one of these bodies falls in toward our sun, executes an orbit about it, and then returns to the depths of space. We have seen how some of these bodies are related to the still smaller bodies of the solar system: the meteoroids, cosmic dust, and the micrometeors of interplanetary space. At the center of all this lies the sun, pouring out vast quantities of light and heat into the frigid depths of space. Its overpowing mass dominates the motions of bodies in its neighborhood.

As we have seen, the age of the earth has been reasonably well established even though the mechanism of its formation remains unclear. By analyzing the chemical content of radioactive materials in rocks and the accumulated decay product, we can determine the ages of these materials. We have assumed that the rates of radioactive disintegration have remained constant throughout the lifetime of the earth. In this way we discover that the earth is at least several billion years old. Most of the igneous rocks appear to have solidified about 3.5 billion years ago. Still older rocks have been discovered, from which we draw the conclusion that the main body of the earth probably coalesced about 4.5 billion years ago. To this information we can now add something about the moon through analysis of the rocks brought back by various Apollo missions. Some are up to 4.8 billion years old.

The ages of stony meteors, recovered after their falls, are generally consistent with the above figures. They too are at least several billion years old. One thing we have ascertained is that the chemical composition of a meteoroid orbiting the sun in interplanetary space will not remain absolutely constant with the time. It is continually subject to the bombardment by energetic cosmic rays from interstellar space. When one of these cosmic rays strikes the nucleus of an atom in the meteor, part of the nucleus disintegrates, throwing off certain decay products that generally accumulate within the solid meteor itself. This phenomenon, known as "cosmic ray exposure," also enables us to get some idea of the age of the meteor. Since cosmic-ray particles do not penetrate our larger meteoroids to a depth of more than a few feet, the cores of the meteoroids remain unaffected by such exposure. Hence the age measured in this way will depend upon what part of the body we examine. These determinations generally range around a few million years but sometimes reach a billion years. The chemical analysis is limited by the fact that some of the decay products, such as helium, neon, and argon, are gaseous and hence likely to escape from the rock.

Facing page: Nebulous Cluster M 16 (NGC 6611) in Serpens, about 4600 light-years away. The interaction of dark and luminous clouds of gas and dust shows tube-like condensations called "elephants' trunks" and dark globules, which may be proto-stars. (Lick Observatory)

The analysis of radioactive decay enables us to measure the time that has elapsed since the primordial meteoritic material solidified. The age of many of the stony meteorites determined in this fashion lies very close to that of the earth, that is, 4.5 billion years. Since meteorites are of the same material as other members of the solar system and probably were formed at about the same time, their age provides a reliable lower limit to the age of the entire solar system. Later on, we shall find that many stars similar to our sun also appear to be in the neighborhood of five billion years old.

Can Planets Be Captured?

Some imaginative individuals have surmised that the earth acquired its moon by capture. They visualize the moon as coming in from a great distance, spiraling slowly around the earth like a plane about to land and then settling down in its present orbit. Other persons have hypothesized that the sun may have captured the various planets in the same way. As a matter of fact, Newton himself showed that a single body cannot possibly capture another body by means of its own field of gravitation. According to the laws of celestial mechanics, if a body moves in closer and closer to the sun or to a planet it finally reaches a point of nearest approach; it must then recede in an orbit that is the mirror image of the one coming in. The laws of gravitation rule out spiral paths. The orbit is a hyperbola, or at any rate an open-ended parabola, and celestial mechanics tell us that the body must recede to infinity if it came in from infinity. Thus, to make capture possible, we should have to find some way of circumventing the law of gravitation.

We can do this for the moon by invoking the aid of a third body, such as the sun, or of introducing some form of friction. A large meteorite from outer space, hitting the earth a glancing blow, might be sufficiently slowed down by atmospheric friction to permit the earth to capture it and thus acquire a satellite. Some theories of lunar origin postulate that such an event occurred long ago. However, a meteor so captured would, after receding to a distance, return again and again, each time suffering other retarding interactions with the earth and its atmosphere. After a few revolutions, the meteor would have slowed down to the point where it would fall to earth—unless the sun's attraction changed the orbit so that the meteor no longer struck the earth.

The force of gravitation has many remarkable consequences. As long as no frictional forces are involved, the universe could run just as well backward as forward. If we lived on a planet revolving around the star Sirius and if an astronaut brought back moving pictures of the solar system, we could not tell which way to run the pictures. From the motions of the planets alone we have no major way of distinguishing the future from the past. A hot body tends to radiate energy to a cool one. Heat flows out of the sun, not back into it. The moon's gravitation drags the tides around the earth once a day. The friction of these tides against the continental shelf slows down the earth and speeds up the moon, causing the moon to recede slowly. The friction causes heat, which radiates away into space. So the thermal properties dictate which direction in time is past and which is future. The universe is running down and will continue to do so unless some unpredictable force "winds" it up again.

Theories of the Origin

A body revolving around the sun possesses what is known as angular momentum. For a circular orbit—and for our purposes we may consider all major planets as having circular orbits—the angular momentum is the mass of the planet multiplied by its velocity and its distance from the sun. The sun and planets have a certain amount of rotational angular momentum in themselves which we compute by dividing up each body into several volumes, as if each part were in orbital rotation about its own axis. We must also add the angular momentum of the satellites as well as of other small bodies in the solar system. But these contribute very little to the total. Although the sun is very massive, its rotational velocity is relatively low and

Part of the nebula around Eta Carinae, showing silhouettes of dark globules that may condense into stars. (Harvard College Observatory, Boyden Station)

the distance from the center so small that it contributes only about 1 per cent of the total angular momentum of the solar system. Jupiter provides almost 60 per cent. Together, the four giant planets contribute over 98 per cent of the total angular momentum.

Angular momentum is well known to ballerinas and figure skaters. For example, a skater executing a whirl starts spinning slowly upon one foot with both arms and one leg extended, then draws the arms and leg closer to the body. The nearer the arms and leg reach the axis of rotation, the faster the spin.

A fundamental theorem of the mathematics of planetary orbits is that the total angular momentum remains constant with time, no matter what happens within a given system, unless acted upon by some external force. On this basic theorem many theories of the origin of the solar system have foundered.

Laplace's Nebular Hypothesis

For a long time, the most widely-accepted idea of the solar system and its origin was that of the great French astronomer-mathematician Pierre S. Laplace (1749–1827). Laplace conceived of a time when all matter in the universe was dispersed through space in the form of a cloud or nebula. In time, here and there within this vast cloud, small condensations occurred and began to grow by virtue of their own gravitational force, so that matter rained into each condensation from the cloud as a whole. Now, if the original cloud had any rotation whatever, Laplace was well aware that, as it contracted, its velocities would have to increase. He hypothesized that because of its accelerated rotation this slowly contracting nebula would become more and more flattened, or disk-shaped. Finally, he decided, the rotation would be so fast that the body would become unstable. A ring of gas would detach itself from the equator and thus temporarily relieve the instability. The compression was supposed to continue so as to produce another instability, the release of a second ring, and so on, with the sun, now hot enough to become a star, at the center. Each ring was then supposed to coalesce to form another body, the *proto-planet*. This object, condensing and increasing its rate of rotation, repeated the process, shedding rings that eventually became satellites.

Some doubt developed concerning this theory in 1898 when the Harvard astronomer William H. Pickering (1858–1938) discovered Phoebe, satellite of Saturn, the first known object that revolved counter to the general motion prevalent in the solar system. The discovery of Phoebe was not as fatal to the nebular hypothesis as some persons imagined, since an asteroid, captured by a planet with an assist from the sun's gravitation, can readily become a satellite that revolves in retrograde fashion. But numerous other difficulties became apparent.

The trouble with Laplace's view of the solar system was that it was merely qualitative. When subjected to rigorous mathematical analysis that takes into account the law of conservation of angular momentum, it becomes untenable. We can calculate the result by reversing time, allowing our sun to expand until it filled the orbit of Mercury. This condition would have been precisely what prevailed immediately after the sun, as Laplace postulated, shed the ring that formed Mercury. The sun would then have required something like 475 years to turn just once on its axis. If, now, the sun were to expand a trifle more, just enough to swallow up the planet Mercury, the rotation time would have decreased by about one hour! Rotation once in 475 years is still quite slow. The sun would certainly not be unstable enough to shed a ring of matter to form Mercury. And if the sun were to continue to expand, swallowing planet after planet, no instabilities could possibly have occurred. Hence scientists were forced to discard the old nebular hypothesis.

The Planetesimal Hypothesis

About the turn of the century, a theory proposed by geologist Thomas C. Chamberlin (1843–1928) and astronomer Forest R. Moulton (1872–1952) of the University of Chicago commanded attention for several decades. Using the law that the total angular momentum of a system must remain constant unless acted upon by some external force, Chamberlin and Moulton hypothesized that this force was the close approach of a passing star that produced huge tides in the outer layers of the sun. These tides caused the sun to spew great quantities of material into space, some of which chased along after the star and started revolving around the sun. The intruding star disappeared into the distance, leaving the sun enveloped in a hot, spinning cloud. The mass of gas eventually cooled, congealing into small solid lumps, the *planetesimals*. A few of the larger lumps acted as centers of condensation, sweeping up the smaller planetesimals and gradually clearing out the debris caused by the near collision with the hit-run star.

The planetesimal hypothesis proved especially popular with geologists because it supposed that the mantle, or outer covering of the earth, grew by the accretion of cold planetesimals rather than by the cooling of a large gaseous and later molten mass. Certain characteristics of the earth, such as a dense core and the chemical composition of its atmosphere, seemed to accord better with the concept of planetesimals. The proponents of the hypothesis pointed to the scarred surface of the moon as further evidence of the impact of numerous small bodies upon a larger mass.

A variant of the planetesimal hypothesis, called the "tidal hypothesis," was suggested by the British astronomer Sir James Jeans and polished by Sir Harold Jeffreys. This theory also relied on the gravitational effect of the passing star. The sun, however, instead of virtually exploding and squirting matter in all directions, was said to have ejected a long snake-like filament that stretched out between the two bodies. This filament cooled and eventually broke up into large condensations, the proto-planets of our solar system. Many fragments and a large gaseous envelope were formed at the same time. The orbits of the primitive planets were highly eccentric, that is to say they moved in long ellipses, coming in fairly close to the sun and then receding deeply into space. Friction with the gas and the planetesimals slowly changed these original orbits into the present nearly circular ones.

About 1936, R. A. Lyttleton of England developed a variant of this tidal hypothesis based on the assumption that the sun was once a double star. We shall see that many stars in the sky—perhaps as many as one-third—are double, so the basic concept was not unreasonable. Lyttleton also invoked the aid of a passing star, which was supposed to have pulled out a gaseous ribbon, as in the Jeans-Jeffreys concept. However, the ejected ribbon came not from the sun, but from the other star. This alternative had the advantage of starting the ribbon in an orbit that was nearly circular. As a finale, the passing star was supposed to have captured the sun's primitive consort, running away with it into space, and leaving the sun to take care of the offspring of this unusual cosmic triangle.

Lyman Spitzer of Princeton University, studying the whole tidal theory anew, objected that the gravitational force of such a filament could not possibly hold either it or its component parts together. The hot gas would evaporate away into space with almost explosive violence. At best we should have a cloud of gas filled with rocky fragments, not unlike the debris from the planetesimal hypothesis, and we have to start over again from there.

Fred Hoyle of Cambridge University proposed still another ingenious variant on this theory. Like Lyttleton, Hoyle postulated that the sun was initially a double star. But at some early stage, one of the pair became unstable and exploded, as stars do when they form what we call novae. The star took off like a jet plane and became lost in space, leaving behind the usual train of dust and gas. The planets then developed from the debris of the explosion. Although altogether speculative, this theory does seem more probable than those based on interstellar collisions, which must be very rare. Despite the immense number of stars in our galaxy, such encounters are so infrequent that our solar system, if formed in this manner, would be almost unique in the universe.

Variants of the Nebular Hypothesis

The concept of a nebula that condenses, forming the sun and planets in the process, seems to be fundamental in all theories. Fred Whipple, a Harvard-Smithsonian astronomer, thought that the original sun, perhaps surrounded by a cloud of gas, may have encountered a swarm of large meteorites. The resistance of the solar gaseous envelope enabled the sun to capture these meteors, which acted as the condensation cores that eventually built up into planets by the accretion of interplanetary gas and dust. Hannes Alfvén, the distinguished Swedish physicist, invokes the action of electromagnetic forces in addition to those of gravitation. The sun, coursing through interstellar space, encountered a cloud of gas and dust and some of this material cascaded toward the sun. If nothing intervened, some of the matter would have fallen into the sun and the rest would have swept on past. But as the sun began to enter the cloud, its ultraviolet radiation detached electrons from the atoms, ionizing them. The sun, as we have seen, possesses a magnetic field, and billions of years ago the magnetism may well have been far greater than it is at present. Such a field could have deflected charged particles from their orbits of direct approach into roughly circular orbits around the sun. Thus the nebular material might have been captured by the sun, leading to the production of condensing planetesimals and the planets.

Fashions change. And none more so than beliefs about the universe and man's relation to it. For example, the Italian philosopher-cosmologist Giordano Bruno (1548–1600) was burned at the stake for declaring that the stars were independent suns and might have planets revolving around them. But today man is prepared to believe in a plurality of worlds. So we end up with a slowly rotating sun surrounded by a swarm of planetesimals. How might this have happened?

We have seen that the sun, apparently in defiance of gravitation, shoots enormous clouds of gas into space. Most of this material cascades back to the surface in threads or condensations many times larger than our earth. But some of it permanently leaves the sun under the impetus of the solar wind. Two features of this process stand out. These clouds of glowing hydrogen move against gravity and at tremendous velocities, sometimes as high as several hundred miles a second. Furthermore, and surprisingly, they do not dissipate in space. Some force tends to keep them from expanding. Motion pictures of solar activities suggest that the forces tending to drive these clouds—the solar prominences—are electric currents and their associated magnetic fields. Such an electric current can overcome the explosive character of a gaseous filament perhaps long enough to permit condensation.

Some evidence suggests that solar electric currents must be slowly dying. Billions of years ago, when the sun was new, the electric currents may have been very much more powerful than they are today. The details are vague, but one may reasonably theorize that an electric current of very great intensity may once have flowed around the equator of the primitive sun and caused the equator to bulge. We can even see how such a current might tear itself loose from the sun, carrying with it a ring of matter, so that the sun may momentarily have resembled the planet Saturn. Even today we see the sun ejecting great rings of glowing gas into space. Moreover, such a ring could exert a braking action, slowing down the sun's rotation and at the same time speeding itself up so as to acquire the angular momentum from the sun. Most stars, especially young ones, tend to rotate more rapidly than our sun. Hence the idea of a braking action is not unattractive. On this hypothesis, every star with a powerful magnetic field and associated electric current becomes a potential parent of a planetary family.

One may briefly sum up this idea in a sentence: the solar system resulted when the sun "blew a fuse." It borrows significant features from most of the major earlier hypotheses, but it has the merit of being a unitary hypothesis, that is, it does not require the cooperation of a second star or outside body. The sun ejects a ring or rings of matter, as in Laplace's theory, though the

224

Today astronomers realize that spiral nebulae, such as M 51 in Canes Venatici, shown above, are independent Milky Way systems consisting of many billions of stars. A century or more ago, however, these objects were sometimes thought to be solar systems in evolution according to the nebular hypothesis. Proponents of the planetesimal hypothesis suggested that these spirals were the result of near-collisions between two stars, and hence also evolving planetary systems. (Hale Observatories)

motive power consists of electric currents instead of the centrifugal force of rotation. The theory relies on the naturally explosive character of the solar atmosphere, as in the planetesimal hypothesis of Chamberlin and Moulton, but the explosion occurs naturally rather than because it is induced by a passing star. The ejected ring possesses features of the filament of Jeans and Jeffreys. The electric current seals the gases in, allowing them to condense rather than dissipate. A nova-like, or perhaps a true nova, outburst occurs, like the one postulated by Hoyle.

As with most of the other theories, we end up with the sun, a swarm of planetesimals, and centers of condensation. From there on the evolution must roughly parallel that generally assumed by other theories. One exception may be that the regular satellite systems, especially those of the larger planets, may also arise from a repetition of the electric explosion on a smaller scale.

Since it is still popular today, one other theory of solar-system origin deserves mention. First conceived by the German astronomer C. F. von Weizsäcker, and later extended by G. P. Kuiper, it also starts with a large, distended nebula that slowly condenses. It differs from Laplace's theory however, in that a number of condensations besides that of the sun occurred. These were the proto-planets, which continued to sweep up the nebular material after they achieved orbit around the condensing sun. For a time, some of these bodies would have even been inside the sun's extended atmosphere. The theory further postulates that when the sun was young and new, the force of its wind, and perhaps the pressure of radiation, expelled a large part of the original material, filtering it out into space and leaving the planets behind. Some concentrated material eventually went to form the comet belt.

We do not know enough to say that this theory is certainly correct and that the others are wrong. Probably all contain some truth as well as certain errors. Still newer theories will be suggested. Space exploration will surely throw light on the problem of origins. What about the future? Will our sun go on forever? Or will some catastrophe bring our solar system to an end? Since the answers are to be found literally in the stars, let us turn from our own little solar system and survey the universe.

16

Stars and Nebulae

Our sun is just one of 100 billion stars—all suns in their own right—in our own Milky Way system. We have seen how complex our sun is; and yet most of its features, such as the chromosphere, corona, prominences, spots, flares, and solar activity in general would have been invisible to us if the sun were as far away as the other stars.

Distances Among the Stars

Early astronomers, surmising that the stars were suns, made the only assumption they could at the time: that all stars were equal to the sun in brightness. Had they been able to determine the ratio in brightness between a first-magnitude star and the sun, as they appear in the sky, they would have found that the sun is about 4×10^{10} times brighter. Hence, using the fact that the intensity of light varies inversely as the square root of the distance, they would have taken the square root of this brightness ratio and found that the stars are 2×10^5, or about 200,000, times farther away than the sun. And the faintest naked-eye stars would be about 10 times more distant than that. In fact, most of the stars one sees with the naked eye are 10 or even 100 times brighter than the sun. Accordingly their true distance from the earth appreciably exceeds that calculated by the above rule.

Astronomers determine the distance of a star by detecting and measuring its apparent motion against the background of more distant stars as the earth moves around the sun. The apparent displacement that would result from the motion of the earth through a distance equal to the radius of its orbit is called the *parallax* of the star. The largest measured parallax, corresponding to the smallest distance, is at least 100 times smaller than the minimum angle the unaided eye could possibly detect. Thus all efforts to determine stellar distances prior to the invention of the telescope failed. And, for more than

Nebulosity in Monoceros, located in the south outer region of NGC 2264. The "Cone" Nebula consists of a dark "elephant trunk" diverging from the bright star at left. (Hale Observatories)

Right: Figure 16–1. The parailactic ellipse of a star, reflecting the earth's orbital motion.

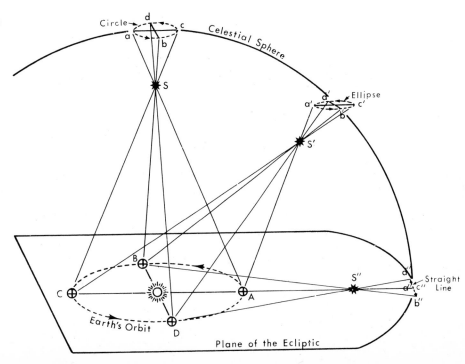

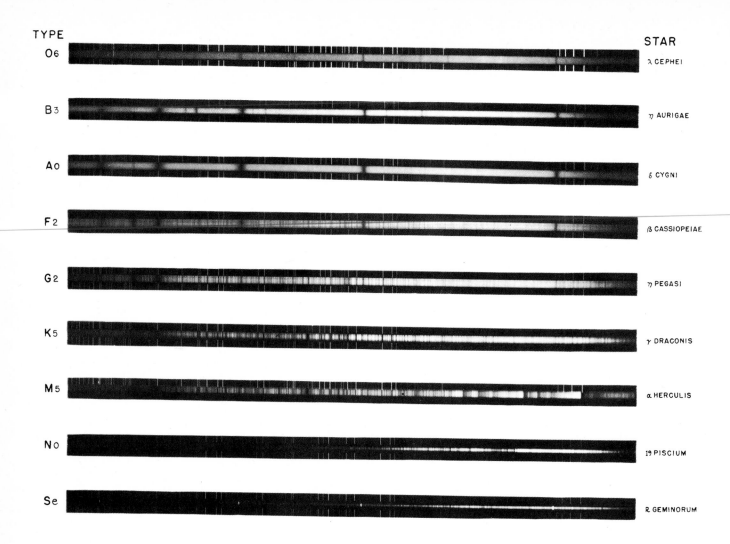

TYPE

O6

B3

A0

F2

G2

K5

M5

N0

Se

STAR

λ CEPHEI

η AURIGAE

δ CYGNI

β CASSIOPEIAE

η PEGASI

γ DRACONIS

α HERCULIS

19 PISCIUM

R GEMINORUM

The principal types of stellar spectra: O, B, A, F, G, K, M, N, and S. (Hale Observatories)

two centuries, telescopes were not sufficiently accurate or sensitive for the purpose. Meanwhile several attempts to measure these distances failed. Even so, the results were of great interest because they led to other discoveries.

Hoping to minimize the effects of refraction, Molyneux, in 1725, installed on his estate near London a fixed telescope specially designed for observations near the zenith, where the correction for refraction approaches zero. Only one bright star, γ Draconis, passed through this zenithal point. However the telescope was so accurate that any deviation of this star from the zenith could readily be determined as it passed overhead. When Molyneux accepted a government post with the admiralty, his young friend, James Bradley (1692–1762), continued the study. The observations were all made visually, of course, because photography was unknown at that time. This star, which forms one of the two bright eyes of the Dragon constellation, lies not far from the northern pole of the ecliptic. In other words, it lies on a line nearly at right angles to the plane of the earth's orbit. One would expect, therefore, that this star would reflect the circular motion of the earth about the sun, itself moving in a small circle on the sky against the background of more distant stars. Measurement of the magnitude of the displacement would provide a determination of the parallax, or distance of the star.

The Displacement of Starlight

The clocks of that period were not sufficiently accurate to enable astronomers to determine the eastward or westward deflections of the star, but only its motion in declination north or south. According to their expectation, the star should have reached its southernmost position in December and its northernmost position in June. The observers found, to their surprise, that the star continued to move southward through January and February into March. It reached its northernmost point, not in June, but in September.

This unexpected behavior led Bradley to extend his observations to other stars. They, too, exhibited a similar pattern. Hence it became clear that this phenomenon resulted, not from the parallactic displacement, but from some other cause. And Bradley presently arrived at the correct explanation. The telescope determines, not the true position of the star, but the direction from which the starlight appears to come. The relationship is analogous to that of a man out in the rain, holding an umbrella over his head. As long as he is standing still, he will hold his umbrella vertically, but as soon as he starts forward, he will have to tilt his umbrella forward, since the velocity of the rain is compounded by its own downward speed and the horizontal speed of an observer. In brief, the small deflection of the apparent direction of the star resulted from the orbital motion of the earth with reference to the velocity of the starlight.

This phenomenon, called the *aberration*, or wandering of light, consists of a displacement of the star from the position it would have if the earth were stationary. An observer of the star, looking back toward our solar system, would see the apparent orbit of the earth as a circle, if the view was from the pole of the ecliptic. From a star in the plane of the earth's orbit, the planet would appear to move back and forth in a line. From other positions, the apparent orbit would be an ellipse. The actual motion of the star, as the result of aberration, reflects this ellipse. The semi-major axis of this ellipse is 20″.5. The total shift from this cause is more than 20 times the parallactic shift of the very nearest star. This discovery was doubly important: it provided the first experimental proof that the earth is moving in an orbit; and it gave a measure of the finite velocity of light (fig. 16–1).

Bradley continued these observations for many years, refining them as he went along. He discovered a second kind of deflection, showing that the axis of the earth does not always have quite the same inclination to its orbit. It has a nodding motion, or *nutation*, which leads to an 18-year periodic variation in the positions of stars. This variation is imposed on the slow, regular drift, or *precession*, of the earth's axis. Thus the path of the north celestial pole among the stars—with a radius of about $23\frac{1}{2}$ degrees and a duration of some 26,000 years—is not a perfect circle. Instead, it has a slightly scalloped edge, deviating from the circle, first on one side and then on the other, by only 9″.2. The wavy outline of the path of the pole departs from its circle by only one part in 9000 of the total radius, but these small changes in the position of the pole affect the positions of stars in the sky.

Figure 16–2. The changes in intensity of various groups of atomic and molecular lines with temperature and spectral class. Neutral atoms are designated I and singly-ionized atoms, II. The molecule shown is titanium oxide.

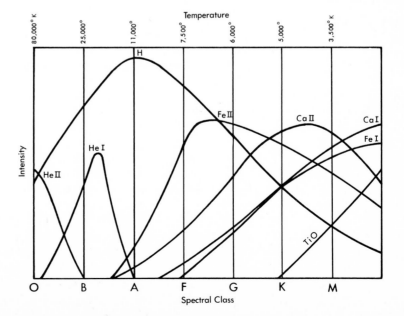

229

About 1800, Herschel made a new attempt to detect the parallactic motion of a star, which is caused by the earth's revolution around the sun. Astronomers had found that a number of the stars in the sky were double. Accordingly, Herschel started measuring the position of one star relative to the other. He did not succeed in determining stellar distances. However, his measurements, continued over a number of years, did show that the directions and distances of the two stars were changing. The stars, therefore, were truly binary systems—one revolved around the other or, to be more precise, they revolved around their common center of gravity.

Modern observations have shown that more than half of the stars in the sky are physical binaries or multiple systems. And the orbital revolutions of these stars, carefully measured by astronomers, have indeed established the universality of the law of gravitation: the stars unquestionably move in accordance with Kepler's laws. Although Herschel had failed in his original objective of measuring stellar distances, he had made a substantial contribution to man's knowledge of stellar systems.

Throughout the first half of the nineteenth century, astronomers continued their attempts to measure stellar parallaxes. They did not succeed; but as the

Figure 16–3. The Hertzsprung-Russell Diagram. The vertical scale represents the absolute magnitude (true brightness) of a star, with the brightest stars at the top. The horizontal scale denotes its spectral type—from hot, blue stars at the left to cool, red ones at the right. The concentration along the main diagonal forms the main sequence. Supergiants lie above and white dwarfs below to the left.

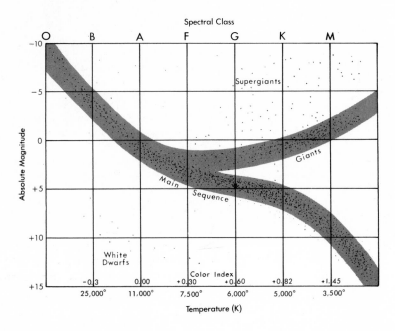

accuracy of their observations increased, they obtained at least one by-product of major importance. Some of the stars appeared to be moving on the face of the sky. Observations over many years confirmed this drift, and it became known as "proper motion." One of the more rapidly moving stars, as determined by Friedrich W. Bessel (1784–1846), bore the assigned number 61 Cygni in a star catalog. Concluding that so large a proper motion meant that the star was a near one, Bessel concentrated his efforts on it. He finally detected the minute shift caused by the motion of the earth around the sun and about 1840 determined its parallax as 0".348. Using a triangulation formula, he calculated that the distance of the star was equal to some 593,000 Astronomical Units.

The Magnitude of Stars

As early as 10 A.D., Claudius Ptolemy had published the first catalog of the positions of 1022 stars, adding eye estimates of the brightness of the stars. The most luminous he called stars of the first magnitude; lesser stars were said to be of the second magnitude, and so on. Those barely visible to the eye were of the sixth magnitude. The original scales were, of course, ex-

The Coal Sack and the Southern Milky Way in the region of the Southern Cross (center of photo). The two bright stars at the left are Alpha (α) and Beta (β) Centauri. (Harvard College Observatory, Boyden Station)

tremely rough. Modern astronomers developed special devices, called photometers, for making accurate measurements of stellar brightness. About the middle of the nineteenth century, N. R. Pogson (1829–1891), of Oxford, proposed a truly quantitative definition of magnitude. Astronomers had already found that, according to the ancient scale of Ptolemy, stars of the first magnitude were approximately 100 times brighter than those of the sixth. Pogson suggested that the brightness ratios be equally apportioned between the difference of five magnitudes. Thus

$$2.512 \times 2.512 \times 2.512 \times 2.512 \times 2.512 = (2.512)^5 = 100$$

almost exactly.

Astronomers adopted Pogson's suggestion, so that stars of the first magnitude were accepted as being 2.512 times brighter than stars of the second; stars of the second magnitude were 2.512 times brighter than stars of the third; and so on. This scale can be extended upward to brighter stars through the introduction of "minus" magnitudes. Thus Sirius, the brightest star in the sky, has a magnitude of minus 1.42 (—1.42). On this scale, Venus at its brightest has a magnitude of —4.3. The magnitude of the full moon is about —12.5 and of the sun —26.7. Since these figures represent brightness as perceived by the human eye, they are referred to as *visual magnitudes*.

An ordinary photographic plate is more sensitive to blue and less sensitive to red than is the human eye. Thus a blue star tends to appear brighter on a

231

photographic plate than a red one, and the red one will appear brighter to the eye. In other words, magnitudes determined photographically—the other kind of apparent magnitude—will not ordinarily agree with those measured visually. When we subtract the visual magnitude from the photographic magnitude, the difference obtained is called the *color index*, because it provides a measure of the actual color of the star. For red stars, this index tends to be large and positive; for white or blue stars it tends to be small.

The apparent magnitude of a star depends on two factors: its true physical brightness and its distance. Therefore, if we wish to compare the intrinsic luminosity of various stars, we must somehow or other compensate for their different distances. For example, if all of the stars lay at the same standard distance, their magnitudes would truly measure the total amounts of energy they were radiating in the spectral region under observation.

The units we have hitherto employed for expressing the distances of stars —such as the centimeter, kilometer, mile, or even the Astronomical Unit—are inconveniently small. As we now know, light traveling at the rate of 186,000 miles a second moves approximately six million million miles in one year. This distance is called a *light-year*. Astronomers have also adopted another somewhat more convenient unit, one related to the concept of parallax itself. A star having a parallax of one second of arc lies at a distance of 206,265 Astronomical Units—which is equal to 3.083×10^{13} km, 1.92×10^{13} miles, or 3.258 light-years. This unit of measurement, the distance at which a star would have a parallax of one second of arc, is known as a *parsec*.

To compare the intrinsic brightness of stars, astronomers arbitrarily adopted the distance of 10 parsecs as the standard. We thus use the term *absolute magnitude* to designate the apparent magnitude that a star would have if it were removed to this standard distance of 10 parsecs (or 32.58 light-years). Simple formulas are available for making the calculation once we know both the apparent magnitude of the star in the visual, photographic, or any other system, and the parallax or distance of the star.

Two remarkable facts stand out in any extensive table of stellar absolute magnitudes. Most impressive, perhaps, is the enormous range over which these magnitudes extend. Our sun, for example, if placed at the standard distance, would have an apparent visual magnitude of about 4.85. It would be about a magnitude brighter than the faintest stars barely visible to the naked eye. A few stars have an absolute magnitude of —5, which means that they are intrinsically ten magnitudes, or ten thousand times, brighter than our sun. Others are as faint as the fifteenth magnitude, ten magnitudes fainter, or ten thousand times less brilliant, than the sun. The sun seems to stand somewhere near the middle of this range. And occasionally exceptional objects appear that are even brighter or fainter than any we have mentioned. Most of the naked-eye stars are intrinsically much brighter than our sun. Although they are far less numerous than stars of much fainter absolute magnitude, we can see them at much greater distances.

The Motion of the Stars

The spectrum of a star gives us additional important information. Having once identified the origin of various spectral lines, we can measure their wavelengths and compare them with the values determined in the laboratory. The measured difference in wavelengths enables the astronomer to determine the motion of the star toward or away from us—called the *radial velocity*—by means of the Doppler effect. The speed of the star, thus calculated, is usually expressed in terms of kilometers per second. We must then subtract the earth's orbital velocity toward or away from the star in order to find its motion relative to the sun. Presumably, we have also determined the star's drift across the sky, its proper motion in seconds of arc per year. Again, if we know the distance of the object, we can compute its apparent velocity in the plane of the sky, termed the *tangential velocity*. Knowing both the radial and tangential velocities, we can calculate the star's true velocity relative to the sun.

The measured velocity of a star is the result of two motions: the motion of the star itself, and the motion of the sun relative to its neighbors. The data from proper motions and from radial velocities clearly indicate that the sun is moving through space, carrying all of the planets with it, at a speed of about 12 miles per second. It is moving toward a point in the sky near the bright star Vega in the constellation of Lyra. We term this point the *apex* of the solar motion. The point diametrically opposite is called the *antapex*. Stars in the vicinity of the apex show maximum radial velocity toward us; those near the antapex show a maximum velocity away from us. The proper motions show results consistent with this conclusion. In brief, the stars are slowly opening up in the direction of the apex, drifting past us, and closing in on each other toward the antapex. The changes are, however, very slow. The familiar constellations show a negligible change in 10,000 years. Major changes would occur in 100,000 years, and, after the lapse of 1,000,000 years, earth-dwellers will see a completely new set of bright stars and constellations.

Many of the stars possess variable radial velocities, alternately approaching and receding from us in a period as short as a few hours or as long as a few years. In many instances we can see two superposed spectra, each spectrum from a different star. One of the stars seems to approach us while the other is receding; then they cross over and reverse directions. These stars are spectroscopic binaries, revolving around their common center of gravity. Again, an extension of Kepler's laws enables us to determine the individual masses of the stars. Even though we cannot always see the spectrum of the companion star—it may be too faint—we can infer the existence of the star.

It is of some interest to note that the first star discovered to be a *spectroscopic binary* was Mizar, which, as we have seen, was also the first star to be recognized as a visual binary. As a matter of fact, each of the two visual components is itself a spectroscopic binary. In the brighter visual component, both spectra appear. The period of revolution about their center of gravity is about 20.5 days. The fainter visual component shows only one spectrum, but the variation in radial velocity clearly reveals its binary character. As we shall see, not all stars with variable radial velocities are binaries.

The Colors of Stars

Astronomers studying stellar spectra during the second half of the nineteenth century found enormous differences among them. At the Harvard College Observatory Miss A. C. Maury (1866–1952) and Miss A. J. Cannon (1863–1941) painstakingly examined thousands of high-dispersion stellar spectra and discovered that they could be arranged in a sequence in which a given spectrum differed just perceptibly from those on either side. A system of letters—O, B, A, F, G, K, and M (with R, N, and S as possible alternatives for M)—was introduced to designate the main classes of stellar spectra. Numbers from 0 to 9 were used to devote the decimal divisions between one class and the next.

The spectral sequence clearly depends on the temperature of the stellar photosphere. The star colors range from blue at the head of the sequence, through white, yellow, and orange, to deep red among the classes M, N, R, and S. The color indices previously mentioned show a close correlation with spectral types. Indeed, when stars are too faint for their spectra to be obtained, astronomers often use the color index as a substitute. The blue stars, of course, are the hottest. The photospheric temperatures gradually decrease toward the end of the sequence, beyond which infrared stars not even visible to the unaided eye have been found.

Although most stellar spectra display dark absorption lines, occasional stars, expecially those in the W or early O classification and some of those near the very end of the sequence, have emission lines as well. Astronomers use the terminology "early" and "late" as an indication of order in the sequence, without any implication concerning the evolutionary development of the stars.

The Bubble Nebula in the constellation
Cepheus. (Lick Observatory)

Spectral Types

At one time astronomers attributed the wide variety of stellar spectra to differences in chemical composition. But that was before the discovery of the spectral sequence and the recognition that temperature of the stellar atmosphere is the primary factor controlling the spectral types (fig. 16–2).

The three sub-sequences, M, S, and R-N, which run more or less parallel, may well result from differences in chemical abundance. The M-type stars apparently have plenty of oxygen, so that metallic oxides can form. The most prominent of these is titanium oxide, TiO, which has characteristic bands in several regions of the spectrum. Stars of type S show, instead, strong bands of zirconium oxide (ZrO). Note the chemical relation, in the Periodic Table, between titanium and zirconium, which fall in the same column of the table. Some true differences in abundance of these two substances may be responsible for the spectral differences between types M and S, although stars of type S may be somewhat cooler than those of type M. Stars of classes R and N show intense bands of molecular carbon. If oxygen were a dominant substance in these atmospheres, one would expect the carbon to have been literally "burned" into carbon monoxide or carbon dioxide. The absence of this reaction indicates the presence of a reducing atmosphere, for hydrogen inhibits the burning. In the spectra of these later types, the spectral lines of hydrogen are unexpectedly strong, far more intense than simple theory would indicate. At these low temperatures, theory indicates that the Balmer lines should be nonexistent. Most of these stars have very extensive atmospheres, and they may contain some regions hot enough to produce the unexpected hydrogen absorption. This suggests phenomena encountered in our solar atmosphere—extremely hot prominences and an even hotter corona.

Stars of class W derive this abbreviation from the fact that they were once referred to as Wolf-Rayet stars, after two astronomers who had made special studies of their characteristics. Their absorption spectra closely resemble those of class O. However, these stars also show broad emission lines, which probably originate in large expanding shells of gas escaping from the stars. The broadening results from the Doppler effect. There seem to be two classes of W stars, one with strong lines of carbon and the other with strong lines of nitrogen. Again we may be dealing with differences in chemical abundance.

Miss Maury, carefully examining the spectra of different stars of essentially the same spectral type, occasionally found some stars with extremely sharp lines. To the designation of such stars she appended the letter "-c" after the main spectral type. We now know that such stars are generally the most massive, the most luminous, and possess the most distended atmospheres of all stars in that particular classification.

Two very different methods are available for photographing the spectra of stars. In one, the telescope focuses the light from the star upon the slit of a spectroscope. By this method the spectrum of only a single star can be obtained on one exposure. A much more efficient method employs a camera that would ordinarily photograph over a wide field of the sky many hundreds or even thousands of stars in a single exposure. A thin prism placed in front of the telescope lens objective disperses the light and brings the various colors to different foci. Each star image is thus spread out to form a spectrum, with violet at one end and red at the other. The telescope is allowed to drift slightly in order to widen the spectrum so that the lines become visible. In this way, one may record the spectra of large numbers of stars on one plate.

The most extensive study of stellar spectra to date was carried out by Miss Cannon between 1911 and 1924. She listed the spectral types of almost a quarter of a million stars brighter than about the tenth magnitude. With the information concerning the spectral types and absolute magnitudes of many thousands of stars, we are now in a position to study the evolution of and relationship between the various stars. The results appear in the *H-R diagram*, named after its formulators, Ejnar Hertzsprung (1873–1967) and Henry Norris Russell (1877–1957). In such a diagram, the horizontal scale representing the spectral types is essentially a sequence of temperature, with highest temperatures to the left and lowest to the right. One might also use the scale of color index, with numerical values increasing toward the right, as a substitute for the spectral types. The vertical scale consists of the absolute magnitudes of the stars, with brightest stars at the top and faintest stars at the bottom (fig. 16–3).

Such a diagram reveals that the stars are not scattered at random. They fall into well-defined regions, of which the most conspicuous is the main sequence, which extends diagonally across the figure. The small group of stars, commonly referred to as white dwarf, appears in the lower left corner of the diagram. A group of luminous stars with absolute magnitudes of about 0, stretching from spectral type F to type M, represent what have come to be called the giant stars. Near the top of the diagram lie the supergiants, stars of tremendous luminosity.

The red M stars fall into two groups—one with extremely high and the other with extremely low luminosity. The spectrum and color of these stars tell us that both groups have approximately the same temperature and, hence, each square inch of surface must have about the same luminosity. The huge differences in total brightness, therefore, must derive from the fact that the giant stars are truly giants as compared with the faint red dwarf stars near the bottom of the main sequence. This dichotomy occurs in most of the spectral types. The supergiants are even more luminous than the giants and, hence, for a given spectral type, must be even larger.

Astronomers found that the "-c" characteristic applies to most supergiant stars. Thus one can tell by merely looking at the spectrum whether a star is a supergiant or an ordinary giant. The former have much smaller surface gravities and much more extensive atmospheres. At the other extreme, the dwarf stars along the main sequence have atmospheres that are much more compressed and have correspondingly higher pressures. As we noted for the sun, lowered pressure tends to favor ionization. Thus, for two stars whose spectra appear at first sight to be almost identical, one can find that the lines from ionized atoms are much stronger in the spectra of giant stars than in those of the dwarfs. In fact, the degree of this intensification makes it possible to determine, by simple examination of the spectrum, the luminosity or absolute magnitude of the star. This figure, in turn, permits one to calculate the parallax, or distance of the star. By this means astronomers are able to determine "spectroscopic parallaxes" of stars whose distances are so great that ordinary parallaxes cannot possibly be measured.

The H-R diagram should also reveal something about the evolution of stars. Sir William Herschel once compared the situation of an astronomer to that of a botanist who spends a day walking through the forest. On every side the walker sees evidence of tree growth—fallen seeds, seedlings, slender saplings, sturdy oaks, fallen trees, decaying stumps, and mold. Although he may not see a single leaf unfold in the course of a day, the botanist should be able to put together what he has observed and arrive at a fairly clear picture of the life history of a tree.

The atronomer, however, is at a disadvantage. The preconceptions of earlier astonomers led him to an entirely erroneous picture of the evolution of a star. Believing that stars condense out of rarefied clumps of gas to form the large, bright giant stars, he inferred that a star begins its life as a red giant, then slowly condenses, growing hotter but smaller until it becomes an O- or B-type giant. Here, so the argument went, partial exhaustion of the stellar fuels caused the star to continue contracting, cooling off in the process. This theory appeared to give a reasonable explanation of the main features of the H-R diagram, and was widely accepted. But it was wholly erroneous. We shall presently return to questions of stellar evolution, but we must first discuss the characteristics of certain unusual stars, variable stars, and stars so peculiar that we may even find it difficult to fit them into the H-R diagram. And we must also recognize that objects other than stars are vital parts of our galaxy, that is, those hazy, distended objects known as nebulae, of which there are several varieties, both bright and dark.

The Galactic Nebulae

A nebulous haze—a sort of interstellar smog—pervades our galaxy. The *nebulae* are enormous clouds of dust and gas, often thick enough to obscure still more distant glowing clouds of stars. Some are clearly visible to the naked eye, the most obvious being the cloud of dust silhouetted against the bright summer Milky Way, and splitting it down the middle, through the constellations of Cygnus and Aquila. Even more conspicuous than this giant "rift" is the sharply-outlined region called the Coal Sack, in the constellation of Crux, the Southern Cross. Other clouds are found some distance from the Milky Way but they are much less conspicuous because the stellar background they obscure is relatively faint.

At first, astronomers thought that these dark patches were regions more or less devoid of stars. But then they came to realize that if gaps had originally occurred among the stars, the random motions of the stars themselves would have filled in such gaps. The final proof of the physical nature of the obscuring clouds came when astronomers found luminous O- or B-type stars in the complex—the nebula itself became visible either through light reflected from such a star or by light characteristic of the gas associated with the cloud.

The *bright galactic* or *diffuse nebulae* owe their luminosity to specific atomic processes. As elsewhere in the universe, hydrogen is by far the most abundant of all the chemical substances in these objects. Helium is the second most abundant element, and oxygen and nitrogen are also important constituents. Neon, which we on earth generally consider a "rare gas," ap-

Enlarged section of bright and dark nebulosity in Monoceros, surrounding an open star cluster. (Hale Observatories)

pears to be equally prominent in the gaseous nebulae and in other celestial objects. Apparently the earth has lost its primitive neon. Other components of the gaseous nebulae include sulphur, argon, and occasionally iron; however, the metals do not appear to be abundant.

Nebular Luminosity

The spectra of gaseous nebulae are characteristic of gas emission at extremely low density and high temperature. The atoms absorb the stellar light in the far-ultraviolet and undergo multiple ionization. The lines of hydrogen, helium, and ionized helium are prominent and a few ordinary lines of oxygen and nitrogen also appear. But the most spectacular feature is spectral lines, some of which have not yet been produced in the laboratory. These spectral lines remained unidentified for many years. Astronomers speculated that some element—which they named nebulium—unknown on earth might be responsible for these radiations. A Mount Wilson astronomer, Ira S. Bowen, finally proved that these lines represent atomic transitions that, in spectroscopic parlance, possess a very low oscillator strength. Where an ordinary atom releases its energy in ten-millionths of a second or less, atoms sometimes take a second or more to emit this particular kind of radiation. Such spectral lines are therefore termed "forbidden." In the extremely tenuous gas of a nebula, the atom can radiate only when it has been excited by collision with a free electron. Under these circumstances ordinary lines—those with high oscillator strengths—become extremely weakened. Forbidden lines then overtake the ordinary lines in brilliance and dominate the spectrum. And that is what happens in the spectra of gaseous nebulae.

Interstellar Dust Clouds

A collision between two clouds of gas and dust can also produce a luminous streak, especially along the interface, or common boundary. Very small dust particles, with diameters less than a few tenths of a micron—smaller than the wavelength of light—tend to scatter blue light more effectively than red light. Smoke or fine dust in the terrestrial atmosphere scatters the blue and reddens the setting sun, producing brilliantly-colored clouds. In the same manner the fine dust of interstellar space reddens the distant stars. Usually, an O- or B-type stellar spectrum indicates that the star will be blue in color. But sometimes, the passage of light through the dust clouds reddens the star until its color index is more characteristic of spectral type M.

Dust clouds can also affect the polarization of starlight. In principle, if a viewer observed a star through polaroid spectacles, the intensity of the light would change as one rotated the polarizer. Actually, the amount of polarization is far too small to be observed so simply, but measurements by photoelectric techniques can detect it. Maps show in addition that the polarizations of starlight from stars in a given area of the sky tend to lie parallel to one another. Spherical, or highly irregular, dust grains could scarcely affect light polarization except in a completely random manner. To produce polarization, the particles must be shaped like tiny needles and some force must hold the long edges of the needles parallel to one another. The evidence suggests that weak magnetic fields permeating the galaxy probably align the particles and cause the polarization.

Thus interstellar dust clouds exert three major effects on starlight: they absorb and weaken the stellar radiation; they redden the starlight passing through the volume; and they produce a small but measurable polarization.

Although the obscuration that takes place may suggest the presence of large quantities of dust, an actual count shows that interstellar space is not so dusty after all. The distance between individual grains of dust is enormous. If, for example, a celestial vacuum cleaner could sweep up all the dust in a volume as large as that inside the earth, probably little more than a cupful would be recovered. The obscuration, therefore, indicates the immense depths of the dust-filled layers through which we are looking.

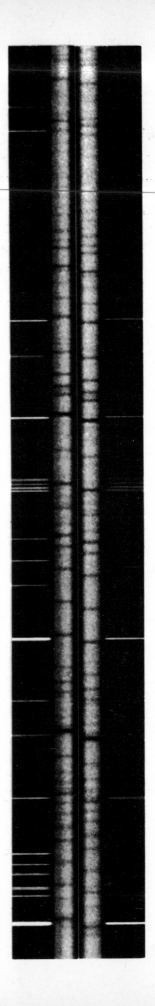

The bright gaseous nebulae are among the most spectacular of all celestial objects. They exhibit a wide variety of forms. Most of them look slightly pinkish, because the red line of hydrogen tends to dominate the spectrum. There are, however, many radiations throughout the region; and the nebula itself, as seen by the eye, rarely shows much color. Many bright diffuse nebulae occur, and such objects provide favorable viewing even through a small telescope.

We have other evidence of the chemical content of interstellar space within our own galaxy. The lines of a spectroscopic binary shift back and forth as the star approaches the earth and recedes from it. But a few such lines do remain essentially stationary. These include the H and K lines of ionized calcium, the D lines of neutral sodium, and a few lines from potassium, iron, and titanium. Some molecules, such as CN and ionized CH, also contribute lines of this type. Astronomers eventually found that these stationary lines were the result of gas in interstellar space. As they plotted the small observed shifts of the spectral lines from this gas over the sky, they were even able to detect some evidence for the rotation of the galaxy as a whole.

Radio astronomy has provided an extremely important new technique for studying the chemical composition of the intergalactic realm. The potential of this technique became evident when the Dutch astronomer H. van de Hulst pointed out that hydrogen atoms could absorb and emit radiation in the radio region at a wavelength of about 21 centimeters. This radiation was soon discovered and launched a new era in astronomical research, with special techniques and equipment.

These radio waves showed a remarkable ability to penetrate, without sensible loss of intensity, the obscuring dust clouds abounding in certain regions of our galaxy, especially toward the galactic center. They had a second advantage: wavelengths and frequencies could be determined with extreme accuracy, so that even small Doppler displacements could be measured. Thus, painstakingly, astronomers began to map the inner regions of our galaxy and find clear evidence for the spiral structure they had long suspected would be there.

The Milky Way—especially the central region—strongly emits a large amount of radio static: a hissing, crackling noise not unlike that heard from an AM radio receiver during a thunderstorm. Grote Reber, an American amateur radio astronomer, recognized the cosmic nature of this static because it varied in intensity with sidereal time. He found it most intense when the bright star clouds of the galactic center, in Scorpius and Sagittarius, were highest above the horizon. Astronomers still do not completely understand what causes this radio static. Most likely the emission comes from free electrons spiralling and oscillating in magnetic fields near hot stars or in the depths of space.

A wide range of radio frequencies is present, producing in effect a continuous spectrum. The 21-centimeter hydrogen line can be superposed in emission upon this background. Sometimes a large mass of hydrogen will absorb radiation from the continuum, producing a strong radio absorption line analogous to the dark, solar Fraunhofer lines.

Astronomers discovered that many other atoms and molecules could absorb and emit radiation in the radio region. The number of substances identified as present in the interstellar medium rapidly increased. The hydroxyl molecule OH produced very strong lines in absorption as well as in emission. Among the other molecules identified were ammonia (NH_3), water (H_2O), and even formaldehyde (HCHO, sometimes called methanal, since it is an oxide derivative of methane). And additional hydrogen lines, produced when protons capture electrons in very high energy levels, have also been discovered.

We shall presently deal with another type of gaseous emission object, the planetary nebula, which is closely related to certain kinds of variable stars.

Two spectra of a single-line spectroscopic binary, Castor (α Geminorum), near maximum velocities of approach and recession respectively. The lines are shifted toward the blue in the former and toward the red in latter with respect to the bright spectral lines of iron given for comparison in the left and right margins. (Lick Observatory)

239

17

Variable Stars, Star Clusters, Galaxies, and Quasars

Certain stars merit our special attention. These are the *variable* stars, which fade and brighten at both regular and irregular intervals.

Variable stars fall into various categories, each usually named after an outstanding body in the group. A few of the brighter stars have specific names, such as Algol or Mira, and others are designated with Greek letters, such as β Lyrae, or ε Aurigae; but most of the known variable stars are too faint to merit special designation. Some variable stars were designated by the capital letters between R and Z; and when more stars were discovered a system of double letters, going from AA through ZZ, was introduced. With this system astronomers could take care of 334 stars in each constellation. However, in certain areas of the sky, especially among the star-rich constellations near the Milky Way, astronomers identified more variable stars, and still another sequence, beginning with 335 and prefixed by the letter "V" (for variable) was initiated.

Eclipsing and Intrinsic Variables

We have already learned that many stars in the sky are binaries. When the plane of the orbit of one these binaries lies nearly in the line of sight, the stars may eclipse one another at regular intervals, causing the light to diminish. The members of such an eclipsing pair often possess very different characteristics. For example a large, faint star may eclipse a small, bright one, causing an immense decrease in brightness (17–1). Algol, or β Persei, suffers an eclipse every 2.87 days and falls from its normal magnitude of 2.2 to 3.47, a decline in brightness amounting to more than a factor of three. This eclipse is only a partial one (fig. 17–2), with a small arc of the brighter star showing behind the fainter one. Both stars are considerably brighter than the sun. The slight decrease in brightness, amounting to only a few hundredths of a magnitude, midway between primary eclipses, occurs when the brighter star eclipses the fainter one. The slight increase of luminosity between the primary and secondary eclipse results from what astronomers call the "reflection effect": the brighter star heats the fainter one so that the side of the darker star facing the brighter star is somewhat more luminous than its other side. Stars having total eclipses have light curves that remain briefly constant near minimum light.

The variable β Lyrae represents an entirely different sort of star, one whose light curve varies continuously. Such binaries consist of two stars so close together that their mutual gravitation distorts them into an egg shape, with the longer axes facing each other. β Lyrae, for example, varies between magnitude 3.4 to 4.3 in a period of slightly less than 13 days.

The periods of eclipsing binaries range from as short as a few hours to as long as 27 years (for ε Aurigae). Eclipsing binaries are also spectroscopic binaries (17–3).

Unlike eclipsing stars, many variables are *intrinsic*, that is, their light changes are inherent in the fundamental structure of the star. Associated with such fluctuations are changes in the heat output and the effective temperature of the star, its color, spectrum, and radial velocity. Changes of velocity, we should note, arise not from the orbital motion but from radial motions—expansion, contraction, or convection—in the stellar atmosphere.

NGC 7293, the Helical planetary nebula in Aquarius. Photographed in red light. (Hale Observatories)

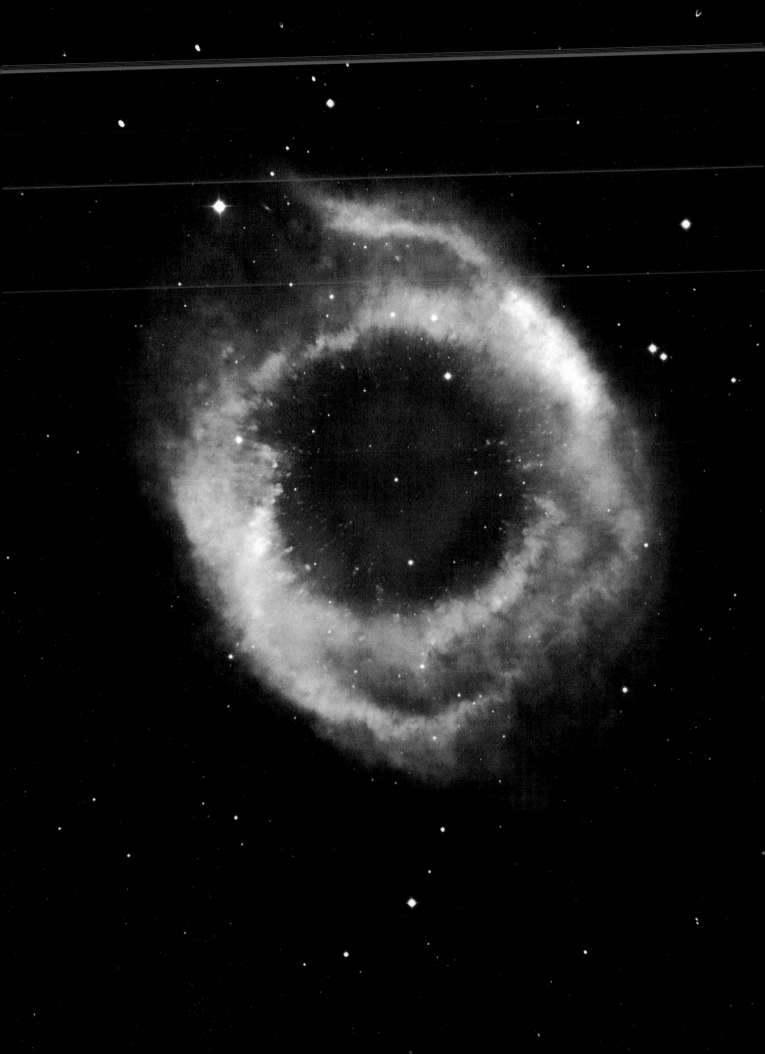

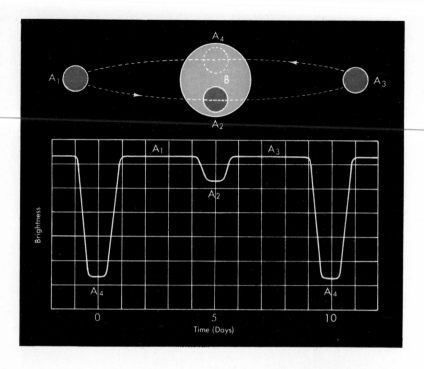

Figure 17–1. Light curve of an eclipsing binary with total eclipses. The brightness is constant during the total eclipse.

The great majority of these stars are periodic or almost periodic in their variability, but many vary unpredictably, often for reasons we do not fully understand. The main objective in studying the variable stars is to identify their probable location in the H-R diagram so that we can understand their relationship to ordinary, nonvariable stars.

The Periodic Variables

Astronomers recognize six somewhat related groups of stars whose variation is periodic or virtually periodic. First come the *long-period variables*, of which Mira, or o Ceti, is the best-known example. At maximum, Mira is a star of the second magnitude, a conspicuous object in the neck of Cetus. Its color is dark red, indicating a low temperature. And the spectral class of this star, M6e, is consistent with its redness. After reaching maximum, the star slowly fades away until at minimum it is about forty times too faint to be seen with the unaided eye. Thereafter the star slowly brightens until it reaches another maximum after a mean interval of about 331 days. The interval may vary by as much as a month either way; such minor irregularities are characteristic of the long-period variables.

Studies have shown that these variable stars are truly giants in size and have enormously distended atmospheres. Spectroscopic evidence indicates that they have layers of luminous hydrogen deep in the atmosphere, where the temperature is higher, even though the density of the gas may still be very tenuous. The variations in brightness are never exactly the same. At maximum, for example, Mira may attain only third magnitude, although sometimes it has been as bright as magnitude 1.2.

Changes in the intensity of the strong titanium oxide bands in the spectra of the long-period variables, or the Miras, tend to exaggerate the variations in brightness in the visible range. The absolute magnitude of these stars' visible light is high, averaging about —1.5; however, since most of the energy lies in the far infrared, the stars are very much brighter than even this figure indicates, with bolometric absolute magnitudes of about —5. Thus the stars are radiating approximately 10,000 times as much energy as our sun. They must, therefore, be relatively short-lived because they use up their energy sources so fast.

Huge clouds of luminous **gas** surround several of the Miras, notably

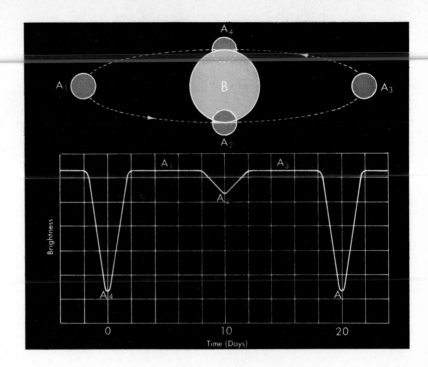

Figure 17–2. Light curve of an eclipsing binary with partial eclipses. The brightness varies continuously.

R Aquarii and Z Andromedae, to form what we ordinarily call a planetary nebula. Since the luminosity of a nebula generally depends upon the absorption of radiation in the far ultraviolet, these stars, despite their redness and low effective temperature, may nevertheless be radiating immense amounts of energy in this spectral region. We shall consider this anomaly when we discuss the planetary nebulae. Not all of the Miras are of spectral class M. A few, such as R Cygni, exhibit S-type characteristics, with strong bands of zirconium oxide replacing those of titanium oxide. Many thousand Miras are known, with periods ranging from about 80 days to several years. Keeping track of the variations in these stars is very time-consuming, and the American Association of Variable Star Observers, with members including many amateurs around the world, has assumed the major responsibility for observing the variations. Maps may be obtained from that organization that show the location of the variable stars and the magnitude of many nearby reference stars useful in estimating the brightness of the variable. Such observations represent a real contribution to science that only the amateur can make.

The term *Cepheid variable* has been applied to several related classes of objects. The name derives from the fact that two of the brighter members of the group were β and δ Cephei. The Germans refer to them by the colorful name of *blinksterne*, or stars that blink. The variations in radial velocity led astronomers to believe for many years that the Cepheids were a form of spectroscopic binary. However, calculations of the orbit usually revealed that the stars were almost in contact or even overlapping. Finally it became evident that the stars were pulsating radially, alternately expanding and contracting.

The star δ Cephei varies between magnitudes 3.8 and 4.6 with a period of 5.4 days. The light curve of δ Cephei varies continuously, with the rise to maximum more rapid than the fall to minimum (fig. 17–4). Most of the standard Cepheids have periods that range between 1 and 100 days. Their spectral types are for the most part F and G. As one might expect, the spectral type varies with the light emission, becoming later when the star is faint. The colors also vary; the stars are reddest and possess the largest color index near minimum light. The spectral type occasionally is as late as K; in other words the stellar atmospheres become quite cool.

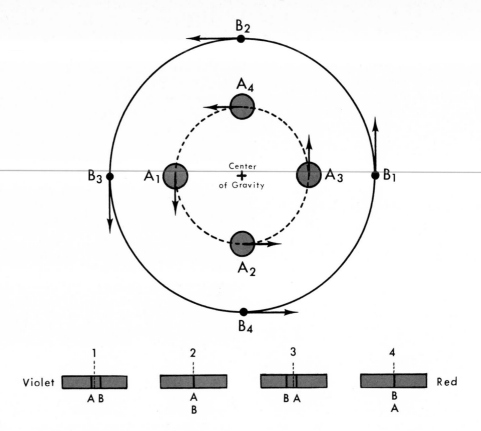

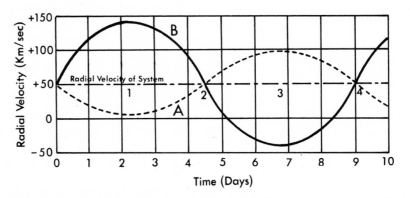

Figure 17–3. Spectroscopic binary with circular orbits. When one star moves toward us the other moves away from us. The first star's spectral lines are shifted toward the blue, and the second star's lines are shifted toward the red. The lines of the whole system are thus doubled. A quarter of a revolution later neither star is moving toward or away from us, and their lines are superposed. The central diagrams show the Doppler shifts of the two components of the binary for their four positions. The lower diagram presents the radial velocity variation of the binary through a full revolution.

The standard Cepheids, usually referred to as type I, are extremely luminous objects, falling among the supergiant stars in the H-R diagram. Not a single one of these supergiants is near enough for its distance to be determined by trigonometric parallax. We have been forced, therefore, to employ indirect methods for distance determination. Miss Henrietta Leavitt (1868–1921), working at the Harvard Observatory, discovered many such variables in the Large and Small Magellanic Clouds, two remarkable objects that appear respectively in the southern constellations of Dorado and Tucana. To the naked eye they resemble fragments of the Milky Way, but a telescope resolves them, as it does the Milky Way, into a huge number of stars. Astronomers now recognize that these clouds are the nearest of all the galactic systems, of which our own Milky Way is a representative. The clouds here are, however, much smaller and belong strictly to a class of dwarf galaxies.

Comparing photographs taken at different times, Miss Leavitt discovered many variable stars, measured their light curves, and determined their periods. The forms of the light curves clearly identified them as members of the Cepheid family. But unlike the Cepheids in our own Milky Way system, which lie at widely different distances, those in one of the clouds must lie at almost the same distance from us. The stars that are visually brighter than others are assumed to be more luminous. The Cepheids of longest period were also found to be brighter than those with shorter periods. This relationship, known as the Period-Luminosity law, has been widely used by astronomers to determine distance. Once the distance of a single star of this type could be determined and its absolute mangitude calculated, it was possible to change the scale of measured apparent magnitudes of all these Cepheids to absolute magnitudes. Thereafter when someone discovered Cepheid variables in an object of unknown distance, measured their magnitudes, and determined their periods, their absolute magnitudes immediately became known along with the distance of the object. This method has been extremely important in determining the scale of our own galaxy and the distance to other galactic systems.

Another group of stars with light curves and periods resembling those of the Cepheids appears to be about $1\frac{1}{2}$ magnitudes fainter than the Cepheids of type I. Their spectra are also of class F and G; but unlike standard stars of these classes, they show emission lines. Their velocity curves are not continuous, but may vary sharply from one radial velocity to another. Such stars, referred to as type II Cepheids, have several recognized subdivisions. Those with the longest periods—between 30 and 50 days—are called the RV Tauri stars, while those with periods between 10 and 30 days are the W Virginis stars. We recognize still a third subdivision, the RR Lyrae stars, whose periods range from a few hours to perhaps as long as one day. These stars were first discovered in the great globular star clusters, concentrated spherical groups containing hundreds of thousands of stellar components.

RR Lyrae itself possesses a magnetic field. The star appears to be rotating very rapidly and the field itself oscillates in a 41-day cycle superimposed on the normal 0.567-day variability. There is evidence that metals may be less abundant in the RR Lyrae and possibly along the entire sequence of type II Cepheids than in ordinary stars. The RR Lyrae variables are very complex and we need much further observation of them before we can hope to understand their relationship to other stars. They have spectral types between A and F and absolute magnitudes of approximately 0. There also may be a group of dwarf Cepheids still fainter than the RR Lyrae stars.

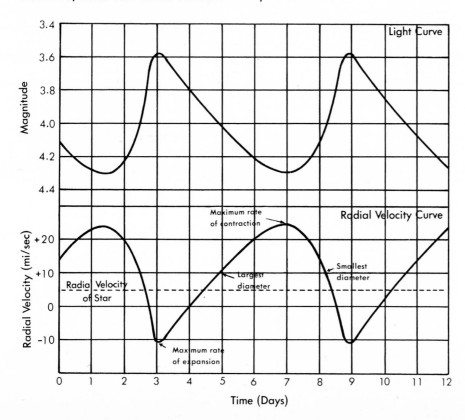

Figure 17–4. Light curve and radial velocity curve of a typical Cepheid variable. The lower curve resembles the upper one turned upside down.

Nova Pictoris, 1925. Top: before outburst; center: at maximum; and bottom:
after maximum. (H. Spencer Jones,
Cape Observatory)

Miscellaneous Variables

The foregoing groups comprise the greater number of known variable stars.
There are, however, many stars that vary irregularly but fall into no specific
type or class. Betelgeuse, the first-magnitude red star in the constellation of
Orion, is the brightest example of an irregular variable. The star is huge and
must possess a highly-distended atmosphere whose diameter fluctuates
constantly and irregularly. Many other giant and supergiant stars of late
spectral type have this characteristic. Changes of spectrum in these stars
indicate that differences in temperature as well as diameter occur. For a few
brighter stars, such as Betelgeuse and Antares, the variations in diameter have
been directly confirmed by measures with an interferometer. The spectra of
semiregular and irregular variables include all of the late classes: M, S, R, and N.

246

R Coronae Borealis is one of the most interesting of all of the truly irregular variables. Its spectrum bears the complex designation cG0ep. The G0 indicates a type that has some features in common with our sun, which is of the same spectral type. The prefix c marks the star as having unusually sharp lines, and the suffix ep indicates that the spectrum has emission lines and is in other respects peculiar. The presence of strong carbon bands suggests that this star, if cooler, might be of class R or class N. Several other similar variable stars are, in fact, of the R or N spectral type.

Since some stars of this group are bright enough to be observed in the Large Magellanic Cloud, we can determine their absolute photographic magnitudes to be of the order of —5, so that the stars are very luminous. The character of the variation in light is noteworthy. The brightness may remain sensibly constant for months or years at a time but then may drop suddenly by six or more magnitudes in a few days or weeks. Thereafter it will fluctuate erratically and slowly return to maximum brightness after many years. The causes of this variation are still unknown.

The *spectrum variables* represent another class. These stars have intense magnetic fields and show minor changes in light. The spectrum may undergo remarkable changes in a period ranging from a day to several weeks. The magnetic fields also vary. Some of these stars, such as α^2 Canum Venaticorum, have peculiar spectra with intense lines of the "rare-earth" elements. These spectra then slowly change over to a more common spectral type. The magnetic field also changes at the same time. It appears almost as if the star has one kind of spectrum on one side and an entirely different spectrum on the other side. Then, as the star rotates, the two spectra seem to alternate.

Probably the most erratic of all variables are the flare stars—red dwarfs of spectral types K or M. Without warning, a star of this kind will suddenly brighten by two or three magnitudes and then fade within a matter of minutes. The stellar flares occur erratically and cannot as yet be predicted. They are thought to resemble solar flares, but on a much greater relative scale. Simultaneous observations by radio and photographic techniques have shown that these stars vary in radio as well as optical emission; in this respect they also resemble solar flares.

Still another class of stars exhibiting erratic variations are the T Tauri variables. Since they usually lie in regions full of gas and dust, astronomers have suggested that the variation may be extrinsic, the result of partial obscuration of the star by interstellar dust clouds. Others have viewed the T Tauri stars as astronomically very "young" objects, just barely condensed out of a vast nebulous cloud and not yet settled down to the steady production of energy by nuclear processes.

Explosive Variables

From time to time stars seem to explode, increasing their brilliance 100,000- or 1,000,000-fold within an interval of one or two days. Every twenty years or so, such a star may reach first or second apparent magnitude, though it originally may not have been previously visible even on long-exposure photographs. It is known as a *nova*.

The actual stellar event constitutes a true explosion, probably caused by the sudden release of an immense amount of atomic energy, as in an H-bomb. The detonation causes the star's outer layers to expand like a huge balloon or bubble. The greater the magnitude of the explosion, the more material that is ejected. Large spectral shifts to the violet indicate that the atmosphere is expanding with high velocity. After the star attains maximum luminosity and begins to fade, bright lines begin to appear. The outer envelope then slowly dissolves into a nebula. Eventually a great gaseous shell surrounds what remains of the now collapsed stellar core. Such an object is a type of planetary nebula, although most of the ordinary planetaries have much smaller velocities of expansion.

Planetary nebulae are special objects very different from diffuse gaseous

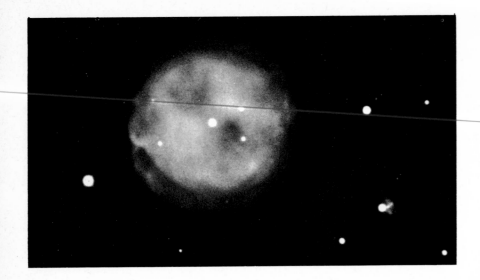

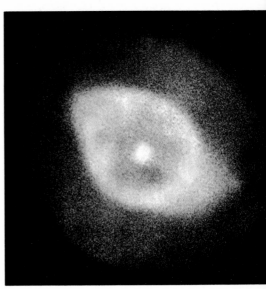

Left: The "Owl" Nebula (NGC 3587), a planetary in Ursa Major. (Hale Observatories)

Below: A planetary nebula in Hydra, NGC 3242. (Hale Observatories)

nebulae, though both require the presence of a hot star to excite their luminosities. Most planetaries have small, sharp-edge disks. In a telescope they look something like a small planet, such as Uranus. Many early observers, seeing one of them, thought they had discovered a new planet until its lack of motion showed that it could not be a planet.

The planetary nebulae are usually quite symmetrical in structure. They are transparent, so that we see both sides at the same time. If a condensation appears on one side of the central star, a similar one will very likely appear on the opposite side. The shape of the nebula often suggested to earlier observers some familiar terrestrial object, giving rise to such designations as the Ring, the Crab, the Dumbbell, the Owl, and the Eskimo. Probably not all planetaries represent old novae. Those that do not may well be caused by some similar type of stellar explosion.

Although truly bright novae are relatively rare, about 25 of them brighter than apparent magnitude 9 when at maximum do appear in the course of a single year. Novae as bright as Sirius or even brighter are not uncommon. The brightest so far this century has been Nova Aquilae 1918 (we label novae in terms of the constellation and the year of appearance), which reached the maximum of magnitude —1.1. What little we know about the pre—nova stage suggests that such stars are dwarfs, slightly variable and perhaps with spectra of an early type.

Supernovae resemble ordinary novae, but are very much brighter intrinsically, perhaps by as much as 10,000 times. Estimates place their absolute magnitudes near —18 at maximum. To give some idea of their almost inconceivable brightness, it may be pointed out that such an object will radiate in a single second as much energy as the sun gives off in several years. Supernovae are rare. One that appeared in 1572, known as Tycho's star, is famous because it stimulated Tycho Brahe's interest in astronomy. Kepler observed a similar star in 1604. The remnants of these objects can no longer be identified. However, a nova that appeared in the constellation of Taurus in 1054 and was recorded in the Chinese Annals can readily be recognized today as the Crab Nebula (color plate 45).

Supernovae are relatively rare events in the history of a galaxy; nevertheless, we have seen many supernovae for two reasons. First, there are millions, perhaps billions of galaxies in the universe. Second, supernovae at maximum are only a few magnitudes less bright than the total brightness of the entire galaxy in which they appear. Hence they are conspicuous objects despite their immense distance—many million light-years—from us.

The Crab Nebula, although ordinarily listed as a planetary, is unique in several ways. First, it has an intense continuous spectrum in addition to the ordinary line spectrum characteristic of such gaseous objects. The light from

The open star cluster M 67 (NGC 2682) in Cancer. (Hale Observatories)

this continuous spectrum is, moreover, highly polarized, probably because of strong magnetic fields that persist in its vicinity. The effect has been compared to that associated with the Van Allen radiation belt surrounding the earth. When we turn our great radio telescopes toward the Crab we can also detect the strong hissing noise indicating that radio emission is still coming from this nebula after more than 900 years. We do not know how long such radiation may continue.

Another class of cataclysmic variables exhibits repeated nova-like explosions at intervals of several weeks or months. These are the dwarf novae, of which SS Cygni and U Geminorum are the prototypes. Such stars remain at minimum for weeks or months, showing only minor fluctuations; they then suddenly brighten in one day by five or six magnitudes, revealing, as they do so, broadened lines of hydrogen and helium. Near maximum some emission lines appear; the star then begins to fade and slowly returns to minimum, at which point many bright lines appear in the spectrum.

A second group resembles ordinary novae except for the fact that they undergo more than one nova-like outburst in a century. These are recurrent novae, such as T Coronae Borealis, which had major eruptions in 1866 and 1946. This star appears to be a binary as well, although how the binary system affects the nova-like behavior is not at all evident. From the foregoing evidence we must conclude that many stars—and perhaps all stars—are subject to nova outbursts, though the maximum brightness and range of magnitude may vary considerably.

Planetary Nebulae, W Stars, and Pulsars

Planetary nebulae are, as we said, huge clouds or envelopes of luminous gas surrounding what is usually a very hot star of type B, O, or W. These hot stars

249

all give off large amounts of ultraviolet radiation. The Wolf-Rayet or W stars also exhibit very broad emission bands in their spectrum, suggesting the presence of an expanding, semitransparent shell of gas. Many of them are binaries. From the orbital data we surmise that W stars possess masses ranging from four to ten times that of the sun. These are much too small to develop into an ordinary nova. One might call them slow for they apparently eject material into space to form the planetary nebulae that now surround most of them. Eventually they will contract to form white dwarfs.

I have pointed out that several planetaries have red Mira variables for nuclear stars instead of the characteristic W star. Some astronomers have postulated the existence of a hot, invisible companion, which conceivably might be responsible for the nebular excitation. On the other hand, one may reasonably picture what could happen if, perchance, a W star were to develop a larger, thicker, and more opaque distended atmosphere around it. Although radiating the same amount of energy, the larger envelope would radiate less energy per unit area. It would thus have to be cooler and, conceivably, might fall in the M-type category. Indeed, the atmosphere may resemble an automobile tire more closely than a large ball, enveloping only the equator and allowing ultraviolet radiation to escape unimpeded from the central core.

What happens during the tremendous cataclysm of a nova explosion is becoming increasingly clear. We have theorized that the cataclysm results from the collapse of a super-massive star, with a release of atomic energy and an explosion of the major portion of the star into space. But there remains a small core in which matter is so compressed that the electrons must combine with the free protons to produce neutrons. This neutron star, to conserve its angular momentum, spins many times a second, vibrating continually. It radiates very short pulses of radio energy with such regularity that astronomers could use them as timekeepers. The most precise measures, however, do indicate a very gradual slowing down of the radio emissions.

Astronomers have found that such objects exist in the universe, emitting pulses of radio waves many times per second. Such objects have received the name of *pulsars*. Initially, a few astronomers jestingly referred to them as L.G.M.s, an abbreviation for "Little Green Men," because their regularity, and the fact that their pulsar radiations bore a resemblance to man-made radio navigation beams, suggested the existence of some extraterrestrial intelligence. Such science-fiction speculation soon disappeared when astronomers were able to identify one of the pulsars with an actual astronomical object: the nucleus of the Crab Nebula. The radio pulses come regularly at the rate of 30 per second, with a tiny but measurable slowing down. The identification of the object became final when photoelectric studies of the star recorded visual variations with the same period as the radio pulsations.

Double and Multiple Stars

Stars, like human beings, tend to be gregarious. In the immediate vicinity of the sun out to a distance of 5 parsecs or about 16 light-years, we have been able to detect 31 single stars, 9 binaries, and 2 triple systems. Thus of the 55 stars considered in this nearby volume of space, almost half are members of complex families. Although we do not have as precise a census of stars at greater distances, our data tend to confirm the conclusion that about half of the stars in our own Milky Way are members of complex or multiple systems.

The very first star recognized as a visual binary, Castor, or α Geminorum, was discovered by William Herschel in 1803. Later studies proved that Castor is an even more complex system, consisting of three pairs of spectroscopic binaries, A, B, and C, with respective periods of 9.22, 2.93, and 0.81 days. A and B revolve around one another in a period of 340 years. C takes several thousand years to execute a single revolution about A and B. The existence of such a complex system poses important questions about its origin and evolution; and still more complex systems exist, with correspondingly greater problems.

A globular star cluster in Hercules, M 13 (NGC 6205). It is about 22,000 light-years away. (Hale Observatories)

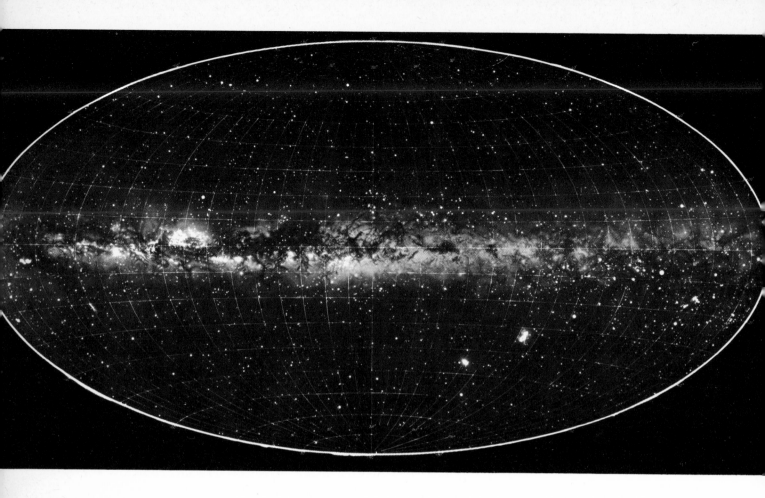

A map of the Milky Way as viewed from earth. (Lund Observatory, Sweden)

Galactic Clusters

Our Milky Way includes many groups of stars containing from a dozen or so members up to several hundred. At first sight, one might assume that such clusters were merely accidental aggregations. However, measurements of their parallaxes and proper motions show that they are truly physically-connected systems. And since all of the stars in each cluster probably originated in a common source, they must have had a similar evolution and are approximately coeval in age.

We call such objects *open* or *galactic clusters*, to distinguish them from the still more complex and condensed globular clusters. Without question, the best-known association of this type is the famous naked-eye cluster called the Pleiades (color plate 41). Where the naked eye sees only six or seven faint stars, even the least optical aid, such as a pair of binoculars, will reveal 30 or 40, and a large telescope will disclose several hundred still fainter members. Clouds of gas and dust surrounding the stars glow dimly, in part from reflected starlight and in part from the excitation resulting from the absorption of the stellar ultraviolet by the gaseous matter.

Such relationships between an open cluster and surrounding nebulosity are by no means uncommon. We find many similar relationships elsewhere in the Milky Way, especially toward Scorpius, Sagittarius, and Centaurus, which lie in the central regions of our galactic system. Among other naked-eye open clusters is the Hyades, not far from the Pleiades, a somewhat less compact group near the bright star Aldebaran, in Taurus. The stars of the delicate constellation Coma Berenices, or Hair of Berenice, comprise the largest of all the naked-eye objects of this type. Still another cluster, which occurs in Cancer and is known as Praesepe appears as a fuzzy object to the naked eye.

The open clusters are themselves not always single. A pair of such clusters, visible to the naked eye as hazy condensations of the Milky Way, are known

252

as h and X Persei. This double cluster constitutes a true physical system of two related and overlapping clusters.

In passing, we may note that five of the seven bright stars forming the Big Dipper are moving parallel to one another. They are in fact part of a loose open cluster, of which the bright star Sirius is also a member, even though we see it in a different part of the sky. The point is that our own sun is moving through this loose cluster, between the Big Dipper on one side and Sirius on the other. The sun, however, is not a true member of the cluster. As a result of this proper motion, the Big Dipper is slowly changing its form. In 100,000 years it will no longer resemble a dipper.

In these open clusters the stars are so far apart that their mutual gravitation can scarcely hold them together. As they wander through the Milky Way, passing stars and groups of stars subject them to varying tidal forces. As a result, the clusters gradually disperse and their members join the aggregates of randomly moving stars that form the background of the Milky Way.

Star Associations

Because stars of spectral types O and B are among the most luminous objects in our Milky Way system, we can detect much larger though much less dense clusters of such stars than we can those of other spectral types. Astronomers have discovered a number of such groups and, to distinguish them from other clusters, have given them the name of *associations*. These groups of stars are so large and their members so few that their mutual gravitation cannot possibly hold them together. The associations, therefore, must be young as compared with the galaxy as a whole. Their age is estimated at something like 10,000,000 years. Also the very fact that these highly-luminous stars are radiating away their energy at a prodigious rate precludes the possibility of their having been in existence for any great length of time. These so-called O associations will rapidly decline in brilliance and fall apart, with the stars evaporating into the galactic background.

The great star clouds of our galaxy, like those in Cygnus, Scutum, Sagittarius, and Centaurus comprise large associations. Such clouds are responsible for much of the light of our Milky Way. Viewed from another galaxy, they would appear as bright condensations along the arms of a spiral galaxy.

Globular Clusters

All of the various groups, clusters, associations, and star clouds that we have discussed are relatively loose in structure. Their shape may be roughly spheri-

Figure 17–5. The spiral arms of our galaxy near the sun as revealed by radio surveys in the 21-cm line of hydrogen.

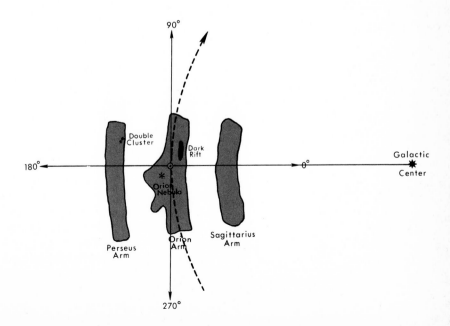

cal, ellipsoidal, or even very elongated. But none shows any decided central concentration. Of an entirely different character are the *globular star clusters*. Photographs show these as highly condensed toward the center; even pictures taken with the greatest telescopes rarely show the central regions completely resolved. By contrast, open clusters often appear as only a slight increase of density against the stellar background.

Observed with the unaided eye, several of these globular clusters are bright enough to be seen as somewhat fuzzy stars. The brightest are ω Centauri and 47 Tucanae, both in the southern hemisphere, the latter being close to the Small Magellanic Cloud. The brightest such object in the northern sky is M13 (NGC 6205) which appears as a fourth-magnitude star in the constellation of Hercules. Its estimated distance from earth is about 22,000 light-years.

More than a hundred such globular clusters are known. They are concentrated in Scorpius-Centaurus toward the center of our Milky Way. However, many of them lie toward the edge of the Milky Way and thus a chart of them more or less delineates the outer boundaries of our Milky Way. Most globular star clusters exhibit a spherical symmetry, although a few are slightly elongated. Actual counts of stars from the photographs are somewhat deceptive because of the crowding near the center of the picture and also because the object undoubtedly contains many stars too faint to appear on the plate. Scientists estimate that there are approximately 100,000 stars in the average cluster. The tremendous combined mass of these stars binds the cluster gravitationally, so that the object is quite stable.

Studies of the spectra of the brighter stars have clearly shown that their stellar composition differs considerably from that of the average star in our galaxy. There are, first of all, a huge number of Cepheids of the type we have referred to as RR Lyrae. Such objects were in fact first discovered in the globular clusters and are often referred to as cluster variables. There are also quite a number of giant M stars in these clusters. Since these objects are largely coeval, we may expect to learn a great deal about the evolution of stars from careful studies of the cluster H-R diagrams.

Many galaxies besides our own have considerable numbers of globular star clusters. The Large Magellanic Cloud, for example, contains such clusters. And so does M31, the Great Andromeda Nebula. The size and brightness of the globular clusters appear to be remarkably constant and hence can be used as a means of determining the distances of the objects containing them. Magnificent when seen through a large telescope, they are unquestionably among the most interesting of all celestial objects. Although we have found it necessary to mention galaxies, they form a group of stars and nebulae of an order significantly greater than those here discussed. We shall find that the gregarious tendencies of stars extends to these and to still higher orders.

The Milky Way

We have viewed our galaxy in terms of its component parts: stars and solar systems, double and multiple stars, open clusters and associations, diffuse gaseous nebulae, planetary nebulae, globular star clusters, clouds of interstellar dust and gas. Now let us try to see the truly complex system of the Milky Way as a whole.

The Milky Way completely circles the sky and divides the entire celestial vault into two hemispheres. Man eventually realized the significance of Galileo's discovery that the light from this band came from the collective glow of myriad stars too faint to be seen individually by the unaided eye. Thomas Wright (1711–1786) was probably the first to understand the significance of the Milky Way. As early as 1750 he conceived of our vast system as having a shape like an enormous grindstone, filled sparsely with stars and with the sun somewhere near the center. Five years later, working independently, the German philosopher Immanuel Kant (1724–1804) came to a similar conclusion. But the first really quantitative study of the problem must be credited to William Herschel, who systematically sampled various areas of the sky, some close to and some far away from the galactic belt. He counted the stars visible in each area—a procedure he called "star gauging"—and in 1785 he published the data from 683 such regions. The counts of individual stars ranged from zero or a very small number in regions far from the galaxy to almost 600 in the galaxy itself. Herschel correctly concluded that these data threw light on the actual structure of the Milky Way.

Scientists now know that our Milky Way resembles the myriads of spiral galaxies, large and small, that we see in all parts of the sky except in the galactic plane itself. Within this region, known as the *galactic equator*, the immense dust clouds obscure the more distant spiral galaxies, which undoubtedly lie farther out. Here and there, even relatively close to the galaxy, the dust clouds occasionally thin out and we can glimpse galaxies lying far beyond.

It appears that our Milky Way is a fairly tight spiral, with a diameter of about 100,000 light-years and a thickness of about 10,000 light-years. Partly from star counts and partly from the dynamics of the stars, whose motions are determined by the gravitational fields within the "arms" of the Milky Way, we deduce that the galaxy consists of about 100 billion (10^{11}) stars. Interstellar space is, on the whole, a fairly good vacuum, containing on the average no less than one atom or molecule in every cubic centimeter.

We have seen how man had to realize, first, that the earth was not the

Figure 17–6. A perspective view (a), and a side view (b) of our galaxy. Note the eccentric location of our system: our sun is about 30,000 light-years from the nucleus of the galaxy.

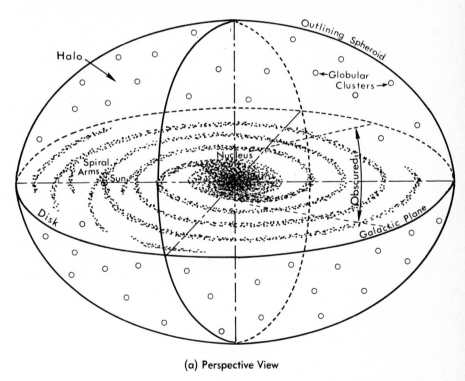

(a) Perspective View

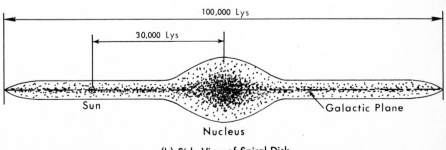

(b) Side View of Spiral Disk

center of the universe. Later, he had to accept the humbling fact that our sun is indeed far from the center of our galaxy, which lies in the direction of the great star clouds of Sagittarius, Scorpius, and Centaurus. The sun appears, in fact, to be about 30,000 light-years from the center of the galaxy, or three-fifths of the way from the center to the edge (fig. 17–5).

We realize that the globular star clusters more or less outline the limits of our galaxy. And, despite the high concentration of stars toward the galactic plane, a halo of stars occurs at somewhat greater distances, forming what is sometimes called the *galactic corona*. This tenuous haze of stars is roughly spherical in shape and can be traced as far as 100,000 light-years in a direction perpendicular to the galactic plane (fig. 17–6). We see similar coronas around other large galaxies.

As one might infer from the spiral structure of our Milky Way and other galaxies, these systems are rotating. The rotation, however, is not entirely uniform, the angular velocities of the outer layers being somewhat less than those nearer the galactic center. As a result, the spiral arms tend to "follow" the rotation and continually stretch out or lengthen. At the distance of the sun from the center, we estimate that a single rotation requires approximately 200,000,000 (2×10^8) years, an interval sometimes called the *galactic year*.

Other Galaxies

Immanuel Kant was probably the first person to conceive of the possibility that the faint condensations of light we now call the galactic nebulae might be independent stellar systems like our own Milky Way. For some reason, the idea was extremely slow to win acceptance. Even in the early twentieth century, many astronomers continued to argue that the objects were relatively near and that their spiral structure represented, not galaxies, but solar systems in the making. But finally, in the early 1920's, Edwin P. Hubble of the Mt. Wilson Observatory took large-scale photographs which clearly resolved some of the larger and brighter spirals into component stars. Furthermore, he found many Cepheid variables among the component stars. He used the Period-Luminosity law to determine their true magnitudes, and then, from their known apparent magnitude, calculated their distance from us. The distances turned out to be over a million light-years. Hence, these nebulous patches of light were indeed Milky Way systems, each one an independent island universe, as they were sometimes called.

Photographs reveal the existence of millions, perhaps billions, of galaxies—far too great a number to study individually. But statistical analyses of the group as a whole, with detailed examination of selected objects, have

Hubble's classification of types of galaxies. E denotes ellipticals; E0 is the most spherical form, while E7 represents the most flattened elliptical galaxy. S denotes spiral galaxies, and SB barred spirals. The small letters indicate the relative size of the galaxy's central nucleus. Objects with large, unresolved centers are designated by a, intermediate by b, and very small by c.

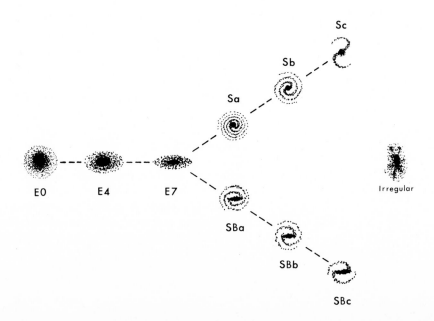

In spiral galaxy M 101 the spiral arms are clearly visible. The bright patches in the spiral arms of this immense system are similar to the gaseous nebula in our own galaxy. It is about 2,000,000 light-years away. (U.S. Naval Observatory)

furnished much information about galaxies and their relationships. They exhibit, first of all, a wide variety of shapes and appearances which must be attributed to genuine differences in physical composition. Our two nearest galaxies, for example, the Large and Small Magellanic Clouds, have quite irregular boundaries. Their distances, as determined from the Period-Luminosity relation, proves to be nearly the same, about 150,000 light-years. They might be called dwarf galaxies, since they are much smaller than either our Milky Way or many other spiral systems.

One of the most famous spirals is the Great Nebula in Andromeda, which one can see with the naked eye as a faint, fuzzy star of the fifth magnitude. On photographs it is a magnificent object, with a small dwarf companion, which is almost five magnitudes fainter even though the two galaxies lie practically at the same distance from us. The mere fact of such a pair illustrates what strange objects the universe contains.

Certain galaxies possess an amorphous structure, lack spiral arms, and have different degrees of ellipticity. It is believed that these objects are, like the spiral galaxies, disk-shaped groups of stars in rotation. The observed ellipticity of such objects depends, therefore, upon the orientation as well as upon the oblateness of the object. The significant feature of such galaxies is their lack of a spiral structure. One may reason that these are galaxies in an early stage of evolution, in which the spiral structure has not yet developed. Indeed, we often find spiral galaxies with arms that can be barely distinguished from the amorphous elliptical type. Many spirals also show a central condensation with an almost straight bar across it, with the spiral arms emanating from the edge of the bar. These carry the obvious name of "barred spirals."

Hubble has grouped these nebulae into classes (fig. 17–7), but this classification is simply descriptive. It does not indicate in which direction the evolution, if any, is taking place. There is, in fact, some evidence that the elliptical galaxies may be the old ones, in which the spiral arms have vanished simply because they have made so many revolutions that they have wound around and around one another. The outer portions of the spiral arms, which seem to contain the more massive and therefore the brighter stars, tend to evolve more rapidly and for that reason have finally disappeared.

Clusters of Galaxies

Like stars, galaxies have a tendency to form clusters or associations. Of these, there are two major types. The regular clusters are roughly spherical. They are considerably condensed toward the center and often possess more than a thousand member galaxies brighter than absolute magnitude —15 and many fainter ones. A cluster in the constellation of Corona Borealis is one of the best-known. The members of such clusters are usually of Hubble type E or S0; in other words, spiral galaxies rarely occur in them. Galaxies also tend to form irregular clusters, which show little central condensation. The member galaxies may be of any of the Hubble class. One of the richest examples of such a cluster is that in Virgo. A less characteristic association, important only because our own galaxy is a member of it, is the so-called local group, which

NGC 205, a dwarf satellite of the Great Nebula in Andromeda, shown resolved into its component stars. (Hale Observatories)

contains 17 known members, including the Large and Small Magellanic Clouds and the Andromeda Nebula. Another important member is M33, the great Spiral Nebula in Triangulum, located about 2,300,000 light-years away.

Double, triple, and multiple galaxies are common. Several thousand clusters have been recognized and that figure probably is merely a beginning, for we are still making a census of only the nearer regions of intergalactic space. We have even found clusters of clusters with individual diameters of more than 100,000,000 light-years. What does this tendency of matter to form families and super-families signify, and where does it end? Are we probing anywhere near the ultimate depths of the universe?

The Red Shift

One indication that we are looking into distant intergalactic space comes from the nature of the spectra of galaxies. The fainter, smaller, and presumably

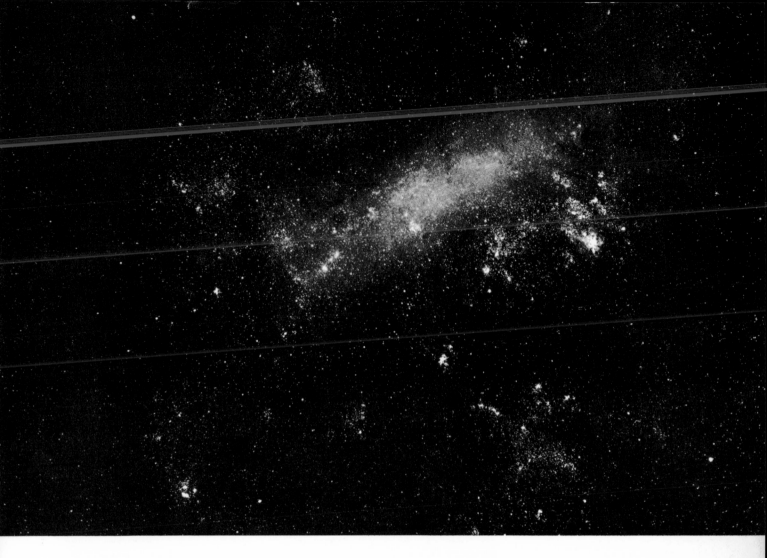

The large Magellanic Cloud. (Harvard College Observatory, Boyden Station)

more distant ones have their spectral lines increasingly shifted to the red, as compared with the larger galaxies. We have been accustomed to interpreting such shifts as a Doppler effect of motion toward or away from the observer. A shift toward the red indicates motion away, and since the shift increases with distance, a literal interpretation of this effect would require the universe to be expanding, with our own galaxy near the center of the expansion.

We noted earlier that the center of our galactic system is a source of radio noise, which is a form of static. Many other galaxies are also radio sources, some weaker and some far stronger than our galaxy. Several objects are truly raucous in their outpouring of static. Optical studies show that such emissions may be associated with the apparent extrusion of a jet-like appendage. In at least one instance, two galaxies appear to be colliding.

Quasars

Radio astronomers have succeeded in detecting a large number of noisy objects that, when photographed with a large telescope, look like stars. These are now called quasi-stellar objects or *quasars* for short. They have two distinguishing features. First, they are decidedly blue in color, indicating that the quasars are very hot objects. Second and more surprising, their spectra are strongly red-shifted, like the distant galaxies. The argument raged for some time concerning the place of quasars in the scheme of the universe. Some astronomers thought they were a type of massive hot star, and attributed the red shift to the presence of a strong gravitational field. Others maintained that the quasars—for all their stellar appearance—were in reality a special form of galaxy. The second point of view has more generally prevailed. We shall meet quasars again as we discuss their possible role in the development of the expanding universe.

The Evolution of Stars, Galaxies, and the Universe

18

In previous chapters we have glimpsed the universe in its immense complexity, from atom to planet to star to galaxy, seeing it as a kind of vast furnace, building stars, blowing them up, and forming others. We know that the secret of the stars lies in the heart of the atom: the atomic nucleus. We also know that there are certain fundamental particles of the atom: hydrogen, or rather its components—the proton and the free electron. There is one other principle of physics that profoundly governs the universe: "the second law of thermodynamics." This law states that heat always flows from a hot body to a colder body, never in the other direction. In this principle lies the secret of the evolution of the stars.

In the beginning—according to one concept of the origin of the universe—was hydrogen: a huge cloud of atoms, protons, and electrons pervading all of space. Whence it came no one knows. The word "space" has a somewhat elusive meaning in a world where time is nonexistent; but even in such a "changeless" world, important events were bound to occur. Irregularities began to appear, initially on a large scale and then on a smaller one. The vast cloud broke up, first into galaxies and then into stars, as the smaller, irregular masses took on a spherical shape and collapsed under the force of their own gravitation. The increasing compression heated the gas and soon the stars were shining—somewhat fitfully at first because the major sources of stellar energy were just being turned on. Deep in stellar cores, protons were colliding and sometimes adhering to one another, releasing energy in the process. The proton-proton reaction had started to build up helium nuclei, converting matter into energy.

In this early stage of the universe there was nothing to regulate the size of these condensations. Yet if a condensation was too small, the gravitational forces were too feeble to take control and the body never became hot enough to shine, unless it chanced to coalesce with other small condensations. Gaseous spheres with masses from about one-tenth to ten times that of the sun did become stars, but they never became hot enough inside to sustain the kinds of nuclear reactions that would build up atomic nuclei even as heavy as carbon. Such objects may have existed as stars for a few billion years before they finally collapsed into the small, very dense stars we call white dwarfs.

The Age of Supernovae

The most important bodies in the primeval state of the universe were those whose masses were a thousand or perhaps even a million times greater than that of the sun. In such objects the gravitational forces dominated and the compression produced high internal temperatures and densities conducive to the formation of the atomic nuclei of heavy chemical elements, through iron and lead up to uranium and beyond. Such stars were extremely luminous and radiated so much energy so rapidly that in a few hundred thousand years—a short time from a cosmic viewpoint—they literally ran out of energy.

In their last stages, these stars collapsed still further under gravitational forces, releasing enough reserve energy to cause the star to explode. Each star flared brilliantly for a few weeks or months as a supernova, while pieces of it flew off in all directions. What remained of the original star collapsed

Facing page: The spiral galaxy M 81 in Ursa Major. It is three to four million light-years away. (U.S. Naval Observatory)

260

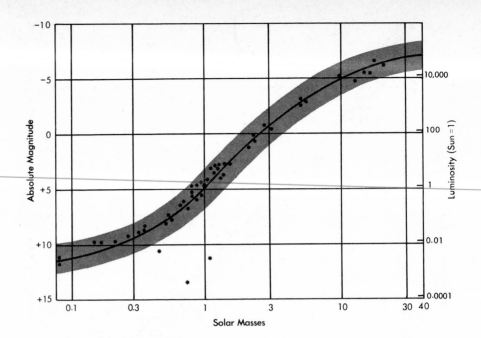

Figure 18–1. The relationship of mass to luminosity. The more massive a star, the brighter it is.

into an object so dense that a cupful might weigh as much as a million tons. The electrons and protons, which were highly compressed, united to form neutrons. Such neutron stars are smaller than our earth and rotate very rapidly—some of them many times a second. As they rotate they send out regular pulses of radio energy and light, called pulsars. One of the best-known neutron stars is the central star of the Crab Nebula, the remnant of a supernova whose explosion was observed, as we noted, in 1054 A.D.

The important fact about such events is that the raw material—hydrogen—had been converted into heavy elements and then returned explosively into space, where it mixed with what remained of the original hydrogen. Some of this material, enriched with the heavy elements, condensed to form a substratum of dust that in turn coalesced to form ordinary second-generation stars such as our sun.

Supernova explosions are not all alike. Some may form planetary nebulae, some may expel a gaseous envelope that continues to expand indefinitely, and some may simply break into thousands or hundreds of thousands of pieces. If these individual pieces are themselves of stellar dimensions, the explosion can produce a star cluster. It has long been my conviction that globular star clusters might themselves be derived from the wreckage of such a catastrophe. Favoring this theory, perhaps, is the fact that globular clusters are generally recognized to be the oldest known celestial objects. The stars that compose them are ancient and decrepit, well on their way to what may be called the cosmic graveyard. We call them stars of population 2, to distinguish them from the young stars of population 1, which are continually being formed in the spiral arms of galaxies where gas and dust occur, from which the stars can condense.

The age of supernovae, which so altered the chemical composition of the substratum of cosmic dust and gas, probably lasted several billion years. At the end of that period the universe was differentiated into the huge units that would eventually form individual galaxies. The globular star clusters and a few individual stars were shining. Condensations were again beginning to form in our galaxy, much as they had formed in the primeval universe. While the smaller condensations failed to grow, the very large ones evolved rapidly, developed instabilities, and finally exploded—but on a scale appreciably less than that of the supernovae. These outbursts, of which perhaps a dozen or so occur annually somewhere in our own galaxy, are the ordinary novae. Those with masses neither too small nor too large became the stars.

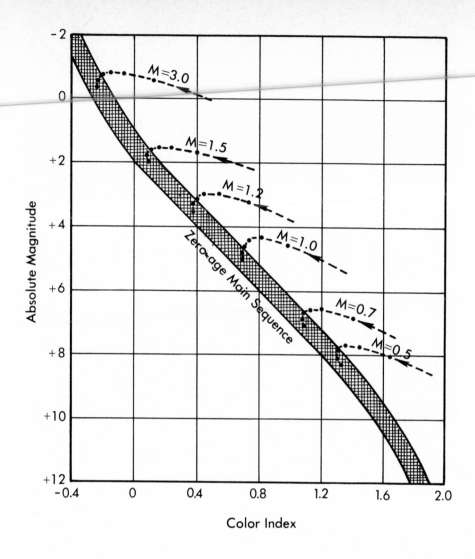

Figure 18–2. Evolutionary tracks of stars contracting toward the main sequence. The numbers give the mass of the star in terms of solar masses.

The H-R diagram, which pictures the relationship existing between the brightness of stars and their surface temperatures, carries information about stellar evolution. To appreciate the significance of this diagram, the reader may here wish to glance again at figure 16–3. The most obvious feature of this diagram is the concentration of points along a diagonal from the upper left to the lower right, the main sequence. This shows that very bright stars tend to be hot and blue and of spectral type O, B, or A, whereas very faint stars are cool and red and of type K or M. Our sun, which lies about the middle of the main sequence, is only of medium brightness. It is a yellow star of spectral class G.

The Life Cycle of a Star

A newborn star does not settle down immediately into its appropriate position along the main sequence. First it is large and cool, collapsing gravitationally until the atomic fires are kindled in its core. Then it coughs and gasps briefly as a T Tauri variable. Then it finally becomes stable and settles down on the main sequence. The more massive the star, the more luminous it will become. A star will hold its position in the sequence until it has exhausted its initial supply of atomic hydrogen in the stellar core, at which time its internal structure begins to change (figs. 18–1, 18–2).

Even when hydrogen is depleted in the stellar core, a considerable supply still exists in the outer layers, which tend to collapse and heat up so that the hydrogen can be consumed. Therefore, paradoxically, as the star begins to run out of fuel it gets brighter. The more massive stars, of course, exhibit larger and more rapid changes of brightness than the less massive ones.

The Sombrero Nebula, M 104 (NGC 4594). This galaxy, seen nearly edge-on, shows the strong concentration of obscuring material in the galactic plane. It is 25 light-years in diameter and 14,000,000 light-years away. (U.S. Naval Observatory)

A star three times more massive than the sun, for example, will radiate about a hundred times more energy and should therefore use up its hydrogen about thirty-three times more quickly. This process continues until most of the internal hydrogen is consumed and converted into helium. The helium core then collapses under gravitational attraction, its temperature rising until the helium starts to burn, building up still heavier atomic nuclei. The star then becomes even brighter. Its outer layers expand rapidly, and it becomes a red giant, like Antares or Betelgeuse.

As noted earlier, stars in a given cluster are probably of the same age. By comparing them we can therefore find out approximately how they have evolved from the main sequence. With the passage of time, the more massive stars of the cluster inflate themselves into luminous, short-lived red giants. The heaviest of these will become novae, explode, and disappear from the cosmic scene, leaving the stars of lesser mass. The latter will in turn increase in brightness less rapidly and less spectacularly to form red giants of lower luminosity. Our sun will eventually become such a star, expanding until it engulfs, in turn, Mercury, Venus, the earth, and possibly even Mars. It may even become a nova before it fades away to dark oblivion. We can draw such a conclusion concerning the fate of the sun as a result of observations of the history of a very old cluster such as NGC 188, which goes back almost ten billion (10^{10}) years (fig. 18–3).

The last stars to leave the main sequence will be the red dwarfs for the simple reason that they are extremely faint and hence do not burn up their hydrogen rapidly. The star evolves rapidly through the giant or supergiant phases. Many of them start to pulsate, forming the Cepheids or RR Lyrae variable stars. These utilize the dregs of hydrogen, helium, and other nuclear reactions before they develop a final major instability, forming a nova if the expansion is rapid or a planetary nebulae if it is slow. The exhausted central star then rapidly collapses to form a white dwarf, a star of extremely high density, or perhaps even a neutron star. Bereft of all sources of energy, the white dwarf cools off and finally fades away into the stellar graveyard of black dwarfs (fig. 18–4).

White dwarfs are so faint we cannot see them at any great distance. Nevertheless, the presence of so many of them in our solar neighborhood indicates that such stellar catastrophes are fairly frequent events. It is estimated that at least 10^{12} years would be required for a white dwarf to cool off sufficiently to become a true black dwarf. Since that figure greatly exceeds the estimated age of our galaxy, one may question whether any black dwarfs exist. Nevertheless, unless some entirely unknown process can rejuvenate the universe, the second law of thermodynamics would seem to require that the entire universe should eventually go down to extinction—into the ultimate graveyard where all stars are cold and black with, perhaps, just a few glowing redly in the chilling darkness of intergalactic space.

The Age of the Universe

In an earlier chapter we discussed the chemical composition of the earth and the universe as a whole, with its hundred-odd chemical elements, some stable and some unstable. In the course of building a few of the unstable elements in our modern atomic laboratories we have recently begun to know their properties.

Of the unstable atoms, radium and uranium are perhaps the most familiar. Their nuclei are radioactive. The nucleus of an ordinary uranium atom can explode a number of times, as we have already noted, forming different atoms in the process and finally ending up as lead. Since uranium is not now being formed in the earth, the uranium we find must be a remnant of radioactive matter left over when the universe, or at least our solar system, was forming. The chemical composition of our surroundings can thus yield definite clues about the "prenatal" state of the universe. Of the two kinds of uranium,

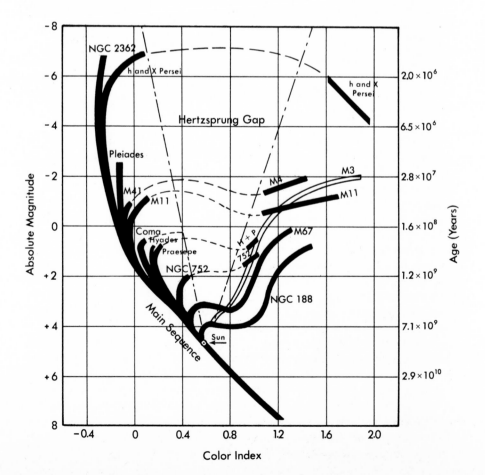

Figure 18–3. Composite H-R diagram for star clusters (after A.R. Sandage). The older stars, for any cluster, are those lying above and to the right. They are the red giant and supergiant M stars of large color index.

265

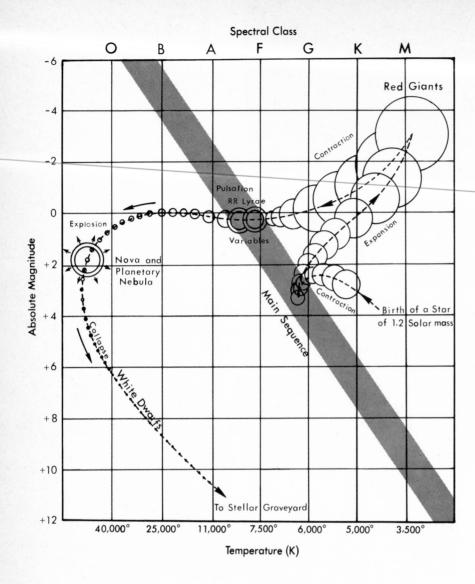

Figure 18–4. Evolutionary tracks on the H-R Diagram, representing the evolution of a star from birth to death.

the heavier kind, U-238, decays to Pb-206. The lighter kind, U-235, which is used for atom bombs, finally decays to form Pb-207. By measuring the relative amounts of these lead isotopes in rocks, we can determine their age. This method is something like estimating the age of a community from the quantity of debris in the local dump or in an ancient buried midden, or from the number of headstones in local cemeteries. The older the rock, the greater the proportion of the lighter lead. And when we study the oldest samples of all, including meteorites and rocks from the moon, they show a maximum age of about 4.6 billion years. We conclude from this that our solar system began some 4.6 billion years ago, or at least that the matter from which our system was formed accumulated at about that time.

There is another important clue in distant galaxies. Spectroscopic determinations of the Doppler effect show that these galaxies are moving away from us, the more distant ones moving more rapidly than the nearer ones. The universe thus seems to be expanding at a tremendous rate, and perhaps even exploding. We infer this staggering expansion from the fact that the spectral lines from these galaxies are all shifted to the red.

The Expanding Universe

Most surprising is the fact that our galaxy seems to be near the center of this explosion. Why should all the galaxies apparently be fleeing from us as from a plague? We found that the earth is not the center of our solar system,

266

and that our solar system is not near the center of our galaxy. It seems most unlikely, not to say astonishing, that our galaxy should be the center of activity among all the billions of galaxies.

But we do have an explanation of this puzzle: Einstein's theory of relativity. It states, in effect, that no matter what galaxy we might happen to call our own, we should find exactly the same thing happening: all the nebulae would be receding from it. Hence, if any galaxy can be the center of the universe, there is apparently no unique center. This thought is a little difficult for our earth-bound minds to grasp. And yet we can find a simple analogy on the earth itself. Except for the poles of rotation, there are no unique points on the surface of the earth because the surface of a sphere has no center. Every city is a hub with roads leading away from it.

Another way of understanding what is happening is to imagine that the earth is expanding like a balloon being blown up from inside. In whatever community an observer was located, he would find the other communities of the world moving away from him. The world of stars is of course not two-dimensional like the surface of a balloon. But mathematicians can reason by analogy that if our three-dimensional world expanded like a balloon, it would constitute a universe similar to the one we live in.

If we project the process backward in time, turning the expansion into contraction, we find that the expansion or explosion seems to have

Spiral galaxy NGC 4565 in Coma Berenices seen almost edge-on. There is a strong concentration of obscuring material in the galactic plane. (U.S. Naval Observatory)

begun between five and ten billion years ago, that is, near the origin of the universe.

We have now examined two independent pieces of evidence which lead us to conclude that something exceptional happened in this universe some five or ten billion years ago. We might well call this event the beginning of the universe, noting that the word "beginning" has a different significance from "creation." These ages, moreover, are not inconsistent with those of the oldest star clusters in our own galaxy. Furthermore, from our measures of the red shift, we find that light from the most distant of the galaxies takes something like five billion years to reach us. The light we see from these galaxies today started coming from them just after they were born.

Let us try to reconstruct what the world was like before the cosmic explosion set enormous clouds of nebulae skyrocketing into space.

The Evolution of the Universe

One theory—perhaps the one most widely held today—is most persuasive. Canon Lemaitre (1894–1966), a Belgian prelate, suggested that all matter in the universe was once concentrated in what might be described as a giant egg. In this egg, the atomic fragments were so closely packed that the electrons could not exist separately. They had to join with the protons to form neutrons. What we had, then, was an immense neutron star. Its density could have been a million times greater than steel. A single pinhead made of this primitive matter might have weighed 100 pounds or, according to some extreme estimates, 1000 or even 10,000 tons!

We do not know the size of this egg. In fact, size is almost meaningless here because it implies the presence of a gauge or independent measuring rod. But with some stretch of the imagination, we may conceive of the cosmic egg as having a diameter between a hundred and a thousand times greater than that of the earth's orbit. In brief, it would probably have filled our solar system.

The egg could, conceivably, have been extremely hot. But no ray of light could penetrate the rock-hard shell of the egg. One might say that there were two completely independent worlds—one inside the egg and one outside it. This does not mean that someone outside the egg would be completely unaware of it. The same law that forbade radiation to escape from the egg would also forbid it to enter; hence, if light from a sun or a star fell on the egg, it would be reflected. The egg would thus be as visible as a rock or any other opaque body.

For countless eons (or for only an instant, according to whatever system is chosen to measure time in so static a universe) this cosmic egg lay incubating. Suddenly, about five billion years ago, the egg hatched, if a violent explosion may be termed "hatching." This bursting of the cosmic body must have been like the explosion of a super-atomic bomb. We do not know what caused this explosion. We may conjecture that mutual gravitational pull tended to hold the mass together. Since the "shell" was flexible, like that of a reptile's egg, it may have been subject to small oscillations. It may have moved spasmodically, like a cat in a gunny sack. Electric currents inherent in the initial mass may have exerted explosive forces similar to those acting on solar prominences and in solar flares. In any event, the mass broke up and the universe was on its way—a colossal, expanding cloud of gas and radiation. Some force, perhaps gravitation, caused the cloud to separate into pieces. These masses formed the clusters of galaxies—the largest cosmic units we identify. At a later stage, these units broke up into smaller masses. These masses—each so large that light takes about 100,000 years to move across one of them—represent the galaxies or Milky Way systems of stars.

Certain results of the Big Bang theory are hard to reconcile with the pure hydrogen idea outlined earlier. The initial explosion of the dense cosmic egg would have produced the heavier elements at the outset and the universe could have skipped the stage wherein super-stars formed the more massive atoms. Such a universe cannot be eternal. We are living in an age of "fire-

NGC 5128, an unusual type of galaxy, in Centaurus, showing intense dust absorption. The galaxy is a source of strong radio emission. (Hale Observatories)

A small cluster of galaxies known as Stefan's Quintet. (Lick Observatory)

works," with stars forming and dying on every hand. This should not worry us too much, perhaps, since it is the only age that could foster the development of life.

But if the universe is expanding and if it continues to expand, as the Big Bang theory suggests, the individual stars and galaxies are growing farther and farther apart. The universe is becoming less and less dense and finally will develop into an essentially empty, dead world. There is one feature, philosophically unattractive, about this theory of the evolution of the universe. We have specifically visualized a world in which the solar system has no unique position in space. However, the Big Bang concept does assign us a unique position in time, about midway between the birth and death of the universe.

To avoid this difficulty, British astronomer Fred Hoyle and his associates investigated an alternative theory in which the universe, despite evolution, always seems to remain about the same.

The Theory of Continuous Creation

According to Hoyle, the universe is continually and inevitably expanding into an infinite space. Where the Big Bang theory has the density of the universe constantly decreasing, Hoyle's theory suggests that atoms of hydrogen come into being here and there, like grains of exploding popcorn, and thus

270

keep the density constant. These atoms will eventually collect into stars and galaxies, which will replace those that have either become extinct or, through expansion, vanished into the cosmic distance.

Hoyle's theory postulates a universe infinite in both time and space. The world is expanding symmetrically in all directions from any point one chooses. This means that constantly at a very great distance some galaxies are moving away with a velocity equal to that of light. Whenever that happens, those galaxies have forever passed beyond our vision. They may exist somewhere but they have ceased to exist for us. But for every galaxy that vanishes over the horizon at infinity a new one appears within our view. And so the world never changes to any marked extent. Only the individual stars and galaxies are different. Thus the old matter and the newly formed atoms keep the density constant in this expanding universe. Hoyle terms this process "continuous creation," but something less subjective such as "constant density" would seem to be more appropriate.

At first sight, the idea that atoms should come into existence automatically seems rather farfetched. But, after all, Lemaitre's Big Bang theory postulated in effect that all the matter in the universe came into being at one instant. The primary difference between the two concepts, one may say, is that Lemaitre theorized that matter appeared in one "big bang," whereas Hoyle postulates its appearance in a series of "little pops." Hoyle's theory does not assume that enormous quantities of atoms are constantly coming into existence in this way. In an entire year only one hydrogen atom would appear in a volume the size of an average 40-story building.

A crucial assumption of the Hoyle theory is the uniformity of the universe in space and time. Apart from minor fluctuations, the universe should look the same wherever or whenever one observes it. The data we so far have on

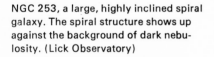

NGC 253, a large, highly inclined spiral galaxy. The spiral structure shows up against the background of dark nebulosity. (Lick Observatory)

this subject are not entirely clear. The more relevant information comes from radio telescopes, largely because they penetrate to greater distances and hence provide information about older objects near the visible limits of the universe. Hoyle himself has concluded that the evidence fails to support his ideas of a continuing universe and has announced that he has abandoned the theory. But investigation of this general approach continues.

The Importance of the Quasars

The key to the problem may well be the quasars, whose precise place in the cosmic scheme still remains to be established. Their noisy radio emission fairly screams at us, commanding our attention. Their blue color indicates that they must be very hot and very luminous. Their large red shifts strongly support the idea that they are some special type of galaxy. If so, most of them lie at distances of ten or fifteen billion light years suggesting that more of them existed in the more distant and hence younger parts of the expanding visible universe. But if this interpretation is correct, then the universe is not the same at all times and in all places!

Some of the quasars vary in brightness within intervals of a few weeks or months. This sets a strict upper limit to their size because if their diameters much exceeded a few light-weeks or light-months the variation in brightness from one part of the object would tend to cancel out that from another part. Light can travel across the solar system in about eleven hours. This means that the diameters of the quasars will not exceed thirty times that of our solar system, which is small indeed for objects so conspicuously bright.

Both of the possible explanations for the cause of the red shift lie by coincidence within the framework of Einstein's theory of relativity. We have

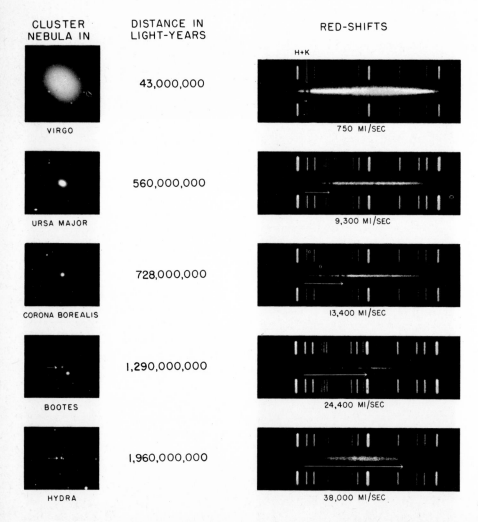

CLUSTER NEBULA IN	DISTANCE IN LIGHT-YEARS	RED-SHIFTS
VIRGO	43,000,000	H+K 750 MI/SEC
URSA MAJOR	560,000,000	9,300 MI/SEC
CORONA BOREALIS	728,000,000	13,400 MI/SEC
BOOTES	1,290,000,000	24,400 MI/SEC
HYDRA	1,960,000,000	38,000 MI/SEC

The relation between red-shift (expressed as velocities) and distance in extragalactic nebulae. The pair of dark H and K lines have shifted to the right (red) for the fainter, smaller and more distant galaxies. (Hale Observatories)

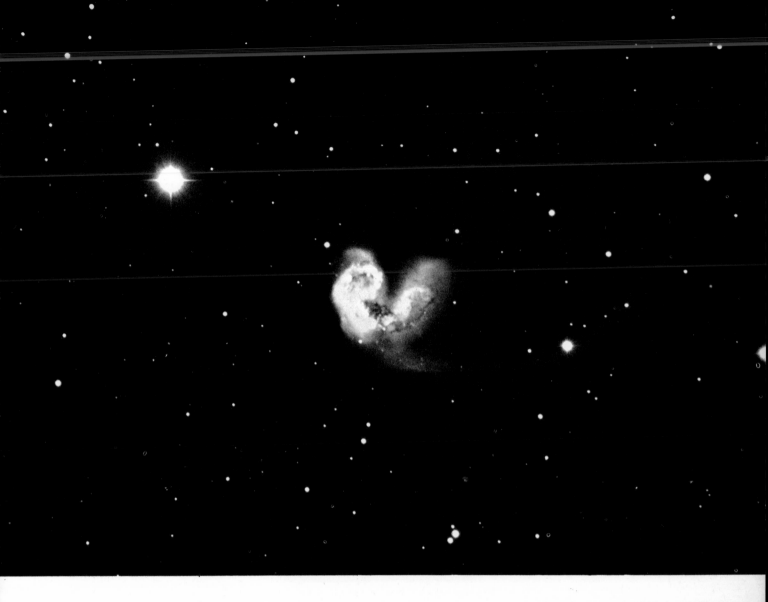

NGC 4038-9. Interacting galaxies, a source of radio noise. (Hale Observatories)

already discussed one explanation: the expanding universe with its nebular velocities that increase with distance. Einstein also showed that light emitted in an intense gravitational field would be red-shifted. In fact, if we were to squeeze the mass of a quarter of a million suns into a volume equal to that of the sun, the intense gravitational field would not even permit light to escape. This is another way of saying that the light would be red-shifted out of sight.

There is no way of deciding which of these two possible explanations applies to the red shifts of the quasars: the expanding universe or the gravitational field of an extremely massive object. Both, however, indicate that quasars must be very massive bodies, and may even represent the prenatal state of an entire galaxy. The presence of initial rotational energy would tend to retard the collapse of the original mass. It may even break up into a number of fragments revolving madly around their common center of gravity. This would allow some of the radiation to escape into space. The fact that one of the noisiest quasars seems to have a long filament projecting from it shows that disruptions can occur.

We tentatively conclude, therefore, that a quasar consists of a swarm of small, extremely massive bodies that may eventually break up into stars and evolve into a galaxy. They are the most distant objects yet observed. As such they may provide the key to the ultimate fate of the universe. And even more probably, they will yield the clue to the beginnings of the universe, the gravitational condensation of clouds of gas and dust into vast masses, and the eventual evolution of such condensations into galaxies.

273

19

Life in the Universe

The secret of the origin and development of life lies in the atom. Atoms are remarkable building blocks. Atomic nuclei can, under certain circumstances, unite with one another to form heavier nuclei, releasing energy. Atoms can join chemically with other atoms to form molecules of various degrees of complexity. They can form not only stars, planets, oceans, atmospheres, and rocks, but even living organisms.

Cells of all kinds need energy if they are to continue living, reproducing, even surviving. Such energy is chemical. There are two basic processes in the creation of such energy. One, which takes place in the absence of air, is called anaerobic. Yeast cells, for example, can break down molecules of sugar by fermentation, releasing a certain amount of heat and forming alcohol and releasing carbon dioxide. Anaerobic activity, though common in the more elementary forms of plants and animals, is far less efficient than the aerobic, which uses the oxygen of the earth's atmosphere to burn sugar or other foods chiefly into carbon dioxide. The heat and energy thus generated support life. These two processes require foods such as sugar or fat. This raises the question as to where the foods themselves come from. The most efficient food production depends primarily on photochemistry. The cells in the leaf of a growing plant, for example, absorb carbon dioxide from the atmosphere and, with the energy of sunlight captured by chlorophyll, build up cellulose, starches, sugars, or other plant substances, releasing free oxygen in the process. Animals use the oxygen and discharge carbon dioxide. This is a fundamental ecological relationship.

The various processes may materially alter the nature of the environment if they do not reach equilibrium. It is certain that the chemical composition of the earth's atmospheric environment has changed many times over the millenia and will probably continue to change in the future. Our survey of the planets of our solar system has revealed how diverse their atmospheres are. Venus, with its thick atmosphere of carbon dioxide, hydrochloric acid, hydrofluoric acid, and other lethal compounds, could not possibly support human life as we know it. On the other hand, some forms of terrestrial life could be transported to Venus and survive, perhaps eventually changing the atmosphere to something more favorable for human existence. Or is the present atmosphere of Venus the result of some unfavorable ecology in the distant past? Our airless moon and Mercury scarcely come under consideration as possible abodes of life. But we cannot automatically exclude the giant planets, particularly Jupiter and Saturn, since we know so little about the physical or chemical makeup of the layers just below their visible surfaces. Methane and ammonia, their major atmospheric constituents, certainly would not support the forms of life we know on earth today. On the other hand, those chemicals are the primary substances that might conceivably have produced the first forms of life on the earth.

Life and Chemistry

All forms of life around us today depend for their existence on the forces of chemistry. Chemical substances may be broadly divided into two different classes: inorganic, which do not contain carbon; and organic, containing carbon, which are built within the living cells. A few materials containing carbons, such as carbon monoxide, carbon dioxide, and the carbonates were not, however, generally regarded as organic. For many years chemists were unable to make some of the more complex organic substances, such as indigo, quinine, or chlorophyll, which plants appear to synthesize so easily. In time they began to doubt their ability to construct such substances, even arguing that it was an impossible task because these substances possessed some special "vital force" or "spirit of life" that was beyond man's power to impart to a molecule.

However, back in 1828, a chemist experimenting with ammonium cyanate, which was regarded as an inorganic substance, suddenly saw it turn under the action of heat into long, silky crystals of urea. The two substances happened to contain the identical number of atoms of carbon, hydrogen, and oxygen, but arranged in a different way. After this one success, chemists slowly overcame the difficulties that had held them back and they managed to construct organic substances of ever-increasing complexity. However, the major successes of organic chemistry are less than 25 years old.

It turns out that carbon atoms have the amazing property of being able to string together in long chains, with combinations of hydrogen, oxygen, nitrogen, and sometimes phosphorus and sulphur—all light atoms in the first part of the Periodic Table of the chemical elements. Where ordinary atoms will sometimes string together in groups of as many as 8 or 10, the addition of more atoms causes the chain to split and break. But with carbon, chains of thousands or even millions of atoms are quite common. They may also form rings or linked rings, of which benzene is perhaps the most familiar example. As a result, organic substances are far more numerous than inorganic.

The origin of life must have depended greatly on the chemical properties of the earth's primitive atmosphere and oceans. With hydrogen and helium so abundant in the sun and stars, it seems reasonable to assume that the early atmosphere contained many hydrogen compounds, such as methane, ammonia, water, and possibly free hydrogen as well. Such other compounds as phosphine, hydrogen sulfide, hydrofluoric acid, and hydrochloric acid, could also have been present in some abundance. At least we infer the occurrence of methane and ammonia from the present chemical composition of the giant planets, which are massive enough to have retained most of their original material. The earth, on the other hand, gradually lost its hydrogen, helium, and other lighter atoms, including neon. As the hydrogen evaporated into space, some of the oxygen remained behind to form carbon dioxide and produce an atmosphere similar to the one we now observe on Venus. The primary difference probably lies in the scarcity of water and the high temperature on Venus, which is too hot for water to exist in liquid form.

In our chemical laboratories we can trace at least some of the steps that may have promoted the genesis of life on earth. Lightning flashes cause chemical changes in the earth's atmosphere, producing some of the simpler organic compounds containing carbon, oxygen, hydrogen, and nitrogen. These include the amino acids, which appear to be fundamental in life processes. We can induce similar chemical changes in our laboratories with the aid of powerful electric sparks and ultraviolet light. Over the millenia the oceans became richer and richer in such primitive organic molecules. Biochemists have identified 29 basic substances, of which 4—Adenine, Cytosine, Guanine, and Thymine (which we can identify by their initial letters)—are known as nucleotides because they are vital constituents of the nucleus of a living cell. Of the remaining 25, 20 are amino acids, which can be used for the production of proteins. The other 5 are fats or sugars, useful primarily as sources of energy.

The 4 nucleotides are not in themselves particularly large as organic molecules go, having only 15 or 20 atoms apiece. But they do have the remarkable property of being able to form extremely long and intricate chains and, sometimes, double chains. The molecules always chain in pairs in such a way that T always lies opposite to A and G opposite to C. Thus, if along one side of the chain the molecules should occur in the order: T G G C T A A C A G, along the opposite side of the chain the order would necessarily be: A C C G A T T G T C. Moreover, the chain is twisted like the strands of a rope to form what is termed a "double helix." This complex molecule is deoxyribonucleic acid, abbreviated DNA. It is the key to the production of life of every sort, both animal and vegetable, on this earth. And since the four basic nucleotides are relatively simple and occur naturally, there is no reason to believe that they would be different elsewhere in the universe. We can, therefore, draw general conclusions about life anywhere from a detailed examination of life processes on earth.

The role played by DNA is immense. It literally holds the key to the individual: the order of the nucleotides along one side of the chain somehow provides a code containing the complete directions for the making of an individual. In the process of cell reproduction, each chain is torn precisely in half. When this fission occurs, the two fragments select from available nucleotides those that match so that, as before, T comes opposite A, and C opposite G. In this way, the two rebuild themselves to form two chains exactly like the original. Every cell of every living creature contains an identical molecule of DNA.

Occasionally nature makes a mistake and binds the wrong molecule into the chain, so that when the splitting occurs, the two molecules that form will not be identical. There will be corresponding changes in the code of instructions and the individual will deviate from the original pattern. A mutation in the species is usually detrimental to the product, and individuals so afflicted often fail to survive. Occasionally, however, the mutation proves beneficial to the species. Such mutations are better equipped than their non-mutant relatives and are better able to compete—which is an oversimplified statement of Darwin's doctrine of "natural selection" or "survival of the fittest."

In the mating process, the DNA of the sperm unites with that of the ovum in such a way that the resulting cell contains contributions from both parents. Each person has his own unique DNA unless he or she happens to be an identical twin, born from the same egg. Thus the development of ever more complex creatures from simpler ones is a natural consequence of molecular chemistry. Not all of us can, as Pooh-bah claimed in *The Mikado*, trace our ancestry back to a "protoplasmo primordial atomic globule." But such a relationship is implied and, indeed, may be expected to occur wherever chemical conditions are favorable.

A gene consists of from 100 to 1000 nucleotides. The order of the appearance of the nucleotides along the chain comprises a sort of code that the cell-building material can read. A single bacterium may contain as many as 3000 to 5000 genes and more than three million nucleotides. An organism as complex as a man, however, will contain as many as three billion nucleotides and millions of separate genes.

On earth alone the diversity of species, which most certainly number in the millions, exhibits clearly the huge assortment of forms that DNA, with its four basic nucleotides, can assume. Each species tends to reproduce itself but it cannot mate with other species. Some species, such as the dinosaur, disappeared long ago, probably because they could not adapt to a changing environment. Or perhaps, as has been suggested, some small mammal developed a special taste for dinosaur eggs. Nature is a patient experimenter, ruthlessly destroying or discarding not only the weaker individuals but also the weaker species. Nevertheless, among living things on earth, one interesting fact emerges. More than half of all living creatures, with the exception of bacteria and other microorganisms, belong to the order of Coleoptera, commonly known as beetles. These insects seem to have an extraordinary power to survive the severest conditions of heat and cold, drought and moisture. They are found all the way from pole to equator, including high mountains. One must conclude that beetle DNA possesses some special quality that permits these species to proliferate so widely. Trying to visualize what forms of life might develop on other planets boggles the imagination. But if there is life elsewhere in the universe, it would be surprising indeed if beetles or beetle-like creatures were not among such life.

Whether or not beings on other planets will resemble those on earth will not depend on atomic chemistry since atoms are the same wherever one finds them. Minor differences in chemical composition may occur in various parts of the universe because of differences in evolutionary history of the star or planet. It does seems probable that this vast universe will contain billions of solar systems and that at least some of these will have planets favorably endowed for life in terms of mass, size, and temperature. Liquid water is, I am convinced, one condition vital for the development of life of any kind, as is an atmosphere containing molecules or compounds of the four basic elements: carbon, nitrogen, oxygen, and hydrogen. The action of lightning flashes and ultraviolet radiation will produce the same amino acids that they do on earth. And as the concentration of such material in the warm seas reaches a critical point, the tendency of the nucleotides to cling together and form rudimentary DNA is likely to assert itself. At some point the random shuffling of molecules starts to follow an orderly pattern. The DNA comes alive and begins to build cells out the available food stuffs.

What happened on earth hundreds of millions of years ago can most certainly repeat itself elsewhere in the universe. For the earth is not unique and has no exclusive power to produce living things. But what such living things will look like no one can say. Natural selection or survival of the fittest, however, does provide an impetus for the improvement of species with time. There is no reason that there should not exist somewhere in the universe, perhaps in many places, beings with intelligence. Here and there we may expect to find a kind of life that may seem monstrous to our man-conditioned standards. Certain planets may be mainly oceans, in which case all forms of life would have to be aquatic.

But if life does exist somewhere out there, how can we become conscious of it and perhaps even communicate with it? Indeed, is there any evidence at all of other planetary systems? To this last question, one can definitely answer, "Yes." For the tiny star known as Barnard's star pursues a slightly wavy path through space as it revolves around the center of gravity of the bright star and an invisible planet about as massive as Jupiter. The center of gravity moves uniformly through space, carrying both stars with it.

Interstellar Communication and UFO's

The subject of interstellar communication has been frequently discussed. And at least one major experiment in this field was carried out some years ago. A radio astronomer, Frank Drake, at the U.S. National Radio Astronomy Observatory in West Virginia decided to point the antenna of his huge radio telescope toward some likely star and simply record continuously whatever noise might be coming from that direction. But he heard only the random crackling of stellar static and nothing resembling a signal carrying intelligence. The operation proved so boring and unproductive that Project Ozma, as the experiment was called, was discontinued.

Some years later, astronomers discovered several sources of distinct, uniformly-spaced pulses of radio energy emanating from outer space. It was briefly thought that they might originate in some sort of complex interstellar navigating system. But the "pulsars" proved to be rapidly-spinning neutron stars, sending out pulses of radio waves.

There is one more aspect of this subject that needs a brief discussion. In the years since 1948 there has been much speculation concerning a phenomenon referred to as Flying Saucers, Unidentified Flying Objects, or UFO's for short. Reports of mysterious and unexplained sightings of peculiar objects in the heavens stimulated a belief in the possibility that they might represent some form of spaceship visiting the earth from the farther reaches of the universe. Credulous writers wrote vividly about superintelligent beings who had somehow discovered ways of circumventing such basic laws of nature as the conservation of energy in order to visit the earth. The UFO's were not explained by the individuals who made the reports, but accredited scientists soon began to offer reasonable explanations. The manifestations, it was discovered, came from a great variety of natural phenomena, such as bright meteors, satellite fragments reentering the earth's atmosphere, reflections from ice crystals, optical mirages, reflections from balloons, airplanes, and other material objects in the atmosphere, and after-images in the observer's eye. A thorough study of UFO's, directed by a leading physicist, Dr. Edward U. Condon of the University of Colorado, gave no indication whatever that the reported sightings represented a visitation by beings from outer space. The Condon Report, *A Scientific Investigation of Unidentified Flying Objects*, confirmed my own conclusions on the subject, published in 1953 and 1963.

These conclusions make no prediction about what may happen in the future. No one can predict accurately what technical development may eventually be achievable here on earth or elsewhere in the universe by societies more advanced than we. But if Einstein's theory of special relativity is correct, the nature of matter itself severely restricts what we can do about interstellar travel. Each atom carries a finite amount of energy. Even though nuclear-powered space ships will be much more efficient than our present chemically-powered ones, the distances of even the nearer stars are inconceivably greater than those in our solar system. To conquer interstellar space, we should have to construct nuclear spaceships hundreds of times taller and millions of times more massive than those of the Apollo program. No one can say that this is absolutely impossible. But only the future can decide whether such an expanded space program will be economically or industrially feasible.

Meanwhile we have much to learn within our own solar system—by both manned and unmanned exploration of the planets, their satellites, and even the comets. Some carbonaceous meteorites have shown traces of complex organic molecules, which kindle man's hope of finding life elsewhere in our solar system. Mars still offers the best chance, despite the bleak, crater-pitted landscape revealed by the United States Mariner probes. The possibility of finding or communicating with life forms elsewhere in the universe will continue to fascinate every man with any imagination at all.

Constellations and Sky Maps

To early peoples the stars appeared to be fixed on the surface of an enormous globe. In representing the heavenly bodies on the face of this globe, the ancients saw patterns among them and formed them into constellations, many of which we still accept. The brighter stars in the imagined figure provided guides to recognizing the constellation. For example, in the constellation of Pegasus, the Winged Horse, a bright star was called "the saddle." Like many stars, "the saddle" received its name, Markab, from Arab astronomers in the Middle Ages.

Although this system is cumbersome, it is useful for identifying the 21 stars of the first magnitude. The names of 40 or 50 additional stars are reasonably well known, especially to navigators, who must identify them in order to determine the position of a ship at sea from observations made with a sextant.

In 1603 a German astronomer, Johann Bayer (1572–1625), published a remarkably accurate map of the entire sky, north and south. His system of designating the stars by assigning Greek letters to them, usually in order of brightness, proved to be very popular. Thus Vega became "α Lyrae," and so on down the alphabet. When the stars in a constellation were so numerous as to exhaust the Greek alphabet, astronomers continued with lowercase letters in the Latin alphabet. Still fainter stars are identified simply by number, a figure taken from the star catalogue of the English astronomer John Flamsteed (1646–1719). In a few instances, Bayer assigned Greek letters to stars in the order of their occurrence in the constellation. The most notable departure was for the seven Dipper stars of Ursa Major, which are designated by the letters from alpha to eta, going from the first star in the bowl of the dipper to the last star in the handle. In another instance, Bayer misjudged the relative brightness of the stars in Gemini, the Twins, so that Castor is known as α Geminorum and Pollux as β Geminorum, even though Pollux is about four-tenths of a magnitude brighter than Castor. (Astronomers employ the genitive of the constellation name, so that α Geminorum signifies α of the Twins.)

Locating the Stars

The method of locating a star on the celestial globe resembles that of locating a city on the surface of the earth. On the globe we employ latitude and longitude for precision. The axis of rotation is fundamental since it locates the north and south poles. A circle drawn halfway between the two poles is the equator. As the zero for measurements of longitude, we adopt the point where the meridian drawn from the north pole through the old observatory at Greenwich, England, intersects the earth's equator. Thus, if we wish to determine the coordinates of New York City, we draw a circle from the pole to New York City and perpendicular to the equator. The arc from the equator to the pole contains 90°. New York is 40° 24′ north of the equator, which is its latitude. Now, at the equator we note that the arc between the fundamental point on the meridian of Greenwich and the foot of the meridian to New York equals 73° 30′ west longitude. Since differences in longitude correspond to differences in time, the longitude is often expressed in hours, minutes, and seconds. Since one hour of longitude corresponds to 15°, the longitude of New York will be 4 hours 54 minutes.

To locate stars we employ a similar procedure. The points where the axis of the earth's rotation pierces the celestial globe determine the north and south celestial poles. Midway between these poles astronomers have drawn the great circle of the celestial equator, which is directly overhead for anyone standing on the earth's equator. Next, they arbitrarily selected a fundamental point on the equator analogous to the intersection of the Greenwich meridian and the equator on the earth. We noted that the ecliptic, which marks the path taken by the sun in its annual circuit of the heavens, is inclined at an angle of 23° 5 with respect to the equator. Twice during the year, at the vernal equinox and the autumnal equinox, the sun crosses the equator. Astronomers have adopted the vernal equinox as a fundamental point and measure longitude from that point eastward—not both east and west as we do for terrestrial longitudes. They can also measure the angle north or south of the equator to the star. The celestial coordinates analogous to latitude and longitude on the earth are called declination and right ascension, respectively. They locate the star in the sky in the same way as latitude and longitude locate a point on the earth's surface (fig. 20–1).

Sun Time and Star Time

Here we must introduce the concept of star time or, as it is called, sidereal time. A meridian is theoretically drawn on the sky from the north to the south point of the horizon, passing through the pole and zenith and dividing the hemisphere into eastern and western quarters. At the moment that the vernal equinox crosses the meridian, the sidereal clock is set to zero and let run. The rate of the clock must be such that it reads zero (or 24 hours) when the vernal equinox again crosses the meridian.

Sidereal time differs from solar or ordinary clock time. Suppose we are observing on March 21, at the very moment the sun crosses the vernal equinox. Suppose, further, that the sun is on the meridian. The time will then be noon, apparent sun time and zero hours star or sidereal time. A day later, when noon again approaches, the sun will appear to have moved eastward with respect to the stars by about one degree as a result of the earth's revolution around the sun. The vernal equinox will cross the meridian first and the sun will cross it about $1/360$ of a day, or four minutes, later. The solar day is longer than the sidereal day. More precisely, these intervals add up in the course of a year to a full day. The sidereal year consists of $366\frac{1}{4}$ sidereal days, whereas the solar year contains $365\frac{1}{4}$ solar days. We must therefore have two clocks: solar and sidereal. The sidereal clock gains one full day over the sun clock in the course of a year.

Figure 20–1. The relationship of hour angle and longitude in terms of latitude and longitude on earth. Washington, on the 75th meridian, is five hours west (one hour for each 15°) of zero longitude at Greenwich. The arrows point to the celestial meridians of Greenwich and Washington, and to star with an hour angle two hours west of the Washington meridian.

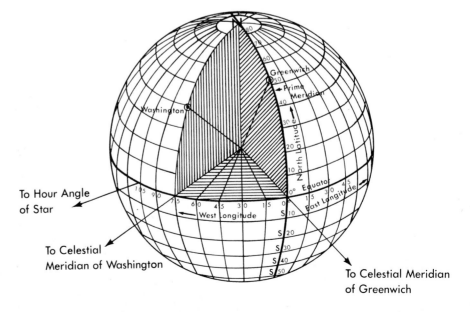

There are at least two kinds of sun time. The first, *apparent solar time*, might well be called sundial time because it depends on the position of the true sun. Unfortunately, there are two reasons that the sun does not move uniformly along the sky. Its path, as we have noted, is inclined 23°.5 to the earth's equator. Near the equinoxes, the sun is moving at an angle to the equator and progresses eastward less rapidly than at the solstices. Also, in June and July the earth's orbital motion is slower because the earth is farther from the sun than in December and January. As a result, sundial time does not progress uniformly through the year. To avoid this complication, we use *mean solar time*, which is uniform. The difference between apparent and mean solar time is called "the equation of time." It can amount to as much as 16 minutes.

Local mean solar time is inconvenient because the sun reaches different meridians at different times. At a latitude of 40°, for example, a location two miles west of an observer will have a local time about 9 seconds slower than the observer. Since such adjustments are nearly impossible to make, nations have agreed to set up standard time zones where all the cities in certain bands employ the same time: standard time. Since 15° of longitude correspond to one hour, the zones are normally about 15° wide, although variations are frequent when, for example, the natural dividing line would cut through some town or city.

A table in the appendix explains the methods and rules for converting standard time into local mean time and further directions for computing local sidereal time. The amateur astronomer often needs to know his local sidereal time in order to find various celestial objects by their right ascensions and declinations. Equatorially-mounted telescopes have graduated circles that, when properly set, point the instrument toward the selected star or other celestial object.

Precession of the Equinoxes

In Chapter 1 we discussed the inclination of the ecliptic to the equator. Since the ancients were more concerned with the moving planets than with the fixed stars, they preferred to employ a system of designating positions in a system that employed the ecliptic as the fundamental circle. Again they used the vernal equinox as their fundamental point. They measured celestial longitude eastward from this point and celestial latitude north or south from the circle just as we determine latitude north or south of the equator on the earth.

History tells us that the appearance of a new star in the constellation of Scorpio in 134 B.C. inspired the great astronomer Hipparchus to construct a new star catalog, one that contained 1080 stars. Comparing their locations with those determined by Timocharis and Aristyllus a century and a half earlier, he noted that the celestial longitudes of all stars seemed to be about 2° greater in his catalog than in the earlier record. From this phenomenon he correctly inferred that the equinox was gradually drifting westward at a rate that turned out to be approximately 1°.4 per century. He also concluded that, since the latitudes of the stars were not changing, the equator itself was moving. Since the equator is in turn defined by the position of the celestial poles, it became evident that the poles themselves are moving. Although the phenomenon is ordinarily referred to as precession of the equinox, the fundamental cause is a slow change in direction of the earth's axis in such a way that an essentially constant angle is maintained with respect to the orbital plane.

As a result of precession, the right ascensions of stars tend to increase constantly and the declinations also show corresponding changes. The magnitude of the change depends on the location of the star in the sky. Hence star catalogs always give the date of the equinox used to define the stellar positions. For example, the chosen equinox will refer to the year 1900, 1950, 1975, or some other arbitrary date.

As a result of precession, the position of the north celestial pole constantly changes. Whereas α Draconis was the pole star about 3000 B.C., α Cephei will be the pole star about 7500 A.D., and in about 14,000 A.D., Vega (α Lyrae) will be the pole star. None of these stars, however, will be as close to the true pole as Polaris is at present.

Isaac Newton was the first to recognize that this movement of the earth's pole results from the gravitational pull of the moon upon the earth's equatorial bulge. The earth, reacting like a gyroscope, stubbornly refuses to move its pole into a position where the axis would be perpendicular to the earth's orbit. As a consequence, the pole exhibits a slow precessional drift, making a complete circuit of the sky in about 26,000 years.

Defining the Constellations

About 270 B.C. the Greek poet Aratos of Soli described in his poem *Phainomena* the constellations as they must have appeared almost 2000 years ago. He mentions 45 star groups; however, today we recognize some of these (for example, the Pleiades) as *asterisms*—small parts of a greater constellation. The main point is that this poem, the only surviving description of its kind from antiquity, provides us with an accurate representation of the sky as conceived by the ancients.

Throughout the centuries many changes have taken place in our representation of the constellations. From the seventeenth century on, some astronomers amused themselves by introducing new constellations and figures. The great majority of these did not survive. Many large gaps between the more conspicuous constellations remained. Several astronomers "formed" new groups from the background of faint stars within these regions. Some of these have proved useful and have survived. When Bayer drew his maps of the southern sky, he delineated a number of new and appropriate constellations to represent the stars in those areas. The French astronomer Nicolas L. de Lacaille (1713–1762) introduced many new southern constellations to represent various scientific instruments, such as a chemical furnace and an astronomical clock. A committee of the International Astronomical Union finally settled on the 88 constellations as we know them today, and accurately defined their boundaries.

Sky Maps and How to Read Them

The accompanying 24 sky maps have been drawn on a new and original plan, which facilitates finding the constellations shown. A number of arrows appear in the margins, each labelled with the name of a month, a compass direction, and the letter L, M or H, signifying respectively, Low, Medium, and High. The lines connecting the brighter stars were drawn to facilitate recognition of the figure.

The arrows indicate the direction of the zenith at 8:30 p.m. on the 15th of the month as indicated. To locate the constellation, find the appropriate month, face in the indicated compass direction—N, NE, E, and so on—and turn the book so that the arrow points straight up. The constellations shown on the map should then be clearly visible. "Low" signifies an altitude within 30° above the horizon; "Medium" indicates a region between 30° and 60°; "High" denotes an altitude between 60° and 90°. Although the maps were drawn specifically for latitude 40° north, they can be used for other latitudes if one allows for the declination of the constellation. Farther north, southern star groups tend to be lower and northern groups higher in the sky.

The charts are complete to magnitude 4.70. Nine additional stars, somewhat fainter than this limit, were arbitrarily included where necessary to improve the outlines of several constellations. The connecting lines serve a dual purpose: they aid the eye in recognizing the group, and assist the memory in recalling its appearance. The right ascensions and declinations of the map centers appear in the upper right-hand corners of the maps.

For days other than the 15th of the month, at 8:30 p.m., try to imagine an arrow part way between two adjacent arrows. For example, on November 1, the arrow should be midway between the arrows for October 15 and November 15. For times other than 8:30 p.m. remember that one month corresponds to a difference of two hours. Stars rise two hours earlier every month. Thus the November arrow will also be good for December 15 at 6:30 p.m., the January arrow for December 15 at 10:30 p.m., the February arrow for December 15 at 12:30 a.m., and so on. The end papers of the book show the constellations centered around the north and south celestial poles, respectively. These are particularly useful since they show how the various constellations are arranged with respect to others.

Four of the maps, numbers 21, 22, 23, and 24, display constellations so far south that they are ordinarily invisible to observers in North Temperate latitudes. Nevertheless, they are interesting, so I have included them for completeness. However, unlike the first 20 maps, the arrows were computed for an observer at 30° south latitude.

The maps indicate the letters (or numbers) assigned to the stars. In a few cases, the star names are also given. Most of the sky maps have a few asterisks, which carry a special designation such as M 101 or a number such as 6543; these asterisks show the location of some objects of special interest for anyone who has a small telescope. The prefix "M" indicates objects that appeared in an early catalog by the astronomer Messier. Those without the prefix were taken from Dreyer's *New General Catalog of Celestial Objects;* their complete designation would carry the prefix NGC. The prefixes I and H indicate respectively an addition to the NGC and an object in the Harvard catalog of star clusters. The accompanying tables list the open star clusters, globular star clusters, diffuse gaseous nebulae, planetary nebulae, and galaxies. Also given are the more important asterisms, which may be described as minor constellations or parts of larger groups. They are interesting sky marks that help in recalling the positions of the configurations. The right ascensions and declinations are given for the epoch 1950. But they change so slowly, because of precession, that the positions are accurate enough for locating stars 20 or 30 years later.

The Dippers and Other Constellations

The stars in the major constellations have traditionally been joined to form easily remembered objects or figures. The best known is Ursa Major (the Big Bear), or the Big Dipper. The two stars at the front of the dipper bowl are called "the pointers" because they point toward Polaris, the North Star. Polaris lies in Ursa Minor, or the Little Dipper, with its two bright stars, known as "the guards," at the bottom of the ladle. Between the two Dippers lies the constellation Draco, the Dragon, with its body curling around the Little Dipper and the two stars that form its eyes located close to the bright star Vega.

The curve of the Big Dipper handle, continued for about three dipper lengths, leads to the orange star, Arcturus, in the constellation of Boötes, the Bear Driver. The hunting dogs, Canes Venatici, are appropriately shown yapping behind the hind legs of the bear. Corona Borealis, the Northern Crown, may be seen as an arm of Boötes, lopped off to form the delicate crown.

Cassiopeia, a W-shaped constellation in the Milky Way, can be found on a line from the bend of the dipper handle through Polaris and approximately an equal distance beyond. In this area we come upon numerous constellations related to the myth of Perseus. The story goes that Neptune—probably represented as Auriga, the Charioteer, rising from the sea on a chariot drawn by sea horses—was angered when Queen Cassiopeia boasted she was fairer than Juno and the Sea Nymphs. As punishment, she was placed in the sky to hang head downward half the time. Her daughter, Andromeda, was chained to a nearby rock, where Cetus, the Sea Monster, is about to attack her. Perseus, flying in on Pegasus, the Winged Horse, is arriving just in time to rescue Andromeda.

283

The Heavenly Waters

The ancients had assigned a large area of the sky to aquatic creatures and Bayer continued this allocation to the southern stars. Three zodiacal constellations—Pisces, the Fish, Aquarius, the Water Bearer, and Capricornus, the Sea Goat—form the northern boundary of this celestial sea. It can scarcely be an accident that the torrential winter rains began to fall when the sun entered this group of constellations.

According to legend, Pegasus struck the rocks with his hoofs and water sprang out. Thus was created the stream of Aquarius, which rains down into the mouth of Piscis Austrinus, the Southern Fish. Cetus lies just south of Pisces. It is probable that early representations of these fish showed them squirting water out of their mouths into streams that splashed against the back of Cetus. But this natural interpretation has been lost and the streams of water have become cords tied to the tails of two dead fish hung up to dry while the splash has become a knot where the two cords come together.

Below Cetus, the river Eridanus flows to its terminus at the bright star Achernar. Dorado, the Goldfish, Volans, the Flying Fish, and Hydrus, the Water Snake, lie near the southern boundary of the celestial ocean not far from the south celestial pole. The great legendary ship Argo lies shipwrecked on the shore of the ocean. The astronomer Lacaille carved up the great ship into four smaller constellations: Puppis, the Prow, Carina, the Keel, Vela, the Sail, and Pyxis, the Compass, to make them more manageable. Columba, the Dove, appropriately flies near the stern of the great ship. Canopus, the second brightest star in the sky, lies directly south of Sirius, the brightest. Two other aquatic creatures, Delphinus, the Dolphin, and Equuleus, the Sea Horse, lie near the northwest boundary of the sea, just below the feet of Pegasus.

The Zodiacal Constellations

There are twelve zodiacal constellations; they lie along the zodiac or the ecliptic, the path of the moon and planets. Several of these are grand and a few insignificant. Aries, the Ram, is an inconspicuous triangle lying between Andromeda and the head of Cetus. Next comes Taurus, the Bull, with the red star Aldebaran marking the eye and with the delicate dipper of the Pleiades—the seven daughters of Atlas—above the bull's back. Next comes Gemini, the Twins, with a pair of bright stars, Castor and Pollux. The feet of the twins lie in a brilliant portion of the northern Milky Way.

Cancer, the Crab, is a minor constellation, notable only for the presence of of a faint cluster of stars visible to the unaided eye, known as Praesepe, the Beehive. Next comes Leo, the Lion, a stately constellation, with the bright star Regulus at the tip of the handle of an asterism called the Sickle. To find Leo follow the dipper pointers in a southward direction instead of north to Polaris. Nearby lies a small triangle known as Leo Minor, the Lesser Lion. Virgo, the Maiden, is the next zodiacal constellation. Its luminary, Spica, lies along a continuation of the curve of the Big Dipper handle through Arcturus.

Libra, the Scales, is not an outstanding constellation, and the ancients sometimes regarded it as part of the claws of its neighbor, Scorpius (or Scorpio), the Scorpion. Antares, whose name aptly signifies "Rival of Mars," has, like Mars, a distinct red color and is one of the most magnificent of all the red giant stars. A small arrow-shaped tip marks the stinger of the scorpion. Sagittarius, the Archer, lies like Scorpius in a brilliant section of the Milky Way. Part of it, as seen from the northern hemisphere, forms an inverted dipper, and it is sometimes referred to as the Milk Dipper because of its location. Nearby, Capricornus, or the Sea Goat, is relatively uninteresting. Aquarius, the Water Bearer, which comes next, is also undistinguished except for four stars that form a "Y." At the end of the series is Pisces, the two Fish, mentioned earlier. The head of the western fish is sometimes regarded as a separate asterism.

The constellation of Hercules lies south of Draco, with the left foot of the giant resting on the Dragon's head. Many of the older mythologies designated this constellation only as the Kneeler; however, some of the ancient coins show Hercules as an archer kneeling on one knee to steady himself for the shot. Sagitta, the Arrow, flies directly away from the bow toward two birds: Cygnus, the Swan, and Aquila, the Eagle. This striking configuration recalls one of the famous labors of Hercules—his slaughter of the Stymphalian birds. The correspondence is even closer when we identify Lyra, the Lyre, with the form that it often takes in some of the older charts: Vultur, the Vulture. The confusion evidently arose from the fact that the Lyre was often represented as having the wings of a bird. The musical instrument, constructed by Hermes from the shell of a tortoise, may have represented the tortoise as well as the instrument. And the beak of a tortoise could easily be confused with the head of a vulture.

Ophiuchus, the Serpent Bearer, may well be an alternative form of Hercules, for the giant frequently had to deal with snakes, beginning in infancy when he strangled the serpent in his crib. He bears Serpens, the Serpent, in his hands, and his right foot is almost touching the stinger of the Scorpion. Other constellations associated with legends of Hercules are nearby. Leo may be the Nemean Lion that Hercules fought. Hercules crushed Cancer, the Crab, underfoot, and Hydra could be the Lernean Hydra of one of his labors. Hydra is the only constellation requiring two maps, rather than a single map, for its complete presentation. Eridanus could be the river that Hercules used in flushing out the Augean stables. The legends mention an encounter with a centaur: Sagittarius is such a creature and, further south, so is Centaurus.

The Orion Group

The hunter Orion and his companions are conspicuous winter constellations. The giant himself is a grand figure, striding across the sky. The bright red star Betelgeuse marks his right shoulder and Rigel his left leg; three bright stars plainly mark his belt. He holds a club above him in his right hand and a shield of lion hide before him in his left as he meets the onslaught of Taurus, the Bull, rearing to the attack. Below the belt lie several faint stars, generally recognized as the Dagger. The middle star of this dagger appears hazy to the naked eye; even through a small telescope, it dissolves into the glorious Orion nebula, a vast cloud of luminous gas excited to luminosity by four bright stars, the Trapezium, imbedded in the cloud. The two hunting dogs, Canis Major, the Greater Dog, and Canis Minor, the Lesser Dog, follow Orion. The Greater Dog is a splendid constellation, with its luminary Sirius. Procyon, in Canis Minor, is much fainter. Between the two dogs stands Monoceros, the Unicorn, a relatively insignificant constellation in a splendid part of the Milky Way. Orion stands upon Lepus, the Hare. The paths of the moon and of the planets Mercury, Venus, Mars, Jupiter, and Saturn always lie somewhere within the zodiacal belt.

Knowing the constellations opens up an entirely new field of interest. The wheeling stars indicate the passage of seasons. Each of the bright stars soon occupies a special place in one's imagination as well as in the sky, for each star is an individual, distinguished by its delicate color, characteristic brightness, and the configuration it forms with neighboring stars. On a clear, moonless night, the Milky Way spans the sky, increasingly bright in the constellations of Scorpio, Sagittarius, and Centaurus, where lies the center of our great galaxy. A small telescope or even a binocular reveals many other notable bodies as it resolves hazy patches of the Milky Way into myriads of stars. Only then can a person appreciate how Galileo must have felt when he first saw the wonders of the sky through his tiny, newly-invented telescope.

The Constellations (1)

Abbre-viation	Latin Name	English Name	Map No.
And	Andromeda	Andromeda	4
Ant	Antlia	Air Pump	22
Aps	Apus	Bird of Paradise	24
Aqr	Aquarius	Water Carrier	10
Aql	Aquila	Eagle	9
Ara	Ara	Altar	18, 23
Ari	Aries	Ram	11
Aur	Auriga	Charioteer	5
Boo	Boötes	Bear Driver	7
Cae	Caelum	Graving Tool	20
Cam	Camelopardalis	Giraffe	5
Cnc	Cancer	Crab	13
CVn	Canes Venatici	Hunting Dogs	2, 7
CMa	Canis Major	Larger Dog	19
CMi	Canis Minor	Smaller Dog	13
Cap	Capricornus	Seat Goat	10
Car	Carina	Keel	22
Cas	Cassiopeia	Cassiopeia	3
Cen	Centaurus	Centaur	23
Cep	Cepheus	Cepheus	3
Cet	Cetus	Whale	11
Cha	Chamaeleon	Chameleon	24
Cir	Circinus	Compasses	23
Col	Columba	Dove	19
Com	Coma Berenices	Berenice's Hair	6, 7
CrA	Corona Australis	Southern Crown	18
CrB	Corona Borealis	Northern Crown	7, 8
Crv	Corvus	Crow	15
Crt	Crater	Cup	14
Cru	Crux	Cross	23
Cyg	Cygnus	Swan	9
Del	Delphinus	Dolphin	9
Dor	Dorado	Goldfish	24
Dra	Draco	Dragon	1
Equ	Equuleus	Little Horse	10
Eri	Eridanus	River	20
For	Fornax	Furnace	20
Gem	Gemini	Twins	13
Gru	Grus	Crane	21
Her	Hercules	Hercules	8
Hor	Horologium	Clock	20
Hya	Hydra	Sea Serpent	14, 15
Hyi	Hydrus	Water Snake	21
Ind	Indus	Indian	18

The Constellations (2)

Abbre-viation	Latin Name	English Name	Map No.
Lac	Lacerta	Lizard	3, 4
Leo	Leo	Lion	6
LMi	Leo Minor	Smaller Lion	2, 6
Lep	Lepus	Hare	19
Lib	Libra	Scales	17
Lup	Lupus	Wolf	23
Lyn	Lynx	Lynx	2, 5
Lyr	Lyra	Lyre	8, 9
Men	Mensa	Table Mountain	24
Mic	Microscopium	Microscope	18
Mon	Monoceros	Unicorn	13
Mus	Musca	Fly	23
Nor	Norma	Level	23
Oct	Octans	Octant	24
Oph	Ophiuchus	Serpent Holder	16
Ori	Orion	Orion	12
Pav	Pavo	Peacock	18
Peg	Pegasus	Pegasus	4
Per	Perseus	Perseus	5
Phe	Phoenix	Phoenix	21
Pic	Pictor	Easel	24
Psc	Pisces	Fish	11
PsA	Piscis Austrinus	Southern Fish	10
Pup	Puppis	Stern	22
Pyx	Pyxis	Mariner's Compass	22
Ret	Reticulum	Net	21
Sge	Sagitta	Arrow	9
Sgr	Sagittarius	Archer	18
Sco	Scorpius	Scorpion	17
Scl	Sculptor	Sculptor's Apparatus	21
Sct	Scutum	Shield	16
Ser	Serpens	Serpent	16
Sex	Sextans	Sextant	14
Tau	Taurus	Bull	12
Tel	Telescopium	Telescope	18
Tri	Triangulum	Triangle	5, 11
TrA	Triangulum Australe	Southern Triangle	23
Tuc	Tucana	Toucan	21
UMa	Ursa Major	Great Bear	2
UMi	Ursa Minor	Little Bear	1
Vel	Vela	Sails	22
Vir	Virgo	Virgin	15
Vol	Volans	Flying Fish	22
Vul	Vulpecula	Fox	9

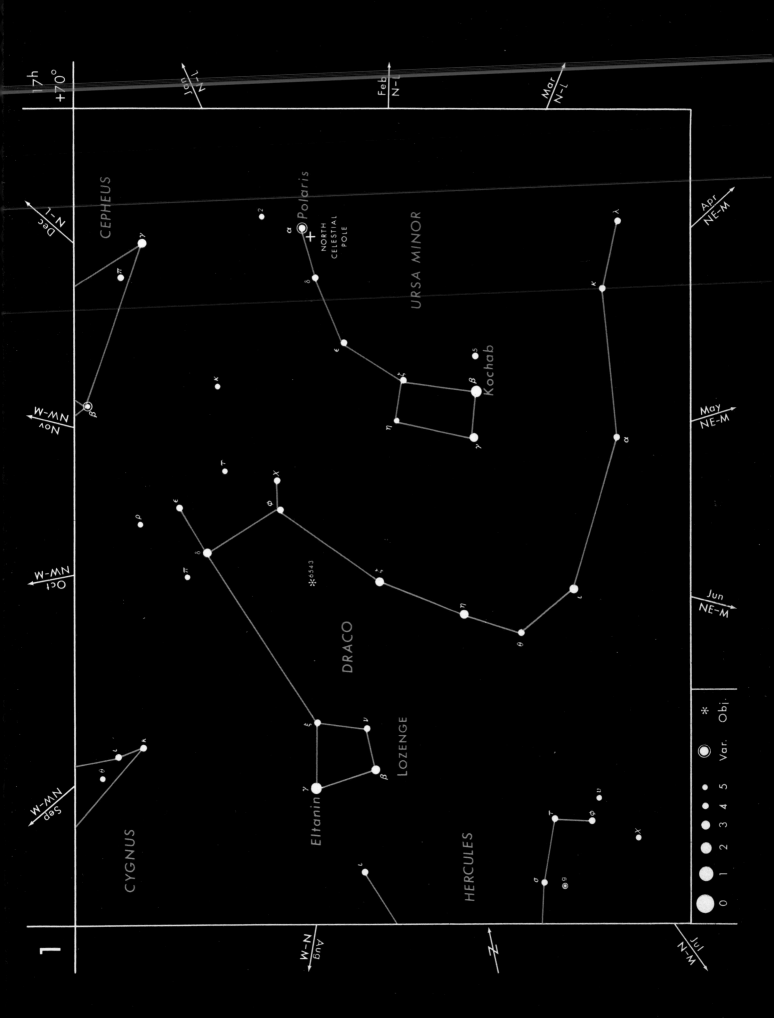

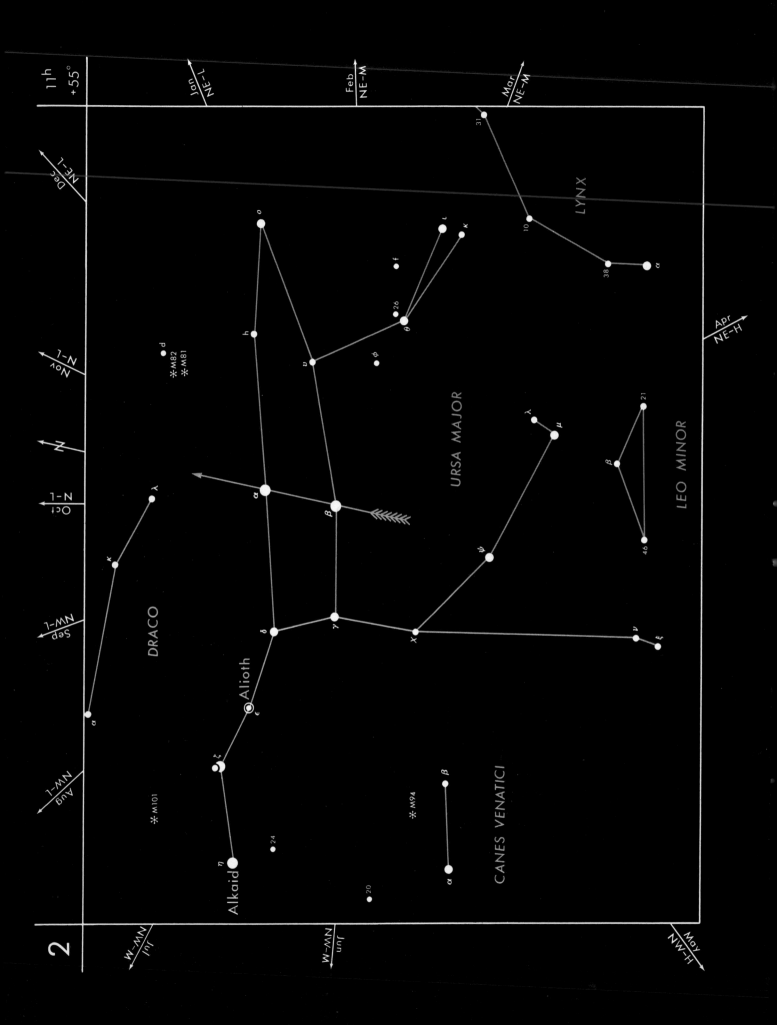

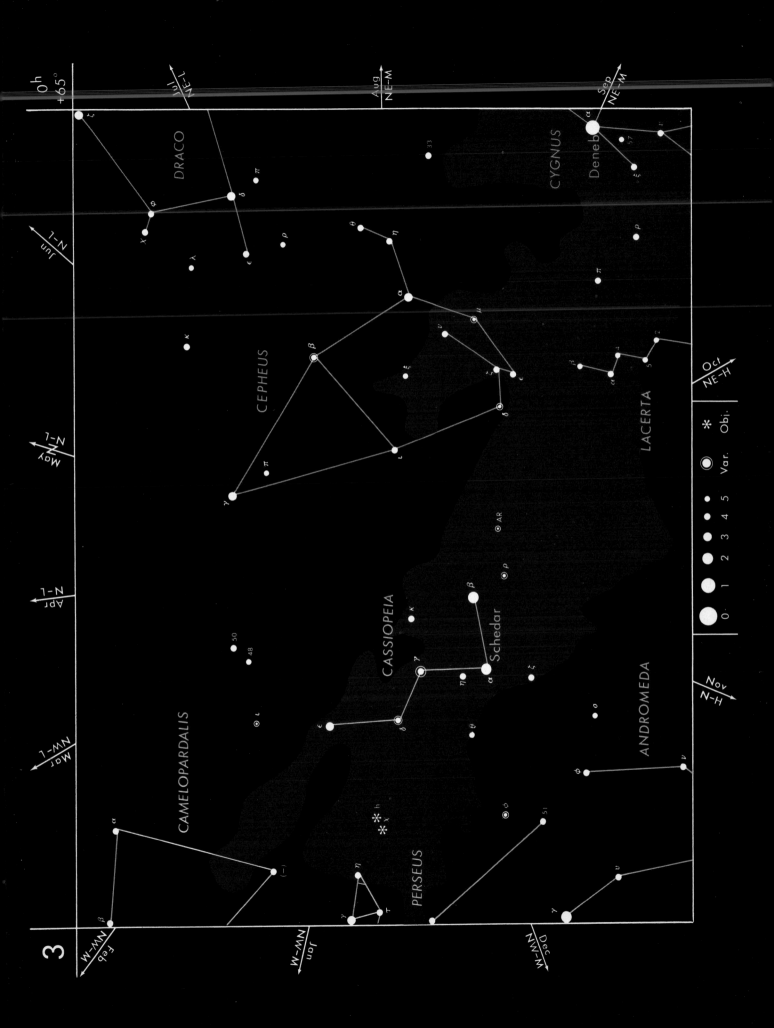

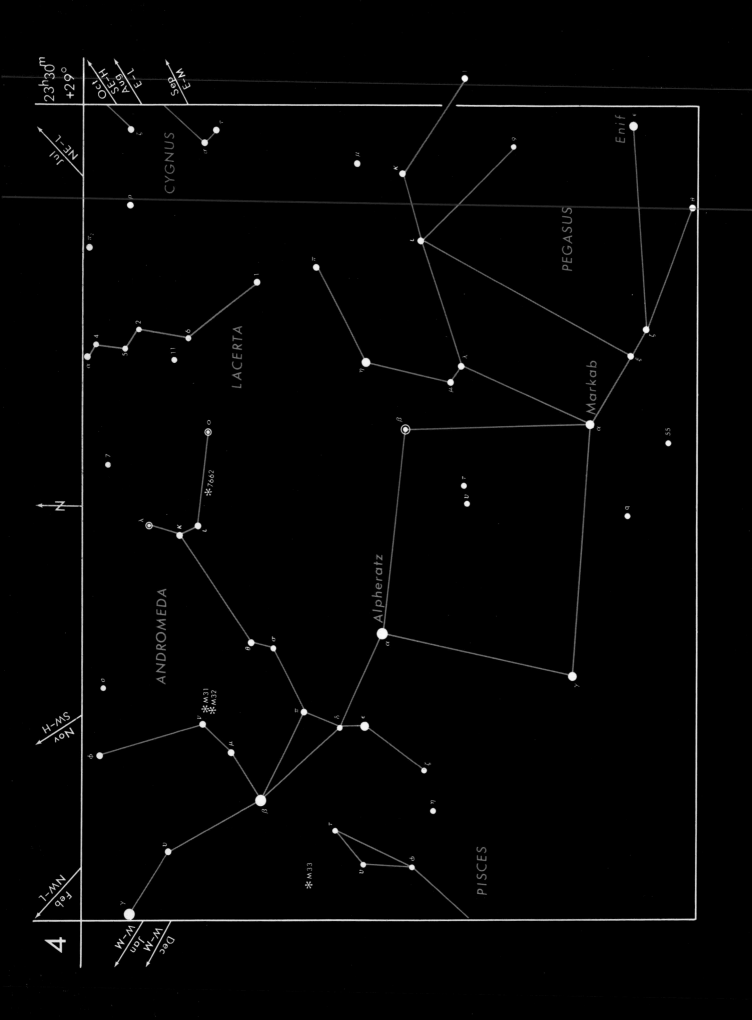

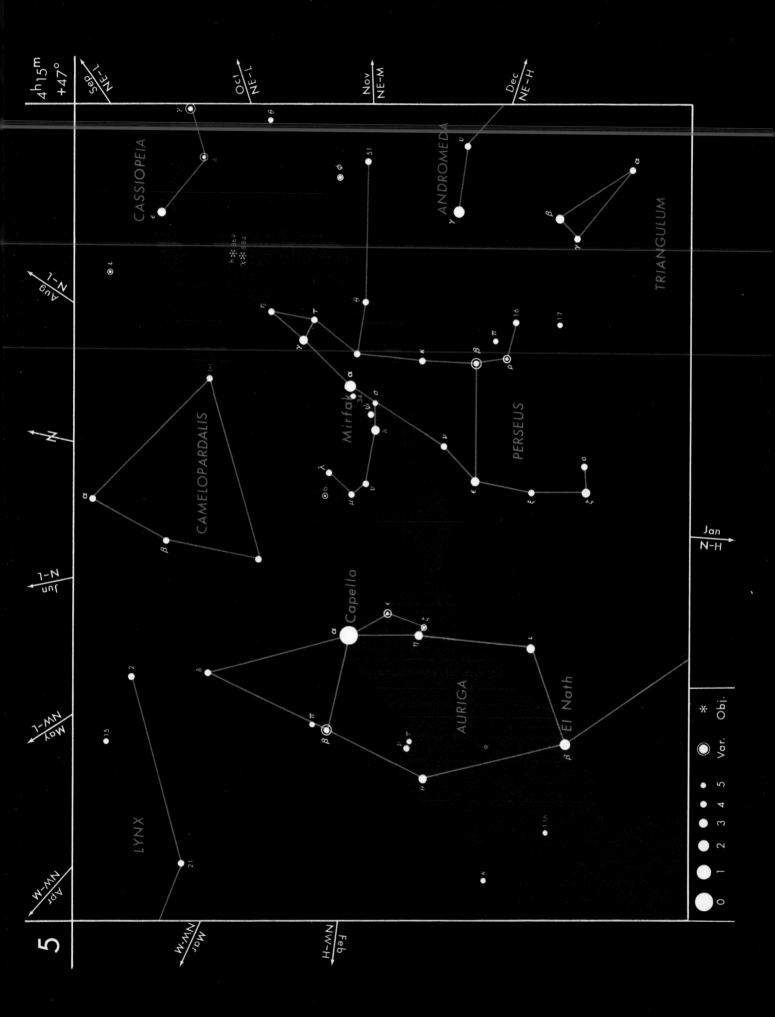

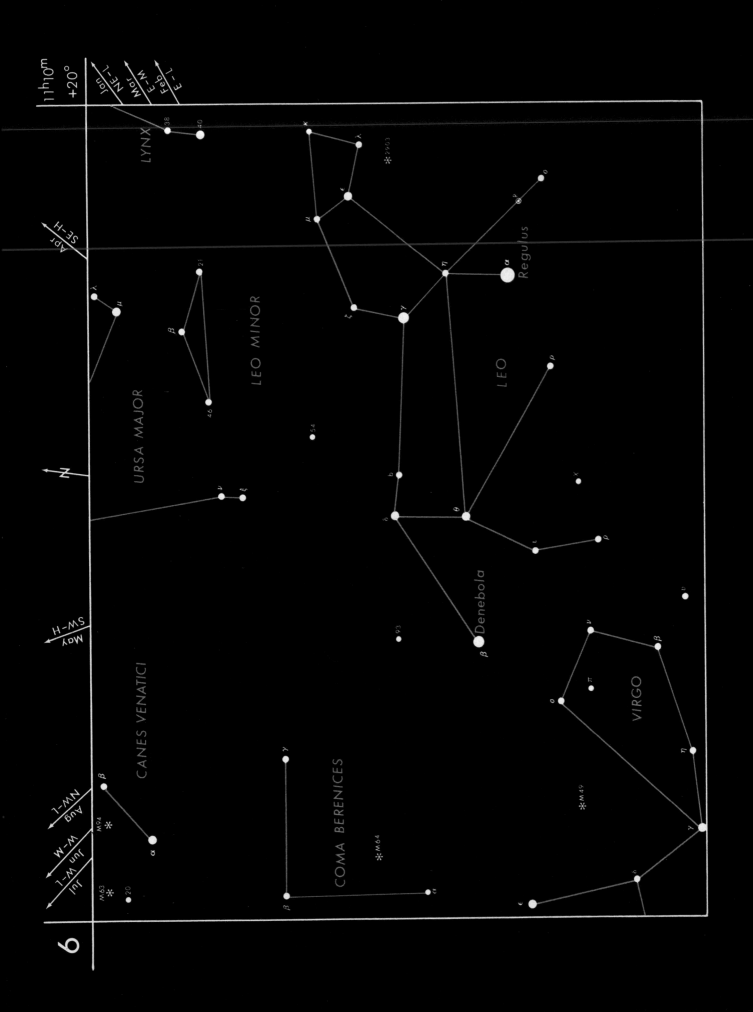

6

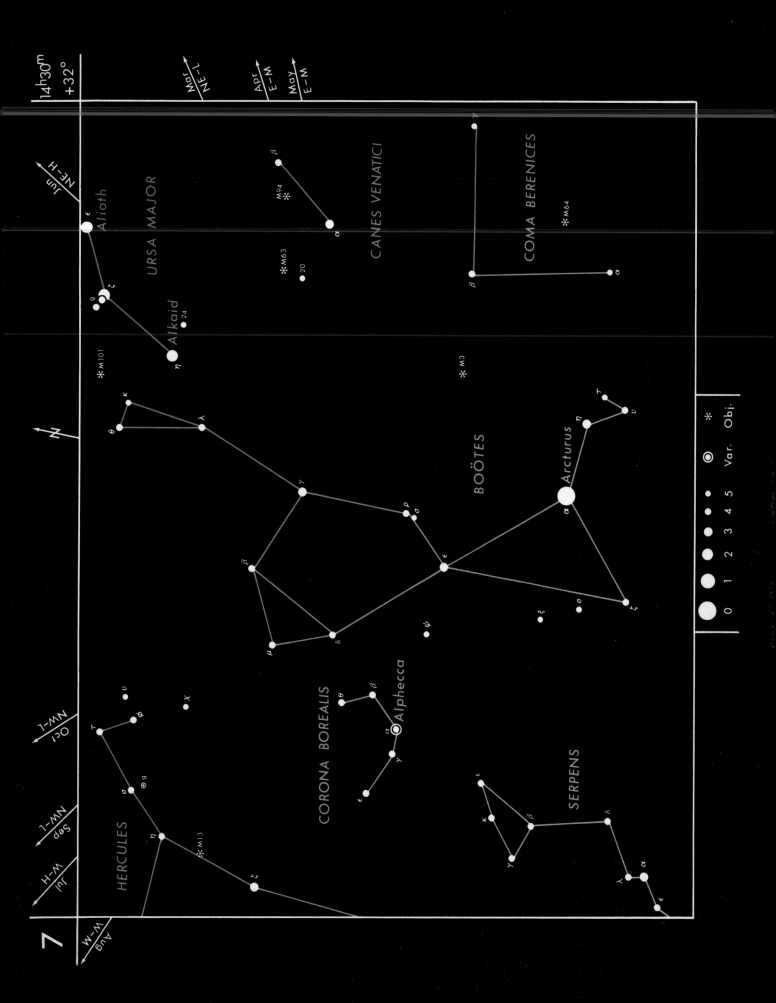

14h30m
+32°

Mar
NE-L

Apr
E-M

May
E-M

Jun
NE-H

URSA MAJOR
ε Alioth
ζ
g
24
η Alkaid
M101

β
M63
20
M94
α
CANES VENATICI

γ
COMA BERENICES
β
M64
α

N

κ
θ
λ
γ
ρ
σ
M3
η
Arcturus
α
τ
υ
BOÖTES
β
ε
ξ
o
ζ
δ
μ
ψ

υ
χ
τ
φ
ω
g
σ
HERCULES
η
M13
ζ

θ
β
Alphecca
α
γ
ε
CORONA BOREALIS

ι
κ
β
γ
δ
SERPENS
λ
α
ε

Oct
NW-L

Sep
NW-L

Jul
W-H

Aug
W-M

* Var. Obi:

0 1 2 3 4 5 ◉ *

7

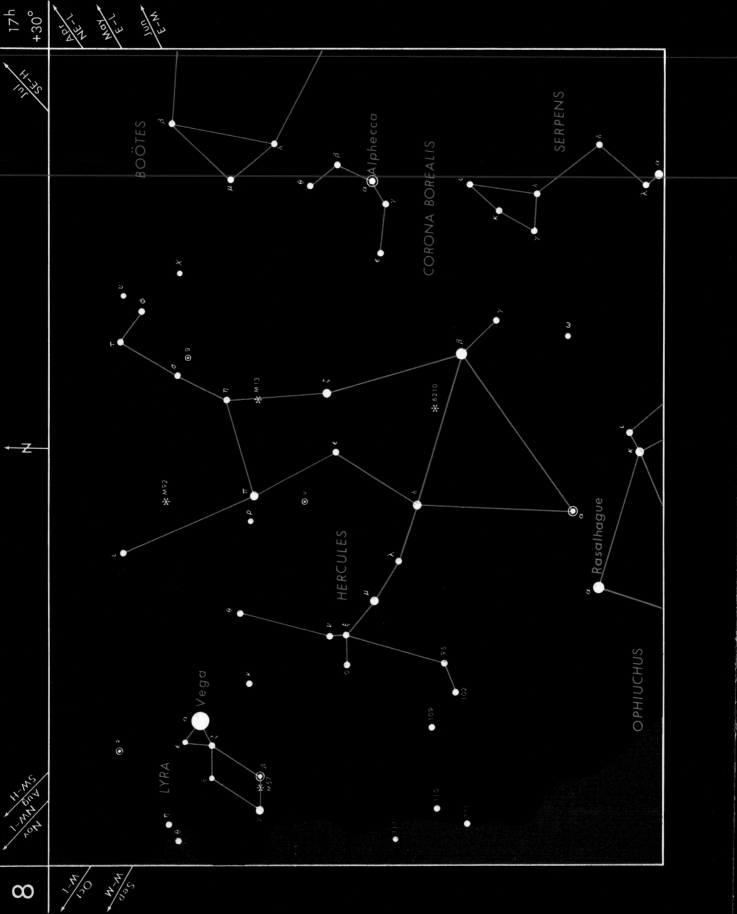

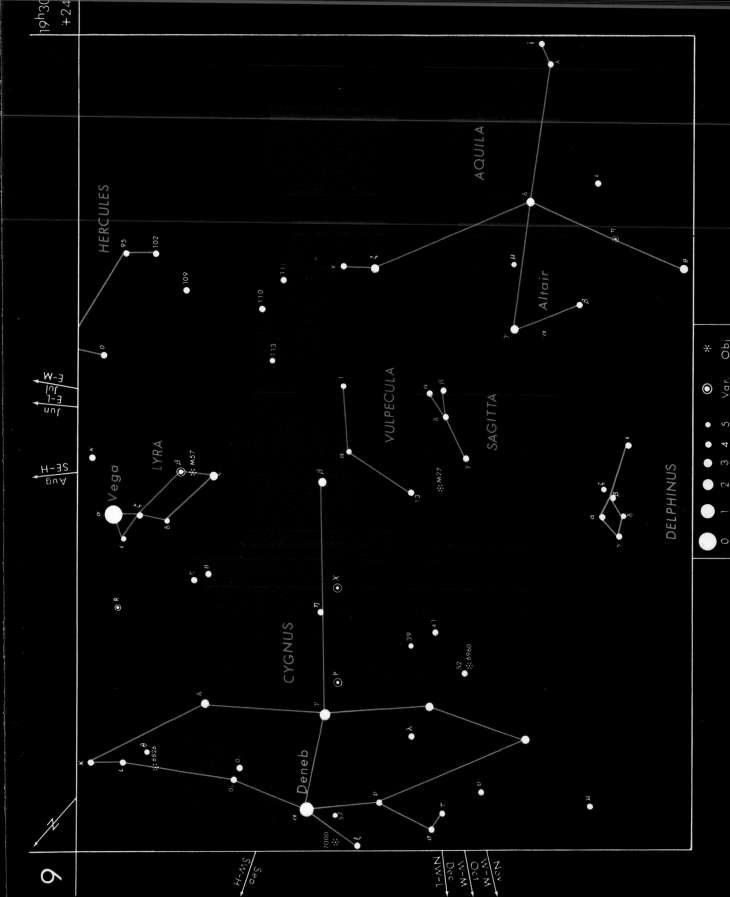

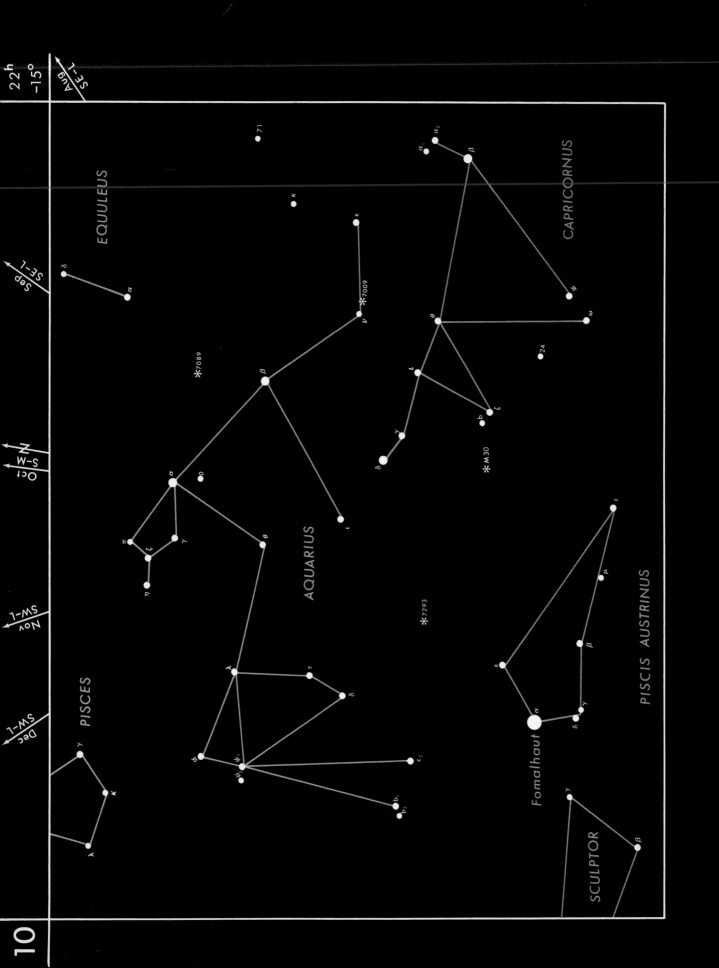

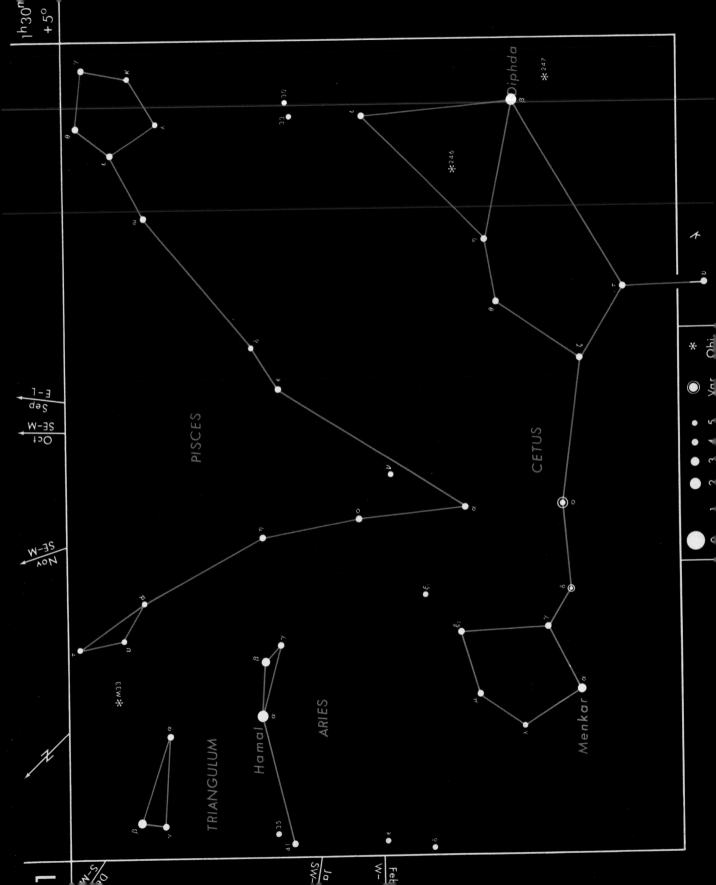

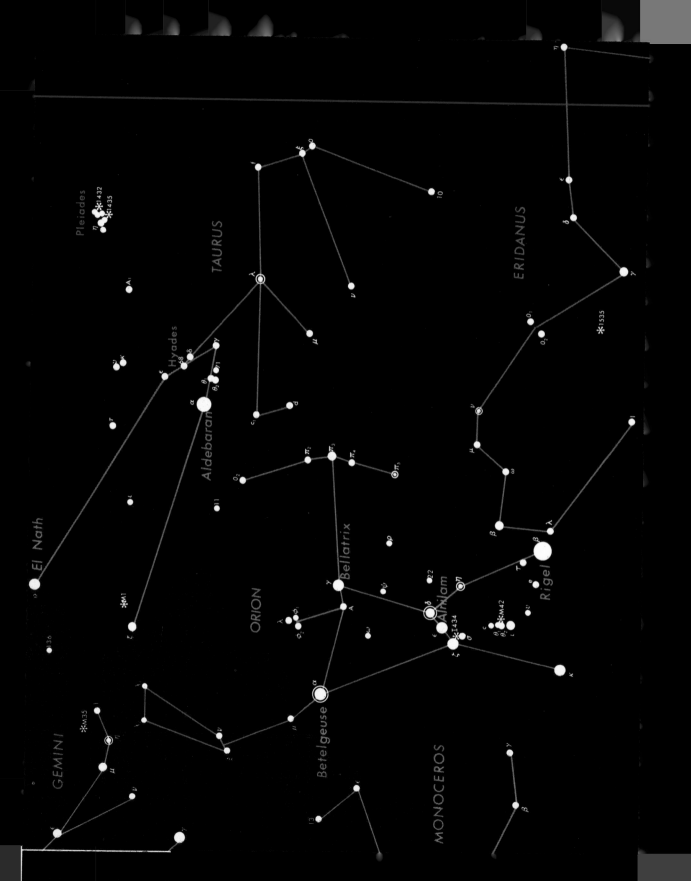

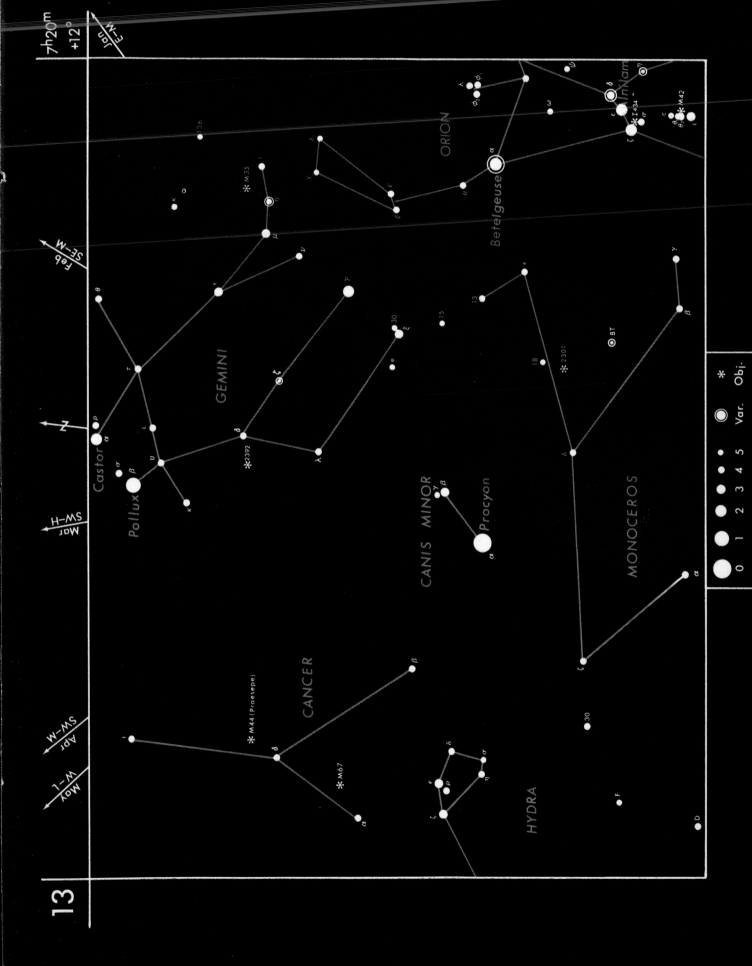

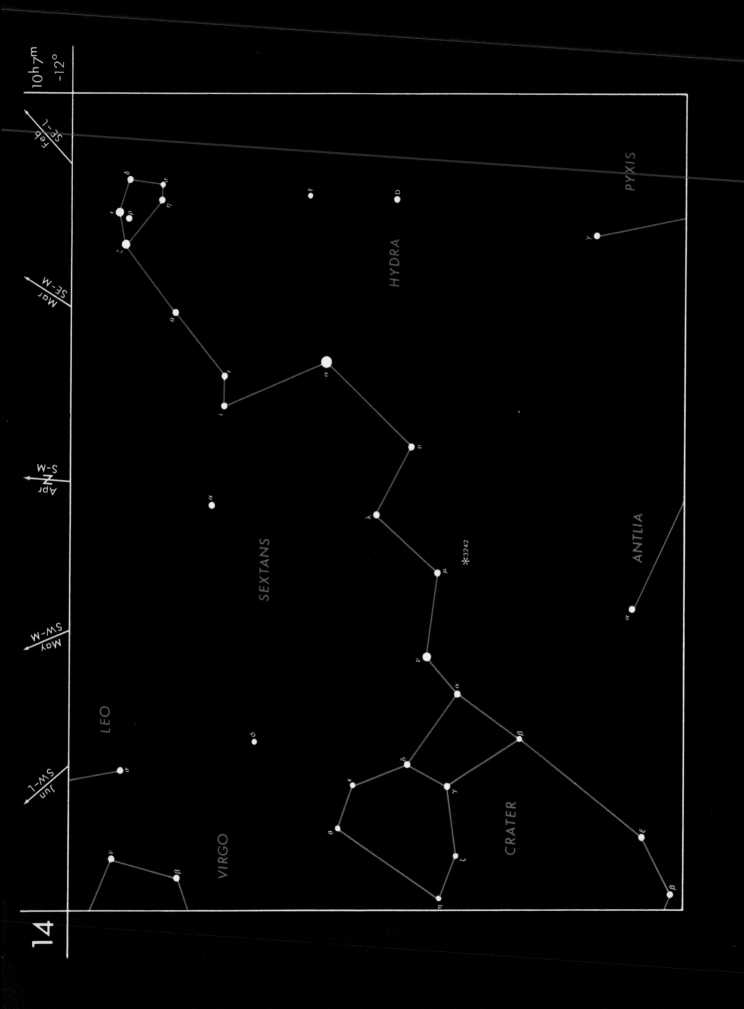

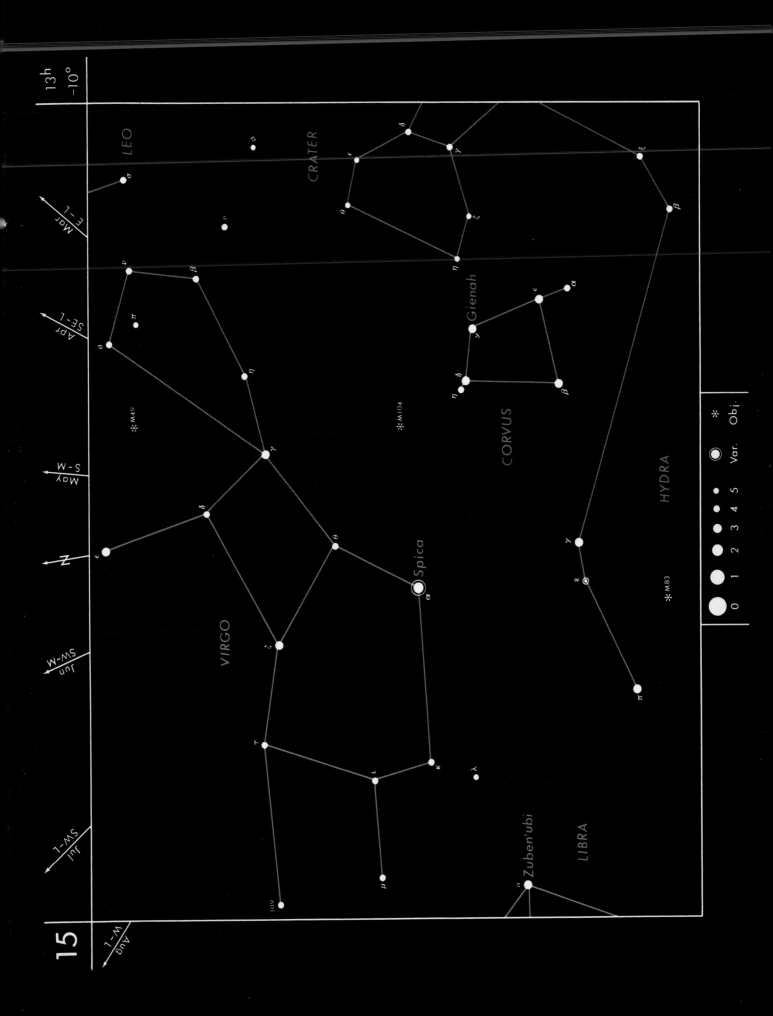

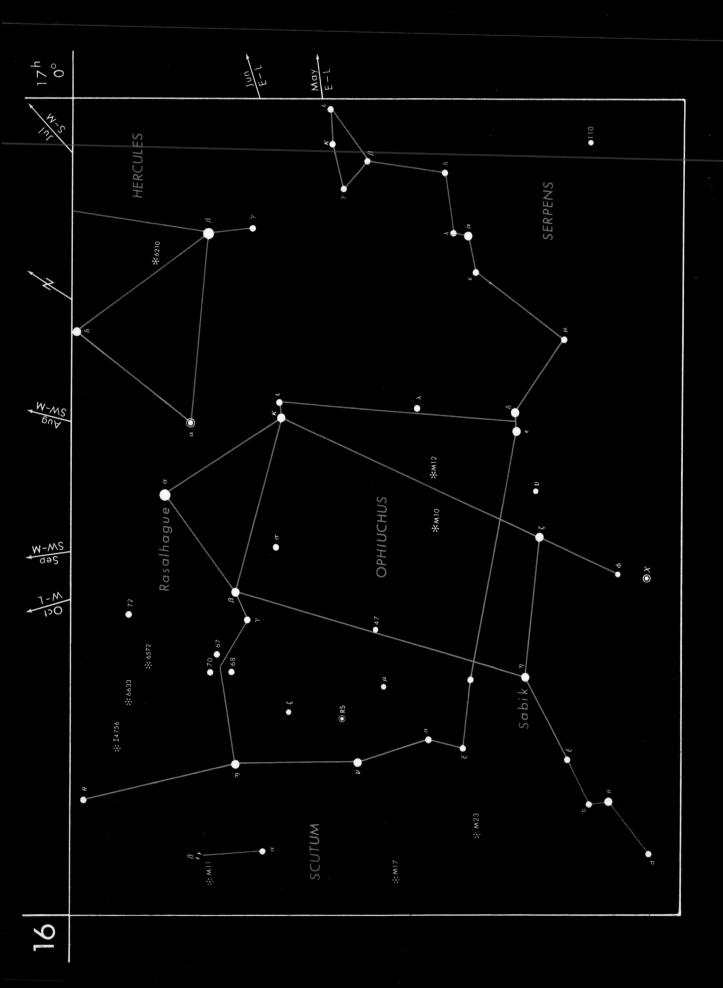

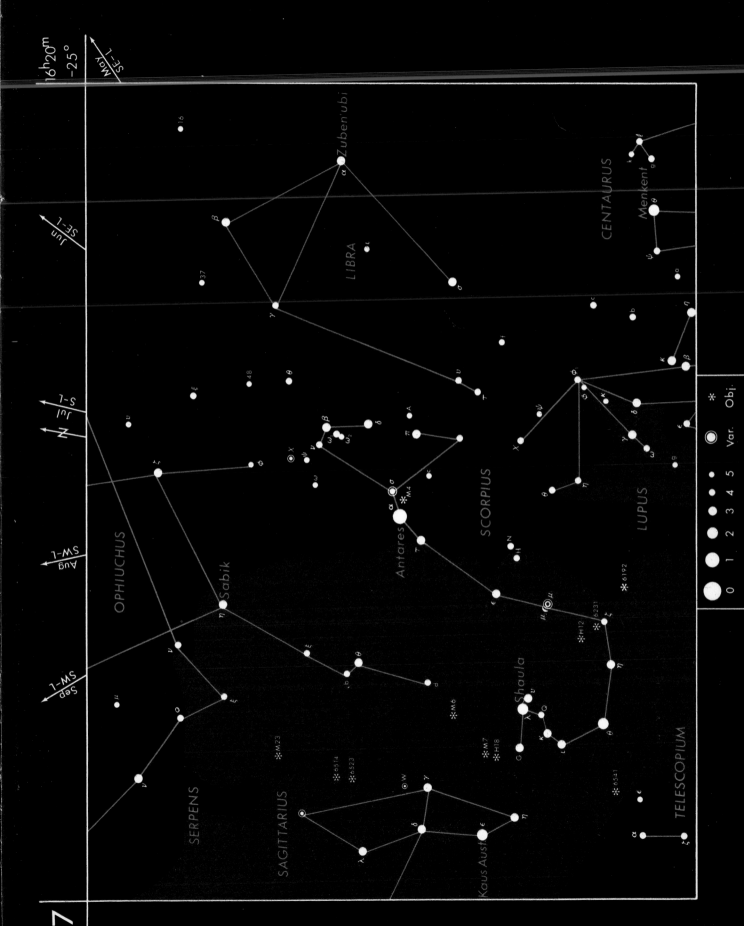

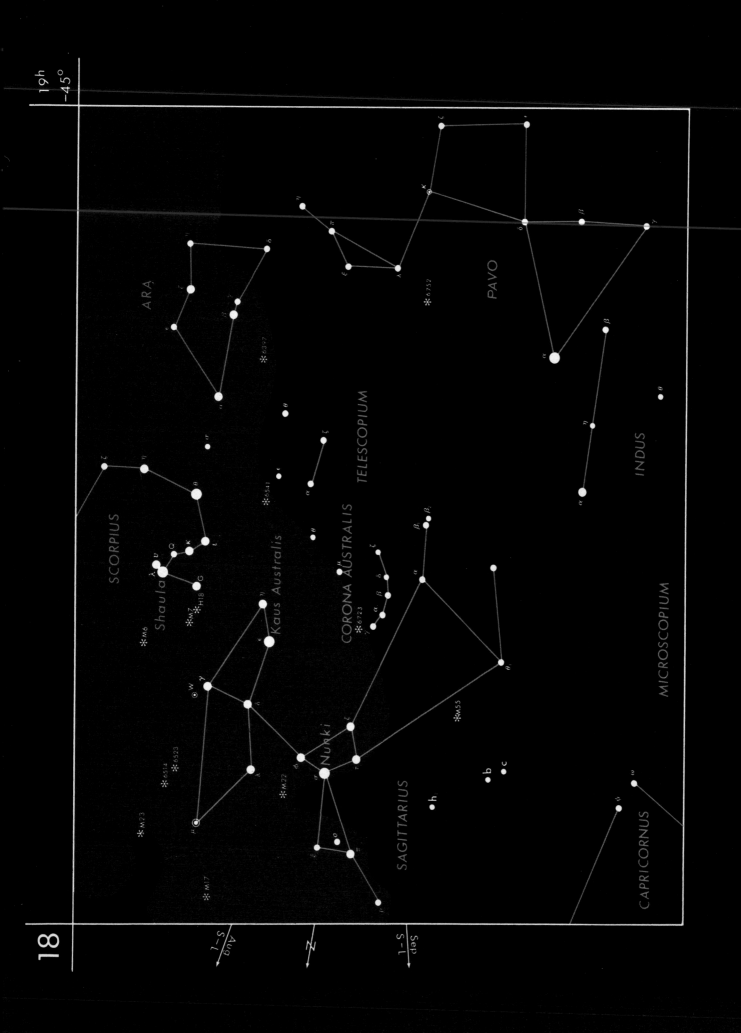

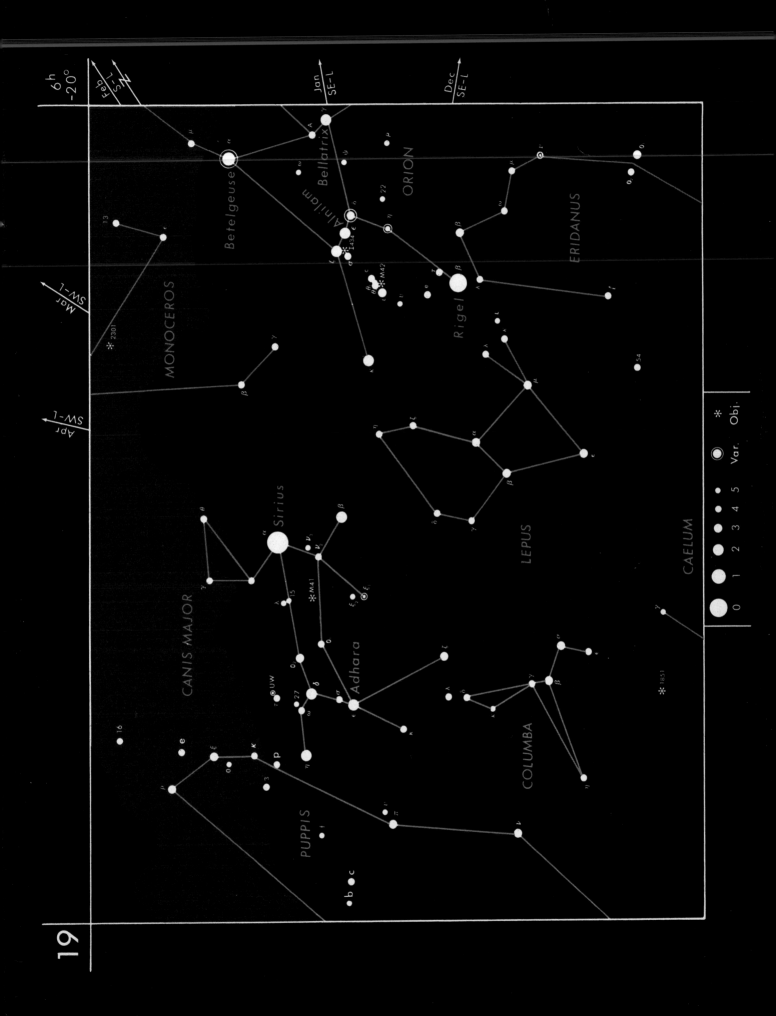

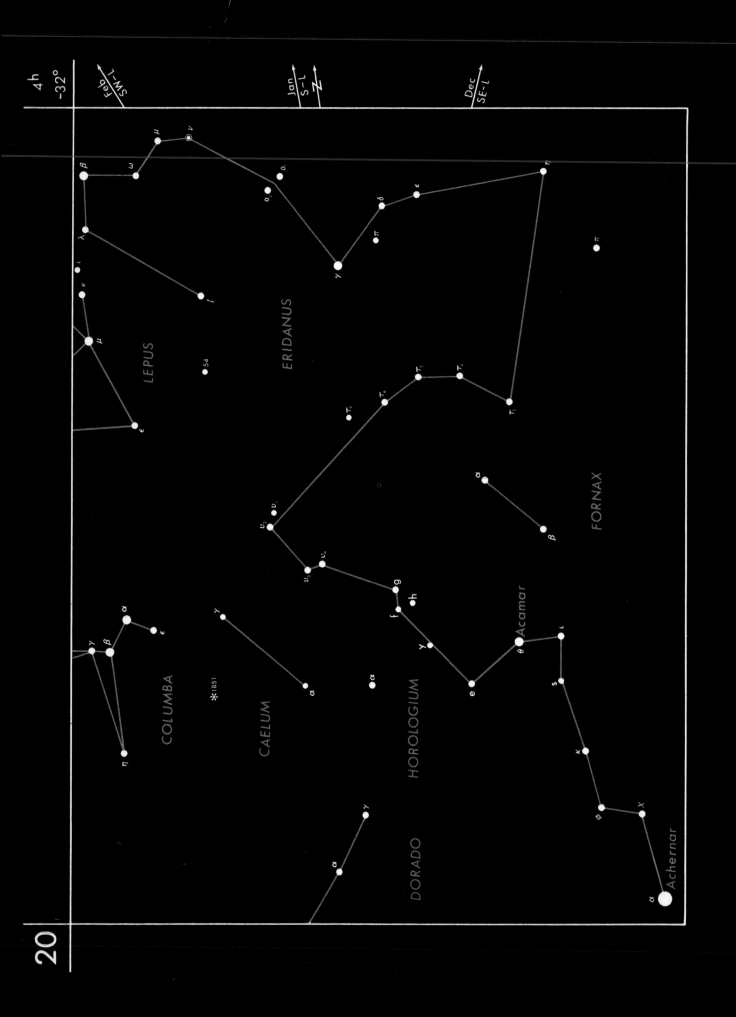

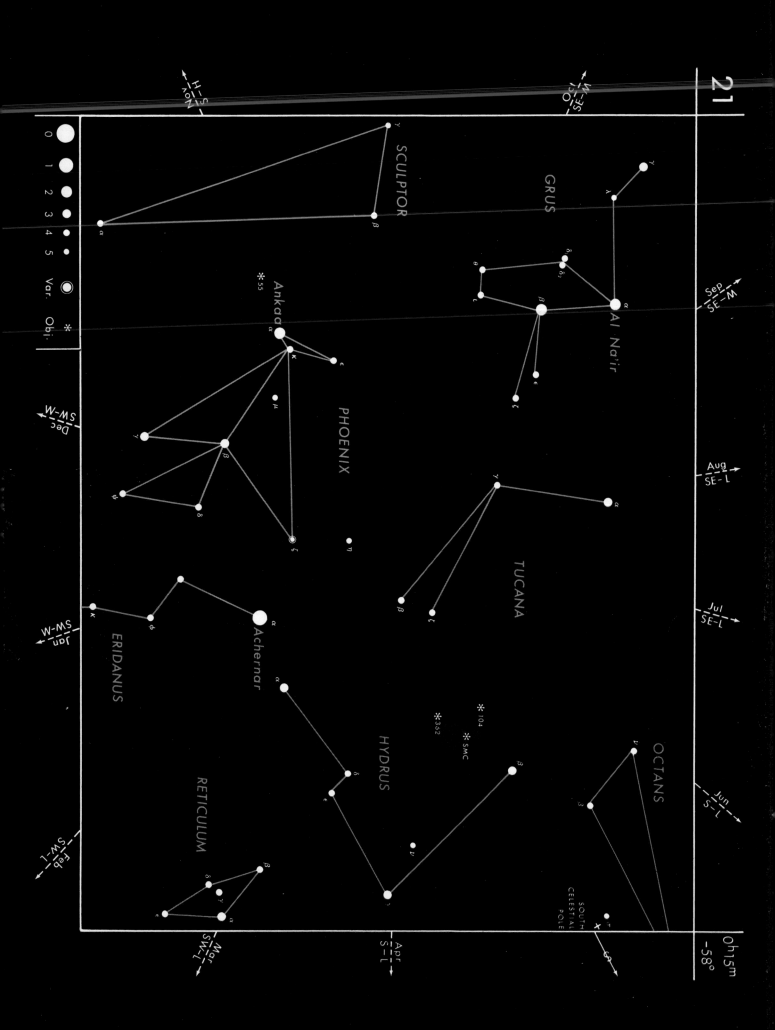

21

SCULPTOR

GRUS

γ

β

α

λ

γ

δ₁
δ₂

η

ι

β

α
Al Na'ir

ε

ζ

*55

Ankaa
α

κ

ε

μ

PHOENIX

γ

β

ψ

δ

ζ

η

γ

α

TUCANA

β

ζ

Achernar
α

ERIDANUS

κ

φ

α

*104

*352

*SMC

HYDRUS

δ

ε

β

ν

OCTANS

ν

β

δ

γ

SOUTH CELESTIAL POLE

χ

τ

σ

RETICULUM

δ

γ

α

ε

β

0h15m
−58°

Sep
SE−M

Aug
SE−L

Jul
SE−L

Jun
S−L

Apr
S−L

Mar
SW−L

Feb
SW−L

Jan
SW−M

Dec
SW−M

Nov
S−H

Oct
SE−H

0
1
2
3
4
5
Var.
Obj.

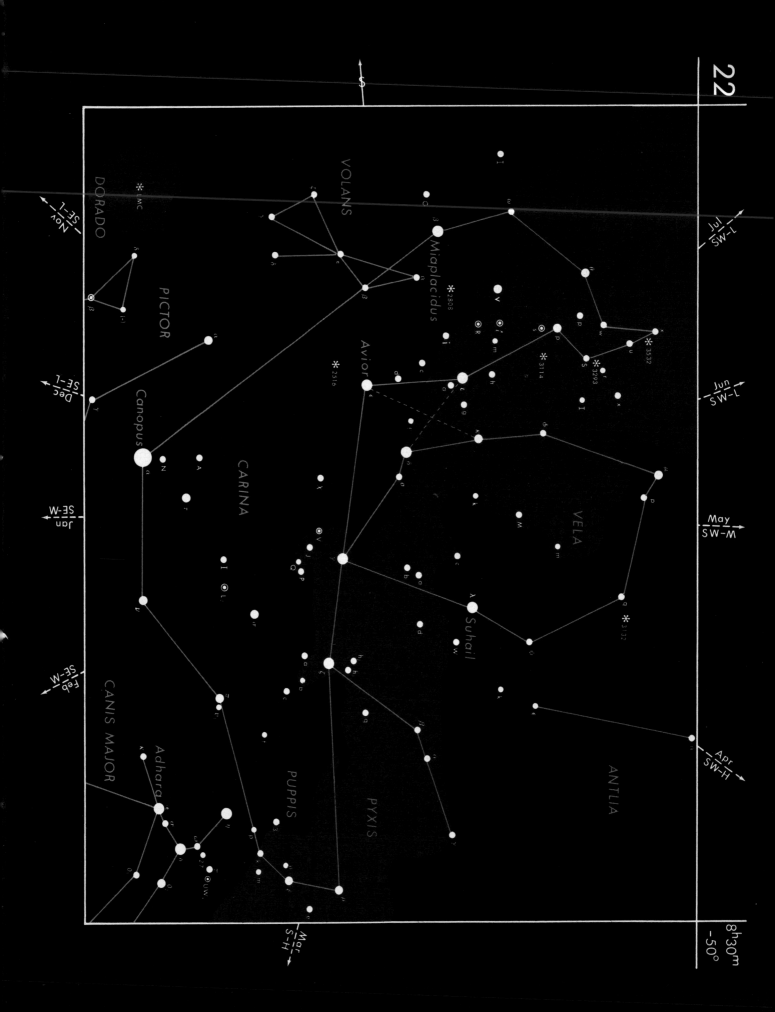

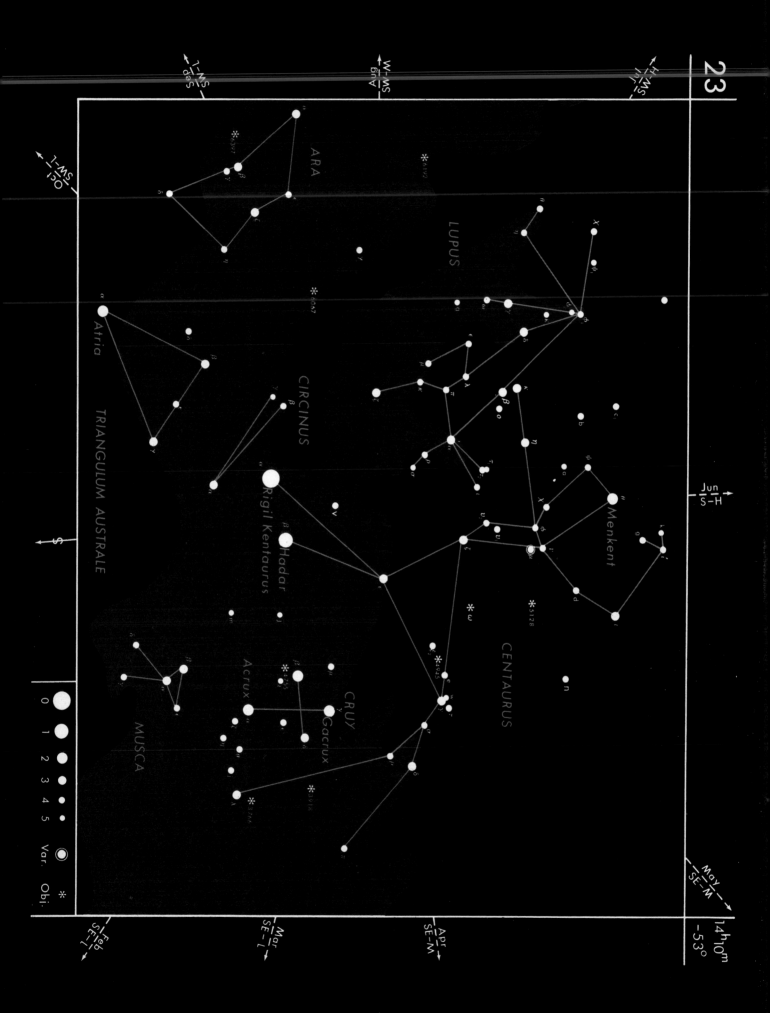

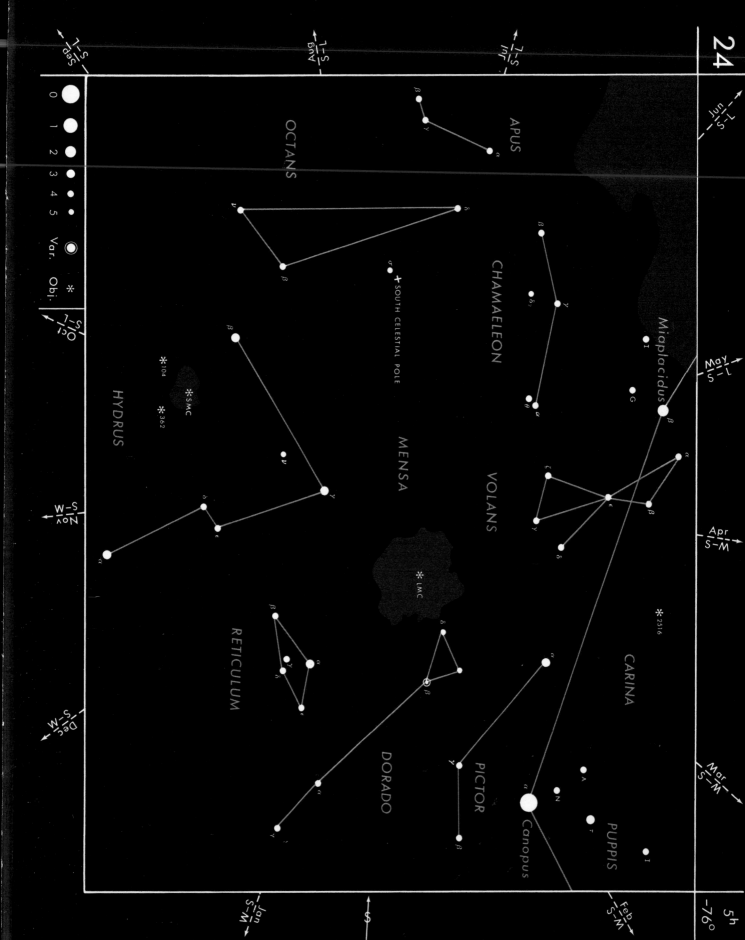

Appendix

Local Mean Time and Sidereal Time

The rotation of the earth causes the sun and stars to move in a daily circuit of the heavens. This motion provides us with a sort of clock since it measures time. Conversely, if one knows the time, he should be able to determine to position of a given star.

We are all more or less familiar with standard time. Encyclopedias and dictionaries have maps showing the twenty-four zones of standard time around the world. Since the circle of the earth's equator contains 360°, each zone contains 360° divided by 24, or 15°. The time in the fundamental zone around the Greenwich meridian is referred to as Universal Time or UT.

To determine the UT in a given area, one must find the difference in hours between his own Standard Time zone and that of Greenwich. The widths of the zones are not precisely 15°; however, 15° corresponds to one hour of time. Thus the eastern United States, on either side of the 75th meridian, has a clock time 5 hours earlier than UT. Most of western Europe employs a clock time earlier than UT, although Rome and Berlin are one hour later, Athens two hours later, etc. Our Local Mean Time is our Standard Time plus (if west of Greenwich) or minus (if east) the difference in hours between Greenwich and our own Standard Time zones. This gives the UT. Suppose someone living in Dallas, Texas, wishes to find his Local Mean Time (LMT) on May 16 at 10:17 p.m. Daylight Time, or 9:17 Central Standard Time (CST). Since astronomers use a day starting at midnight with a clock reading from 0 to 23, he adds 12 hours and finds that the time is 21h 17m. Since Central Standard Time is 6 hours less than UT, the UT will be 27h 17m, or rather 3h 17m on May 17. He then divides the longitude of Dallas, 97° W, by 15, getting 6 with a remainder of 7. He multiplies the remainder by 4, getting 28. Since his LMT is then 6h 28m earlier than UT, he finds that LMT = 3h 17m — 6h 28m =
= 27h 17m — 6h 28m = 20h 49m.

We can then calculate Local Sidereal Time, LST, by the following procedure. We take the number of months and days that have elapsed between the previous September 21 and May 17, that is, 7 months 26 days, multiply this by 2 and call the answer "hours," or 14h, and the number of days by 4, or 104, and call the answer "minutes." Since 104m = 1h 44m, we now add the two figures, obtaining a total of 15h 44m. This quantity is the Sidereal time of Greenwich midnight. Finally, we add this to the LMT to obtain the Local Sidereal Time. Or

Sidereal Time. Or	
LMT	15h 44m
	20h 49m
LST	12h 33m

So calculated, this figure may be as much as three minutes in error, but it is adequate for most purposes.

Once we have this figure we can use it in connection with the right ascensions, RA, to calculate the star's hour angle, HA. Then HA = LST — RA. The hour angle is measured *west* from the meridian. A table of right ascensions resembles the timetable of trains. It gives the time when the star (or object) will be on the meridian. For example, if we wish to locate Regulus, whose RA = 10h 6m, we look at our sidereal clock and find LST = 12h 33m,

Precession of the equinoxes. A slow westward motion of the equinoctial points along the ecliptic caused by the action of the sun and the moon upon the bulge around the earth's equator.

Prominence. Cloud of luminous gas elevated above the sun's surface.

Proper motion. Apparent drift of a star across the sky, compounded from the motion of the star and the sun.

Proton. Atomic particle with a unit positive charge. The nucleus of the hydrogen atom.

Pulsar. Galactic source of pulsing radio waves with very short period; believed to be a rapidly rotating neutron star.

Quadrature. Location of a planet when its longitude differs from that of the sun by 90°.

Quasar. Quasi-stellar object. Blue, starlike object with a large red shift, located at a great distance from our galaxy.

Radial Velocity. Motion of a star toward or away from the earth.

Radioactivity. The natural tendency of certain atomic nuclei to explode and eject various fragments.

Radio Astronomy. The study of radio waves emitted by stars and other celestial objects.

Red Shift. Shift in a body's spectral lines to the red caused by a high receding velocity or an intense gravitational field.

Refraction. The bending of light rays caused by their passing through the earth's atmosphere or any medium of greater density than its original medium.

Retrograde motion. Westward or backward drift of a planet resulting from the forward motion of the earth as it passes the planet.

Revolution. Orbital motion of a body around its primary.

Right ascension (RA). Angle, measured eastward, from the vernal equinox to the foot of a star's hour circle.

Rotation. Turning of an object on its axis.

Satellite. Object in orbit around a planet.

Shooting star. Popular term for meteor.

Sidereal time. Star time; the hour angle of the vernal equinox.

Solar wind. Gases driven from the sun as the result of boiling activity.

Solstice. Position of the sun when farthest north (summer solstice) or farthest south (winter solstice).

Spectral type. The classification of stellar spectra.

Spectrograph. Machine for dispersing light and analyzing its component colors.

Spectrum. Starlight dispersed according to color or wavelength by means of a prism or other device.

Star. A hot ball of glowing gas.

Star clusters. Connected systems of stars. There are two major types: open clusters, a group containing from a few to several hundred stars; and globular clusters, a more complex and condensed group, containing as many as 100,000 stars, highly concentrated toward the center of the cluster.

Sun. Center of our solar system, a star of type G0. Sometimes used generally as a synonym for star.

Sunspot. Dark area of the solar surface, cooler than its surroundings.

Supernova. A star explosion approximately 10,000 times brighter than a nova.

Superior planet. A planet located farther from the sun than the earth.

Synodic Period. Interval between two successive conjunctions of the same celestial bodies.

Synodic month. Period between two successive new or full moons.

Telescope, reflecting. A telescope with mirror objective.

Telescope, refracting. A telescope using a lens (usually achromatic) as an objective.

Terminator. Dividing line between the illuminated and shadowed portions of the lunar or planetary disk.

Time, Local Mean. Solar time for a given location reduced from apparent to mean by application of the equation of time.

Time, Standard Mean. Mean solar time for some standard adapted longitude (for example, Eastern, Central, Mountain, or Pacific Standard Times).

Time, Universal. Standard time of the Greenwich meridian.

Transit. When a small celestial body moves in front of a much larger one (as when Mercury or Venus appears in silhouette against the solar disk or when a satellite passes in front of Jupiter or Saturn). The shadow of a satellite may also transit the disk of its primary.

Van Allen Belt. Region containing energetic ions and electrons trapped in the earth's magnetic field.

Variable star. A star whose brightness varies. Some types are: eclipsing binaries, which are double stars with orbital plane in earth's line of sight, so that they eclipse one another at regular intervals; irregular variables, the result of physical changes of stellar structure; flare stars, which vary because of stellar flares; and cepheids and long-period variables (q.v.).

Wane. The waning moon refers to that portion of the lunar revolution between full and new. Opposite of wax.

Wax. The waxing moon refers to that portion of the lunar revolution between new and full, when the illuminated area is increasing.

Zenith. The point directly overhead, as determined by the indefinite upward extension of a plumb line.

Zodiac. Twelve constellations along the ecliptic through which the sun, moon, and planets move.

Zodiacal light. Soft glow of white light extending upward from the horizon along the ecliptic, particularly in the tropics. Caused by sunlight scattered from small particles of matter in orbit between the earth and sun.

Index

Page numbers in italics indicate illustrations

Planned, prepared and produced by Paul Steiner and the staff of Chanticleer Press. Editors: Milton Rugoff and Susan Weiley, assisted by Mervyn Rothstein. Design: Ulrich Ruchti and Elaine Jones. Production Coordination: Gudrun Buettner. Production Assistant: Ruth Charnes. This book is set in Univers and printed in offset by Amilcare Pizzi, Milan, Italy.

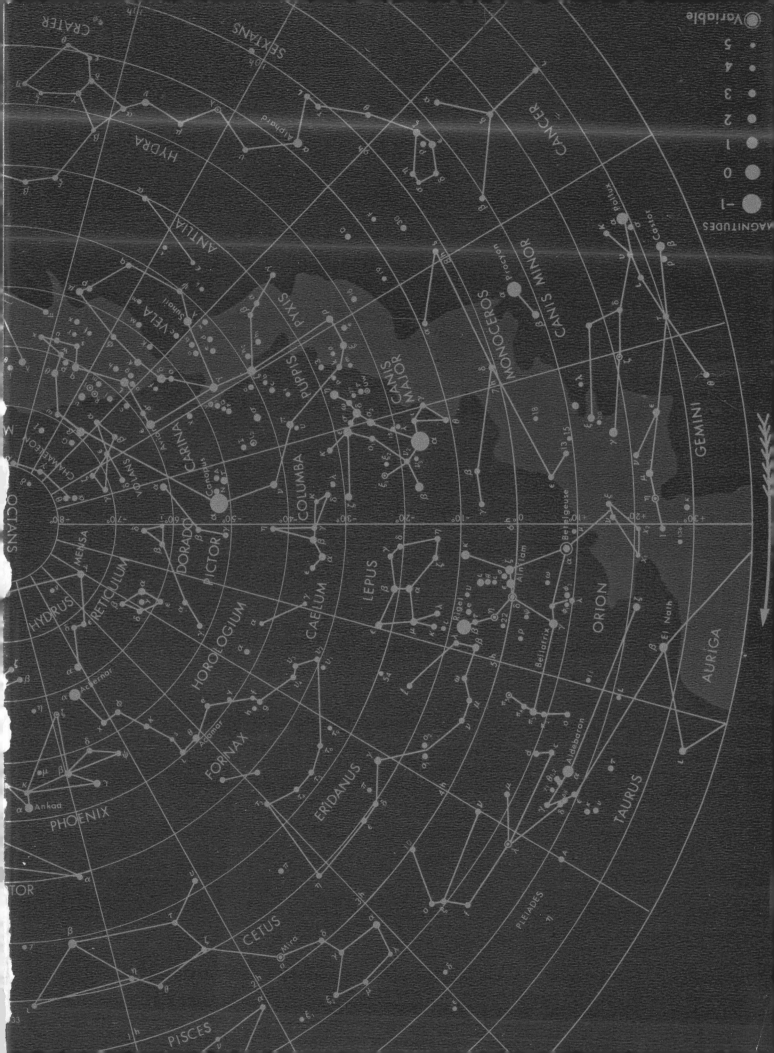